D1387446

EVERYMAN, I will go with thee,
and be thy guide,
In thy most need to go by thy side

JONATHAN SWIFT

Cousin of Dryden, born at Dublin in 1667, of English origin. Secretary to Sir William Temple, 1692; ordained in Ireland, 1694; returned to Temple, 1696; to Ireland again in 1699. Dean of St Patrick's, Dublin, 1713. His mind gave way about 1740 and he died on 19th October 1745.

JONATHAN SWIFT

A Tale of a Tub

AND OTHER SATIRES

INTRODUCTION BY
LEWIS MELVILLE

DENT: LONDON
EVERYMAN'S LIBRARY
DUTTON: NEW YORK

All rights reserved
Made in Great Britain
at the
Aldine Press · Letchworth · Herts
for
J. M. DENT & SONS LTD
Aldine House · Bedford Street · London
First included in Everyman's Library 1909
Last reprinted 1968

NO. *1347*

SBN: 460 01347 5

INTRODUCTION

JONATHAN SWIFT was born at 7, Hoey's Court, Dublin, on November 30, 1667. His paternal grandparents were Thomas Swift, the royalist vicar of Goodrich, near Ross, and Elizabeth Dryden, the poet's aunt; and he was the son of Jonathan Swift by his wife Abigail Erick of Leicester, a kinswoman of the author of the *Hesperides*. Jonathan the elder was steward of the King's Inn at Dublin, and he died seven months before the birth of his famous son, leaving his widow with a little daughter, Jane, in poor circumstances.

Mrs. Swift returned to her family at Leicester, and her brother-in-law, Godwin Swift, charged himself with the boy's education. At the age of six Jonathan was sent to Kilkenny Grammar School, said to be the best of its kind in Ireland, and eight years later was entered as a pensioner at Trinity College, Dublin, where he distinguished himself by failing in two of three subjects taken up for his degree, which, indeed, he did secure, but only by the ignominious "special grace." That Swift, like his distant relatives Herrick and Dryden, showed no signs of precocious genius is true enough, but it is inconceivable that he was a dunce, as more than one writer has urged, and the reason for his failure at Trinity College may more readily be found in his recklessness, brought out, he declared, through his ill-treatment by relatives. Indeed, it seems that Godwin, by his general demeanour, made the bread of charity bitter to the lad, whose high spirit then, as after, made a state of dependence almost unbearable to him.

In 1688 Godwin Swift died, having made no provision for his nephew, owing to his having through unfortunate speculations passed from affluence to the brink of insolvency; and, shortly after the flight of James II., Jonathan joined his mother at Leicester to discuss plans for his future. In the following year he accepted an offer of a position in the household of Sir William Temple, whose wife, Dorothy Osborne, was a connection of the Ericks.

Swift was soon enstalled at Moor Park, Temple's home near Farnham, in Surrey, and there he, "a raw, inexperienced youth," to quote his own description, became, first, humble companion of the statesman, essayist, and later, when his abilities were obvious to his master, secretary and amanuensis. At Moor Park he met William III., who, it is said, offered him a commission in a cavalry regiment and taught him to cut asparagus in the Dutch fashion. He saw the monarch again when Temple entrusted him with a mission to convince his Majesty of the necessity of triennial parliaments; however, the king declined to be convinced, which, said Swift, was "the first incident that helped to cure me of vanity."

Swift could scarcely endure his subordinate position: in his writings there are many indications of his bitterness, and there is an autobiographical note in his posthumous *Directions to Servants*, written towards the end of his life, which suggests that the memory of these unhappy days was still vivid: "To grow old in the office of a footman is the highest of all indignities; therefore, when you find years coming without hopes of a place at Court, a command in the army, a succession to the stewardship, an employment in the revenue (which two last you cannot obtain without reading and writing), or running away with your master's niece or daughter, I directly advise you to go upon the road, which is the only post of honour left you; there you will meet many of your old comrades, and live a short life and a merry one, and make a figure at your exit."

To grow old in service under Temple or another Swift determined should not be his lot. The thing he wanted most in the world was independence, and to secure this he overcame the scruples that forbade him to enter the Church for support. When he first went to Moor Park, he regarded this merely as a place where he might render service, valued at "£20 a year and board," until he was appointed to a living. But after a while he saw, or fancied he saw, that Temple, having realised the value of his *protégé's* services, was in no hurry to part with him, and made only a pretence to secure him preferment; whereupon at last, in 1694, the young man, enlisting other influence on his behalf, returned to Ireland, was ordained, and presented to the small prebend of Kilroot, near Belfast, worth £100 a year. There he met Jane Waring, the sister of a college friend, now generally known as "Varina," the least important of the trio of women with which his name is associated.

Soon wearying of the life of an impecunious country parson, Swift embraced the offer of Temple, who missed his aid, to return to Moor Park, and in May 1696 he again took up his abode there, where he remained, diligently acquiring a profound knowledge of men and books, until the death of his famous master three years later. "I was at his death as far to seek as ever," he said; and, having his bread to earn, he returned to Ireland, and acted as chaplain to Lord Berkeley at Dublin Castle. There one of his duties was to read to Lady Berkeley her favourite Robert Boyle's *Meditations :* one day he read, apparently from the volume, a "Meditation" that Lady Berkeley accepted without suspicion — it was his own *Meditation upon a Broomstick*, that most delightful parody! In February 1700, Lord Berkeley gave him a prebend in St. Patrick's, Dublin, and the vicarage of Laracor, with the living of Rathbeggan, County Meath, worth in all about £200 a year—an income "Varina" thought sufficient for marriage, but after the expression by Swift of an opinion diametrically opposed to this suggestion, the lady passed out of his life.

With two other women Swift's name is inextricably connected, with the passionate Esther Vanhomrigh ("Vanessa") and with Esther Johnson ("Stella"), of whom he wrote: "I knew her from six years old, and had some share in her education by directing what books she should read, and perpetually instructing her in the principles of honour and virtue, from which she never swerved in any one action or moment of her life. She was sickly from her childhood until about the age of fifteen; but then grew into perfect health, and was then looked upon as one of the most beautiful, graceful, and agreeable young women in London, only a little too fat. Her hair was blacker than a raven, and every feature of her face in perfection." The

story of these women is so well known that there is no
necessity to enter into it here. "Vanessa" was but an
episode in his life; but "Stella" was the love of his life,
and with her death in 1728 the solitary gleam of brightness
in his sad existence disappeared. Whether he married her
or not is, with the identity of "Junius," one of the un-
solved mysteries of history; but two things seem certain:
if the union took place, it was after "Vanessa" appeared
on the scene, and it was never consummated.

Though in 1699 the outside world was ignorant of his
existence, Swift was known to the wide circle of Temple's
acquaintance as a man of great promise, and, to a select
few, not only of promise but of performance. He had
already fleshed his pen: he had written verses—though
these called forth Dryden's oft-quoted remark, "Cousin
Swift, you will never be a poet," a prophecy soon to
be falsified; and he had prepared Temple's letters and
memoirs for publication. But this work counts as nothing
when it is remembered that he had composed *The Battle of
the Books* and *The Tale of a Tub*, which, written in 1697 and
circulated in manuscript, did not receive the honour of
publication until seven years after their inception.

The Battle of the Books arose out of an essay by Temple
in 1692 on ancient and modern learning, to which William
Wotton replied in favour of the moderns, and the controversy spread, with Boyle and Bentley, respectively, for
and against the ancients. Swift then took up his pen in
defence of his patron, and, pretending the quarrel had
spread to the books in the St. James's Library, of which
Bentley was curator, wrote the mock-heroic *Full and True
Account of the Battle fought last Friday between the Ancient
and Modern Books in St. James's Library*, describing the
forces, on each side, and the pitched battle, but, with
happy inspiration, leaving the issue in doubt—the "Ad-
vertisement" runs: "The manuscript, by the injury of
fortune or weather, being in several places imperfect, we
cannot learn to which side the victory fell."

Brilliant as was this *jeu d'esprit*, it pales into compara-
tive insignificance before the wonderful *Tale of a Tub*, that
masterly satire on "the numerous and gross conceptions

in religion and learning." Ostensibly the history of three brothers, Peter (the Church of Rome), Jack (Presbyterianism and other forms of Protestant Dissent) and Martin (the Lutheran and Anglican Churches), the whole resolves itself into a tremendous onslaught on hypocrisy and theological shams. The wealth of satire, the deep irony, the terse style, and the brilliant imagination that inspired the pamphlet places it in the very foremost place of its kind in English literature. "Good God!" cried Swift, reading it near the end of his life, "what a genius I had when I wrote that book!" and this opinion has been echoed by every critic of English literature from Swift's days to ours.

Swift was not content to remain at his "hedge-living," as he dubbed it, at Laracor, and he came frequently to England, where he interested himself in all questions of the day, though he contrived, so far as possible, to hold himself aloof from party. The impeachment of the Whig lords in 1701 provoked him to write a *Discourse on the Contests and Dissensions between the Nobles and Commons in Athens and Rome*, which, like all Swift's works, was published anonymously: [1] it was attributed to Somers and to Burnet, and it was only when Thomas Sheridan told Swift that the latter had written it, that Swift avowed the authorship. Then, in gratitude, although there is nothing in the pamphlet committing the writer to Whig principles, the leaders of that party welcomed him heartily when he next visited England, and promised him preferment. Soon after came the publication of *The Battle of the Books* and *The Tale of a Tub*, when, at a bound, Swift took his place amongst the leading men of letters and wits of the day, and made the acquaintance, and eventually became the friend, of Congreve, Steele, Addison, Halifax, and other notabilities.

In 1707 Swift came to London with an official mission to obtain the application of Queen Anne's Bounty to Ireland, and while he was still pressing this proposal upon the government, the bishopric of Waterford fell vacant. There

---

[1] The only work to which Swift put his name was a letter addressed to Lord Oxford in 1712, entitled *A Proposal for Correcting, Improving, and Ascertaining the English Tongue*, and containing suggestions for the foundation of an English Academy of Letters.

is no doubt he expected the preferment, and was disappointed when he was passed over in favour of Dr. Thomas Milles; and in the following year his claims were again ignored when an appointment had to be made to the see of Cork. His anger, however, was kept within bounds, and, though he felt himself injured, he did not break with his untrustworthy friends. However, the breach was to come, and it arose out of Swift's *Letter on the Sacramental Test* (1708), which vexed the Whigs, who were allied with Dissent. The matter that had brought Swift to England made no progress, and Swift returned embittered to Ireland.

On his next visit to England his hatred of Dissenters led him to the Tory camp, where Harley met him with an undertaking to settle the Bounty question. He then threw in his lot with this party, contributed to the Tory *Examiner*, attacked Godolphin and Wharton, and in 1711 wrote *The Conduct of the Allies*, which urged that the war was carried on from corrupt motives, and did more than anything else, it was believed, to make the Peace of Utrecht acceptable to the English nation.

He was the supreme pamphleteer of his, perhaps of any, time, for this benefit he had derived from his years of servitude at Moor Park: he had learnt public business from the inside; and so when he engaged in political conflict, he wrote not as a *doctrinaire*, but as a man of affairs. Sir Leslie Stephen has said that Swift's political pamphlets were blows rather than words, and this effect was undoubtedly produced, not only by the author's inspired common-sense, but also by his practical knowledge of the working of governments. A master of irony and invective and of logic, his simple, forcible style, never decked out with meretricious adornment, made his meaning clear even to the dullest intellect; and made him the most valuable adherent of any principle he thought fit, in his honesty of purpose, to support.

So powerful an ally must be kept in good humour even by the most high and mighty statesmen, and Swift's influence between 1710 and 1714 was enormous. To his lasting credit he never committed a "job," and, equally to his credit, he took advantage of his power to further the interests of men of letters, irrespective of party: he secured the promise of an office for Nicholas Rowe, and did his best to keep Steele's place for him; he obtained subscriptions for Pope's translation of Homer, and rendered yeoman service to Congreve and Parnell, and such minor lights as William Diaper and William Harrison. It seemed as if he could do anything for anybody except himself. The Whigs had done nothing for him, and the Tories seemed equally determined to shuffle out of their obligations—would have done so, too, had not he in 1713 demanded at the point of the sword, as it were, "something honourable;" if that were not forthcoming, he said plainly to Oxford, he would return forthwith to Ireland. Then, and then only, since it was clear he could not longer be put off with vague promises, did they move: they promoted John Sterne, Dean of St. Patrick's, Dublin, to the see of Dromore, and installed Swift in the vacant deanery in June 1713.

We find Thackeray speaking of Swift as an outlaw, who says, "These are my brains; with these I'll win titles and compete with fortune. These are my bullets; these I'll turn into gold!" The accusation sounds weighty, but, when examined, to what does it amount? That Swift desired advancement in his profession, and hoped to secure it because he was head and shoulders above every man in it! How many men of genius are there who do not hope that their talents may secure this delectable end, whether churchmen, soldiers, statesmen, lawyers, novelists? And, so long as they do not prostitute their great gifts, who shall object? It is right and fitting that genius shall have its reward, and it is far better that an intellectual rather than a soulless adventurer shall succeed in climbing the tree and plucking the fruit. Swift may not have been the ideal dean or the possible bishop; indeed he was not; but he compares favourably with many who held these positions. At least his life was clean, his honour untarnished; he wronged no poor man, hurt no woman, and he never wrote a line except as his conscience dictated. It is said he was never promoted to a see because he was the author of *The Tale of a Tub*: we may well agree with Mr. James Hannay who, in his excellent and unjustly forgotten book on *Satire and Satirists*, denounces this as "odious and sickening cant," as indeed it obviously is, when we remember the age in which Swift lived, that age which is revealed in his terrible satires and in Hogarth's prints, that age in which corruption, sensuality, and irreligion was rife, when statesmen intrigued round the deathbed of a queen, and the mistresses of royalty were advanced to the highest honours.

Thirteen months after Swift became Dean of St. Patrick's, Queen Anne died, and, his hopes of a bishopric at an end, anyhow for the time being, he returned to Ireland, where the Whigs, now in power, kept watch, it is said, for any opportunity to impeach their erstwhile ally for high treason. The last stage of Swift's life shows him transformed from an English into an Irish favourite, and this almost in spite of himself. He always looked upon himself as an Englishman, and regarded the Irish as of little political importance, at all events until after he settled there for some years. At first he concerned himself little about the affairs of the nation, and might never have taken an active part had it not been for the infliction of Wood's Halfpence, the injustice of which aroused him, first, to protest privately, and, that failing of its effect, then, in 1714, to attack the disgraceful "job" in the vigorous *Drapier Letters*. Two years later he went to England, visited Pope and Gay, and dined with Walpole, to whom he complained in vain of the treatment of Ireland by the government; and he paid his last visit to this country in 1727, when the death of George I. gave him some hope that he might assist in displacing Walpole from the office of prime minister. He returned to find Stella on her death-bed.

Though, of course, Swift was not on friendly terms with the official society of the capital, his stalwart opposition to the oppression of the hated Saxon, together with his far-reaching charities, drew all hearts to him, and for the rest of his life he was the idol of the Irish people. When Sergeant Bettesworth, whom he had outrageously ridiculed, threatened him with violence, an association was formed to defend the "person of the Drapier," and in such profound reverence was he held by the ignorant that he dispersed a crowd gathered to see an eclipse by sending word that it had been put off by his orders!

He diligently pursued his literary work in the quiet retreat of the cathedral close. In 1726 he made a departure from his usual practice of seeking no remuneration for his writing, and permitted Pope to dispose for £200 of the manuscript of the only lengthy work that came from his pen. This bore upon the title-page the legend, *"Travels into Several Remote Nations of the World*. By Lemuel Gulliver, first a Surgeon, and then a Captain of Several Ships,*"* and, though issued anonymously, was at once ascribed to its author, and set the seal on his fame. If it is not intellectually equal to *The Tale of a Tub*, it is only second to that in the list of his major achievements, and its interest is far more universal. Dr. Johnson might say of this masterpiece, "When we have once thought of big men and little men, it is easy to do the rest:" yet neither he nor any other man had "thought of big men and little men," and it is quite certain that neither he nor even Defoe, nor any other man whose name is proudly enrolled in the annals of English literature, could have done "the rest." It is, indeed, not the conception but the execution that is so wonderful. Granted the postulates, the realism is so remarkable—Emerson accurately but somewhat prosaically remarked that Swift described his fictitious persons as if for the police—and the whole work is so amazingly truthful a satire on existing social conditions, and so convincing an attack on "the animal called man," that it seems almost as if its accuracy could be proved mathematically: and yet—and this is the miracle of the work—its irony is so deep that it has been a favourite gift-book for children!

There are critics who have averred that Swift was mad when he wrote the latter parts of the book, for, they declare, no sane man could have been so cruel, so inhuman; but to express this view is to show a splendid ignorance of the Dean's character. No brain could have been clearer than his, even when, always with that redeeming quality of humour, he described the bestial Yahoos and the passionless Houyhnhnms. Swift knew full well what he was doing: he was no playful satirist desiring, as, for example, Addison did, to please while he instructed, but a man terribly in earnest, realising the weaknesses and the vices of mankind. As another famous philosopher looked for an honest man, so he sought for a good one: "If there were but a dozen Arbuthnots in the world," he said, "I would burn my *Travels !*"

In his later years Swift wrote many things that would have made the reputation of a lesser man. He gave vent to his sardonic humour in *A Modest Proposal for Preventing the Children of Poor People in Ireland from being a Burden to their Parents or Country, and for making them Beneficial to the Public* (1729) and in *Directions to Servants* (written in 1737, but published posthumously); but while he attacked ignoble things fiercely, he could rebuke folly with a gentle hand, and the playful humour that years earlier had inspired the *Bickerstaff Papers* [1] was again apparent in 1730 in the good-natured satire on *Polite Conversation*.

All his life Swift had been subject to attacks of giddiness and deafness, and now as old age came upon him these afflictions became more and more frequent and severe. Young stated that the Dean had once said to him, "I shall be like that tree: I shall die at the top;" and as the years passed, the great man dreaded not death, but life. "Good-night, I hope I shall never see you again," he is reported to have said to his friends when taking leave of them. The fate that he had foretold for himself came to pass: his brain became overclouded in 1738, in 1741 guardians were appointed by the Court of Chancery, and in the following year, after suffering great agony, he fell into a state of apathy which mercifully endured until the end. He died, at the age of seventy-seven, on October 19, 1745, and was buried in his cathedral by the side of "Stella" Johnson. As we pause to reflect upon these last years, and compare them with the virility of those two-score that preceded them, there will surely be none to dispute Thackeray's pronouncement: "An immense genius: an awful down-fall and ruin. So great a man he seems, that thinking of him is like an empire falling."

---

[1] "Written to prevent the people of England from being farther imposed on by vulgar Almanack makers."

This is not the place to enter into a criticism of Swift, but space must be snatched for a few passing words of appreciation. Perhaps there has never been in this country another writer, with the exception of the supreme head of English letters, in whom can be discerned the same force of intellect. Others may amuse, may touch the heart, may arouse good passions and bad, but no man appeals so directly to the brain. Yet, curiously enough, Swift has found his severest critics among men of genius. What Dr. Johnson said of *Gulliver's Travels* has already been recorded, and this great man had so erroneous an impression of the gifts of a man still greater that he would not ascribe to him the honour of having written *The Tale of a Tub*. "Swift has a higher reputation than he deserves," he said in 1763. "His excellence is strong sense; for his humour, though very well, is not remarkably good. I doubt whether *The Tale of a Tub* be his; for he never owned it; and it is much above his usual manner." This may serve to make critics humble, for if in this manner Johnson tripped, who may not fall? Macaulay's estimate is too familiar to be repeated here, and Thackeray's, for the same reason, will not be given. These men were repelled by Swift's ferocity, and they seem not to have inquired what prompted it: yet Swift's apparent malignity arose from a great love of his fellow-creatures, soured by continual disappointment in their nobility, and from a love of truth and of righteousness that on every hand he saw trampled under foot.

This ferocious satirist had a heart as tender as beats in any breast. He was disappointed in material ambition, a victim of hope deferred; far sadder, he was debarred from conjugal love, either by his fear of madness or by some other and more mysterious ban. Yet he won the love of a people, and kept it for thirty years; he was the friend of Gay and Prior, of Pope and Berkeley, of Addison and Arbuthnot, and many more, though it must be confessed he did not suffer fools gladly; and he was beloved in middle-age, as all the world knows, by two devoted women: let those who doubt his tenderness read the *Journal to Stella*, never meant but for the eyes of the person to whom it was addressed. There are those, however, who will not be convinced, and these see only in the inscription, "Only a woman's hair," attached to a lock of Stella's hair, found at his death, a last sneer of him whom Addison pronounced "the greatest genius of the nation!"

LEWIS MELVILLE.

SELECT BIBLIOGRAPHY

SEPARATE WORKS. *A Discourse of the Contests and Dissensions between the nobles and the Commons in Athens and Rome, with the Consequences,* 1701; *A Tale of a Tub, with An Account of a Battle between the Ancient and Modern Books in St James's Library,* 1704 (this includes *The Mechanical Operation of the Spirit*); *A Project for the Advancement of Religion and the Reformation of Manners, by a Person of Quality,* 1708; *The Bickerstaff Papers,* 1708, 1709; *A Meditation upon a Broomstick, and somewhat beside,* 1710; *Miscellanies in Prose and Verse* (including some of the above pamphlets, and other articles), 1711; *The Conduct of the Allies and of the late Ministry in beginning and carrying on the present war,* 1711; *Some Remarks on the Barrier-Treaty between Her Majesty and the States-General, etc.,* 1712; *Some Advice humbly offered to Members of the October Club, in a letter from a Person of Honour,* 1712; *Letter to a Whig Lord,* 1712; *A Proposal for correcting, improving, and ascertaining The English Tongue, etc.,* 1712; *The Public Spirit of the Whigs, etc.,* 1714; *A Proposal for the Universal Use of Irish Manufacture,* 1720; *Letter of Advice to a young Poet,* 1721; *The Drapier Letters* (five in number), 1724, 1725; *Sixth and Seventh Letters,* not published separately, given in works, 1735; *Cadenus and Vanessa,* 1726; *Travels into several remote Nations of the World. In four parts. By Lemuel Gulliver, first a surgeon and then a captain of several ships,* 1726; *A Short View of the State of Ireland,* 1727; *Journal of a Dublin Lady,* 1729; *On Poetry; a Rhapsody,* 1733; *A complete Collection of genteel and ingenious Conversation . . . in three Dialogues,* 1738; *Imitation of the Sixth Satire of the Second Book of Horace,* 1738; *Verses on the Death of Dr Swift, written by himself, in 1731,* 1739; *Some Free Thoughts on the Present State of Affairs,* 1741; *Sermons (On Mutual Subjection, On Conscience, On the Trinity),* 1744; *Directions to Servants in General,* 1745; *History of the last four Years of the Queen,* published from the last MS. copy, 1758.

   The Journal to Stella is given in collected editions of Swift's works, and has been separately edited.

   Among works edited by Swift are *Works of Sir William Temple, with an Account of his Life and Writings,* 1720; and *Memoirs of Captain John Creighton, written by himself,* 1731.

   Swift contributed to the *Tatler,* 1709 and 1710; and to the *Examiner,* 1710–11; and to the *Intelligencer,* which was set up by Swift and Sheridan in 1728.

Besides the edition of *Miscellanies in Prose and Verse* of 1711, there was a fourth edition in 1721; and another in 4 vols., 1727 (the third and fourth vols., 1732). This collection professedly contains all Swift's minor works which he wished acknowledged; a fifth vol., 1735, completes the author's works. An edition of 1745–8 is in 13 vols.

Miscellaneous Works, 1720, contains the *Tale of a Tub* and *Miscellanies in Prose and Verse;* and in 1722 appeared *Miscellanies* which contain some pamphlets, letters, poems, and tales.

Edition of Letters from 1714 to 1738, 1741.

COLLECTED EDITIONS. In 6 vols., 1735–8, revised by the author; other volumes were afterwards added. Ed. by Hawkesworth, 12 vols., 1755; several volumes were afterwards added by different editors; Dublin Edition, 20 vols., 1772; Ed. by T. Sheridan, 17 vols., 1784; by J. Nichols, 19 vols., 1801; by Sir Walter Scott, 19 vols., 1814, 1824; and by Temple Scott, 1897–1908.

The prose works are published in Bohn's Standard Library, 1897, etc.; there are separate editions of the poetical works; the one of 1833–4 (Aldine Edition of Poets) contains the life by Mitford. Johnson's life is given in *Works of the British Poets*, vols. 39, 40 (1779), and in *British Poets*, vols. 37, 39 (1822). There is an edition of Swift's *Correspondence* by F. E. Ball, 1910–14.

BIOGRAPHY AND CRITICISM. *Remarks on the Life and Writings of Jonathan Swift in a series of letters from John, Earl of Orrery to his son*, 1752; and *Dr Delaney's Observations upon Lord Orrery's Remarks*, 1754; D. Swift: *An Essay upon the Life and Character of Dr Jonathan Swift*, 1755; W. H. Dilworth, 1758, 1760; T. Sheridan, 1784; Sir W. R. W. Wilde: *The Closing Years of Swift's Life* (with unpublished poems and remarks on Stella), 1849; Lord Jeffrey, 1853; W. E. H. Lecky: *Leaders of Public Opinion in Ireland*, 1861, 1871, 1903; J. Forster, 1875 (1 vol. only); Sir Leslie Stephen (English Men of Letters), 1882; Sir H. Craik, 1882; J. Hay: *Jonathan Swift: the Mystery of his Life and Love*, 1891; J. Churton Collins: *Jonathan Swift, a Biographical and Critical Study*, 1893; G. P. Moriarty: *Dean Swift and his Writings*, 1893; see also Johnson, *Lives of the Poets*.

Swift has been a favourite subject of biographical and critical study in the first half of the twentieth century and the following is a selection of books published on him in English during the period: G. Aitken: *Swift*, 1912; C. Whibley: *Jonathan Swift*, 1917; J. C. Nicol: *Swift and Stella*, 1926; Sir Shane Leslie: *The Skull of Swift*, 1928; S. Dark: *Five Deans*, 1928; F. E. Ball: *Swift's Verse*, 1929; Carl van Doren: *Swift*, 1931; S. L. Gwynn: *The Life and Friendships of Dean Swift*, 1933; M. M. Ross and J. M. Home: *Swift, or The Egotist*, 1934; M. B. Gold: *Swift's Marriage to Stella*, 1937; R. W. Jackson: *Jonathan Swift, Dean and Pastor*, 1939; F. S. Goodwin: *Jonathan Swift, Giant in Chains*, 1940; R. W. Jackson: *Swift and his Circle*, 1945; R. C. Churchill: *He Served Human Liberty*, 1946; Bernard Askworth: *Swift*, 1947; H. J. Davis: *The Satire of Jonathan Swift*, 1947; E. Hardy: *The Conjured Spirit*, 1950.

CONTENTS

A TALE OF A TUB

WRITTEN FOR THE UNIVERSAL IMPROVEMENT OF MANKIND

Diu multumque desideratum.

TO WHICH IS ADDED, AN ACCOUNT OF A BATTLE BETWEEN
THE ANCIENT AND MODERN BOOKS IN ST. JAMES'S
LIBRARY; WITH THE AUTHOR'S APOLOGY,
AND EXPLANATORY NOTES

[BY W. W–TT–N, B.D., AND OTHERS]

———

Basyma cacabassa eanaa, irraumista diaraba caëota bafobor camelanthi.
—IREN., lib. i. c. 18.

———Juvatque novos decerpere flores,
Insignemque meo capiti petere inde coronam,
Unde prius nulli velarunt tempora Musæ.—LUCRET.

Ridentem dicere verum quid vetat?—HORACE.

ANALYTICAL TABLE

THE tale approved of by a great majority among the men of taste. Some treatises written expressly against it; but not one syllable in its defence. The greatest part of it finished in 1696, eight years before it was published. The author's intention when he began it. No irreligious or immoral opinion can fairly be deduced from the book. The clergy have no reason to dislike it. The author's intention not having met with a candid interpretation, he declined engaging in a task he had proposed to himself, of examining some publications, that were intended against all religion. Unfair to fix a name upon an author who had so industriously concealed himself. The Letter on Enthusiasm,[1] ascribed by several to the same author. If the abuses in law or physic had been the subject of this treatise, the learned professors in either faculty would have been more liberal than the clergy. The passages which appear most liable to objection are parodies. The author entirely innocent of any intention of glancing at those tenets of religion, which he has by some prejudiced or ignorant readers been supposed to mean. This particularly the case in the passage about the three wooden machines. An irony runs through the whole book. Not necessary to take notice of treatises written against it. The usual fate of common answerers to books of merit is to sink into waste paper and oblivion. The case very different when a great genius exposes a foolish piece. Reflections

---

[1] This celebrated letter, which was generally supposed to have been written by Dr. Swift, and by him, with as little foundation, ascribed to his friend Colonel Hunter, was the production of the author of the *Characteristics*, in which collection it holds the foremost rank. It bears date in September 1707 and was written with a view to the French prophets, whose enthusiastic extravagances were then at the greatest height.

occasioned by Dr. King's Remarks on the *Tale of a Tub;* others, by Mr. Wotton. The manner in which the Tale was first published accounted for. The Fragment not printed in the way the author intended; being the groundwork of a much larger discourse.[1] The oaths of Peter why introduced. The severest strokes of satire in the treatise are levelled against the custom of employing wit in profaneness or immodesty. Wit the noblest and most useful gift of human nature; and humour the most agreeable. Those who have no share of either, think the blow weak, because they are themselves insensible.

P.S.—The author of the Key wrong in all his conjectures. The whole work entirely by one hand; the author defying any one to claim three lines in the book.

The Bookseller's Dedication to Lord Somers.—How he finds out that lord to be the patron intended by his author. Dedicators ridiculous, who praise their patrons for qualities that do not belong to them.

The Bookseller to the Reader.—Tells how long he has had these papers, when they were written, and why he publishes them now.

The Dedication to Posterity.—The author, apprehending that time will soon destroy almost all the writings of this age, complains of his malice against modern authors and their productions, in hurrying them so quickly off the scene; and therefore addresses posterity in favour of his contemporaries: assures him they abound in wit and learning, and books; and, for instance, mentions Dryden, Tate, D'Urfey, Bentley, and Wotton.

Preface.—The occasion and design of this work.

Project for employing the beaux of the nation. Of modern prefaces. Modern wit how delicate. Method for penetrating into an author's thoughts.

Complaints of every writer against the multitude of writers, ike the fat fellows in a crowd. Our author insists on the common privilege of writers; to be favourably explained when not understood; and to praise himself in the modern way. This treatise without satire; and why. Fame sooner

---

[1] In several parts of the apology, the author dwells on the circumstance of the book having been published while his original papers were out of his own possession. Three editions were printed in the year 1704; a fourth, corrected, in 1705.

gotten by satire than panegyric; the subject of the latter
being narrow, and that of the former infinite. Difference
between Athens and England, as to general and particular
satire. The author designs a panegyric on the world, and a
modest defence of the rabble.

SECTION I. THE INTRODUCTION.—A physico-mythological
dissertation on the different sorts of oratorial machines. Of
the bar and the bench. The author fond of the number Three;
promises a panegyric on it. Of pulpits; which are the best.
Of ladders; on which the British orators surpass all others.
Of the stage itinerant; the seminary of the two former. A
physical reason why those machines are elevated. Of the
curious contrivance of modern theatres. These three
machines emblematically represent the various sorts of
authors.

An apologetical dissertation for the Grub Street writers,
against their revolted rivals of Gresham and Will's. Superficial readers cannot easily find out wisdom, which is compared to several pretty things. Commentaries promised on
several writings of Grub Street authors; as *Reynard the Fox*,
Tom Thumb, *Dr. Faustus*, *Whittington and his Cat*, the *Hind
and Panther*, *Tommy Pots*, and the *Wise Men of Gotham*. The
author's pen and person worn out in serving the state.
Multiplicity of titles and dedications.

SECTION II. TALE OF A TUB.—Of a Father and his Three
Sons. His will, and his legacies to them. Of the young
men's carriage at the beginning; and of the genteel qualifications they acquired in town. Description of a new sect, who
adored their creator the tailor. Of their idol and their
system. The three brothers follow the mode against their
father's will; and get shoulder-knots by help of distinctions;
gold-lace, by help of tradition; flame-coloured satin lining,
by means of a supposed codicil; silver fringe, by virtue of
critical interpretation; and embroidery of Indian figures,
by laying aside the plain literal meaning. The will at last
locked up. Peter got into a lord's house, and after his death
turned out his children, and took in his own brothers in their
stead.

SECTION III. A DIGRESSION CONCERNING CRITICS.—Three
sorts of Critics; the two first sorts now extinct. The true
sort of critics' genealogy; office; definition. Antiquity of

their race proved from Pausanias, who represents them by Asses browsing on vines; and Herodotus, by Asses with horns; and by an Ass that frightened a Scythian army; and Diodorus, by a poisonous weed; and Ctesias, by serpents that poison with their vomit; and Terence, by the name of *Malevoli*. The true Critic compared to a Tailor, and to a true Beggar. Three characteristics of a true modern Critic.

SECTION IV. TALE OF A TUB, continued.—Peter assumes grandeur and titles; and, to support them, turns projector. The Author's hopes of being translated into foreign languages. Peter's first invention, of *Terra Australis Incognita*. The second of a remedy for Worms. The third, a Whispering-Office. Fourth, an Insurance-Office. Fifth, an Un versal Pickle. Sixth, a set of Bulls with leaden feet. Lastly, his pardons to malefactors. Peter's brains turned; he plays several tricks, and turns out his brother's wives. Gives his brothers bread for mutton and for wine. Tells huge lies; of a Cow's milk that would fill 3000 churches; of a Sign-post as large as a man-of-war; of a house that travelled 2000 leagues. The brothers steal a copy of the will, break open the cellar door, and are both kicked out of doors by Peter.

SECTION V. A DIGRESSION IN THE MODERN KIND.—Our author expatiates on his great pains to serve the public by instructing, and more by diverting. The Moderns having so far excelled the Ancients, the author gives them a receipt for a complete system of all arts and sciences, in a small pocket volume. Several defects discovered in Homer; and his ignorance in modern invention, etc. Our author's writings fit to supply all defects. He justifies his praising his own writings by modern examples.

SECTION VI. TALE OF A TUB, continued.—The two Brothers ejected, agree in a resolution to reform, according to the will. They take different names, and are found to be of different complexions. How Martin began rudely, but proceeded more cautiously in reforming his coat. Jack, of a different temper, and full of zeal, begins tearing all to pieces. He endeavours to kindle up Martin to the same pitch, but, not succeeding, they separate. Jack runs mad, gets many names, and founds the sect of Æolists.

SECTION VII. A DIGRESSION IN PRAISE OF DIGRESSIONS.—Digressions suited to modern palates. A proof of depraved appetites; but necessary for modern writers. Two ways now in use to be book-learned: 1. By learning titles; 2. By reading Indexes. Advantages of this last; and of Abstracts. The number of writers increasing above the quantity of matter, this method becomes necessary and useful. The Reader empowered to transplant this Digression.

SECTION VIII. TALE OF A TUB, continued.—System of the Æolists; they hold wind or spirit to be the origin of all things, and to bear a great part in their composition. Of the fourth and fifth animas attributed by them to man. Of their belching, or preaching. Their inspiration from Σκοτία. They use barrels for pulpits. Female officers used for inspiration; and why. The notion opposite to that of a deity, fittest to form a devil. Two devils dreaded by the Æolists. Their relation with a Northern nation. The Author's respect for this sect.

SECTION IX. DISSERTATION ON MADNESS.—Great conquerors of empires, and founders of sects in philosophy and religion, have generally been persons whose reason was disturbed. A small vapour, mounting to the brain, may occasion great revolutions. Examples; of Henry IV., who made great preparations for war, because of his mistress's absence; and of Louis XIV., whose great actions concluded in a fistula. Extravagant notions of several great philosophers, how nice to distinguish from madness. Mr. Wotton's fatal mistake in misapplying his peculiar talents. Madness the source of conquests and systems. Advantages of fiction and delusion over truth and reality. The outside of things better than the inside. Madness, how useful. A proposal for visiting Bedlam, and employing the divers members in a way useful to the public.

SECTION X. THE AUTHOR'S COMPLIMENTS TO THE READERS. —Great civilities practised between the authors and readers; and our author's thanks to the whole nation. How well satisfied authors and booksellers are. To what occasions we owe most of the present writings. Of a paltry scribbler our author is afraid of, and therefore desires Dr. Bentley's protection. He gives here his whole store at one meal. Usefulness of this treatise to different sorts of readers; the superficial, the ignorant, and the learned. Proposal for making some ample commentaries on this work; and of the usefulness of commentaries for dark writers. Useful hints for the commentators of this treatise.

SECTION XI. THE TALE OF A TUB, continued.—The author, not in haste to be at home, shows the difference between a traveller weary, or in haste, and another in good plight, that takes his pleasure and views every pleasant scene in his way. The sequel of Jack's adventures; his superstitious veneration for the Holy Scripture, and the uses he made of it. His flaming zeal, and blind submission to the Decrees. His harangue for Predestination. He covers roguish tricks with a show of devotion. Affects singularity in manners and speech. His aversion to music and painting. His discourses provoke sleep. His groaning and affecting to suffer for the good cause. The great antipathy of Peter and Jack made them both run into extremes, where they often met.

The degenerate ears of this age cannot afford a sufficient handle to hold men by. The senses and passions afford many handles. Curiosity is that by which our Author has held his readers so long. The rest of this story lost, etc.

THE CONCLUSION.—Of the proper seasons for publishing books. Of profound writers. Of the ghost of wit. Sleep and the Muses nearly related. Apology for the author's fits of dulness. Method and Reason the lacqueys of Invention. Our author's great collection of flowers of little use till now.

A DISCOURSE CONCERNING THE MECHANICAL OPERATION OF THE SPIRIT

The Author, at a loss what title to give this piece, finds after much pains, that of *A Letter to a Friend* to be the most in vogue, of modern excuses for haste and negligence, etc.

SECTION I. Mahomet's fancy of being carried to heaven by an ass, followed by many Christians. A great affinity between this creature and man. That talent of bringing his rider to heaven, the subject of this discourse; but for ass and rider, the author uses the synonymous terms of enlightened teacher and fanatic hearer. A tincture of enthusiasm runs through all men and all sciences; but prevails most in religion. Enthusiasm defined and distinguished.

That which is mechanical and artificial is treated of by our author. Though art oftentimes changes into nature: examples in the Scythian Longheads and English Roundheads.—Sense and reason must be laid aside to let this spirit operate. The objections about the manner of the Spirit from above descending upon the Apostles, make not against this spirit that arises within. The methods by which the assembly helps to work up this spirit, jointly with the preacher.

SECTION II. How some worship a good Being, others an evil. Most people confound the bounds of good and evil. Vain mortals think the Divinity interested in their meanest actions. The scheme of spiritual mechanism left out. Of the usefulness of quilted night-caps to keep in the heat, to give motion and vigour to the little animals that compose the brain. Sound of far greater use than sense in the operations of the Spirit, as in music. Inward light consists of theological monosyllables and mysterious texts. Of the great force of one vowel in canting; and of blowing the nose, hawking, spitting, and belching. The author to publish an Essay on the Art of Canting. Of speaking through the nose, or snuffling: its origin from a disease occasioned by a conflict between the Flesh and the Spirit. Inspired vessels, like lanterns, have a sorry sooty outside. Fanaticism deduced from the ancients, in their orgies, bacchanals, etc. Of their great lasciviousness on those occasions. The Fanatics of the first centuries and those of later times, generally agree in the same principle of improving spiritual into carnal ejaculations, etc.

THE BATTLE OF THE BOOKS

The Preface informs us this piece was written in 1697, on account of a famous dispute about Ancient and Modern Learning, between Sir William Temple and the Earl of Orrery on the one side, and Mr. Wotton and Bentley on the other.

War and invasions generally proceed from the attacks of Want and Poverty upon Plenty and Riches. The Moderns quarrel with the Ancients about the possession of the highest top of Parnassus, and desire them to surrender it or to let it be levelled. The answer of the Ancients not accepted. A

war ensues, in which rivulets of ink are spilt; and both
parties hang out their trophies—books of controversy. These
books haunted with disorderly spirits, though often bound
to the peace in libraries. The author's advice in this case
neglected, which occasions a terrible fight in St. James's
Library. Dr. Bentley, the library-keeper, a great enemy to
the Ancients. The Moderns, finding themselves 50,000
strong, give the Ancients ill language. Temple, a favourite
of the Ancients. An incident of a quarrel between a bee and
a spider, with their arguments on both sides. Æsop applies
them to the present dispute. The order of battle of the
Moderns, and names of their leaders. The leaders of the
Ancients. Jupiter calls a council of the Gods, and consults
the books of Fate; and then sends his orders below. Momus
brings the news to Criticism; whose habitation and company
is described. She arrives, and sheds her influence on her son
Wotton. The battle described. Paracelsus engages Galen;
Aristotle aims at Bacon, and kills Descartes; Homer overthrows Gondibert, kills Denham and Wesley,[1] Perrault [2] and
Fontenelle.[3] Encounter of Virgil and Dryden; of Lucan
and Blackmore; of Creech and Horace; of Pindar and
Cowley. The episode of Bentley and Wotton. Bentley's
armour. His speech to the modern generals. Scaliger's
answer. Bentley and Wotton march together. Bentley
attacks Phalaris and Æsop. Wotton attacks Temple in vain.
Boyle pursues Wotton; and meeting Bentley in his way, he
pursues and kills them both.

[1] Samuel Wesley, rector of Ormesby and Epworth, in Lincolnshire.
[2] Charles Perrault, author of a poem entitled, *Le Siècle de Louis
le Grand.*
[3] The author of *The Plurality of Worlds*, who died in 1756, within a
few days of completing his hundredth year.

THE AUTHOR'S APOLOGY

IF good and ill nature equally operated upon mankind, I
might have saved myself the trouble of this apology; for it
is manifest by the reception the following discourse has met
with, that those who approve it are a great majority among
the men of taste; yet there have been two or three treatises
written expressly against it, beside many others that have
flirted at it occasionally, without one syllable having been
ever published in its defence, or even quotation to its advantage that I can remember, except by the polite author of a
late discourse between a Deist and a Socinian.

Therefore, since the book seems calculated to live, at least
as long as our language and our taste admit no great alterations, I am content to convey some apology along with it.

The greatest part of that book was finished about thirteen
years since, 1696, which is eight years before it was published.
The author was then young, his invention at the height, and
his reading fresh in his head. By the assistance of some
thinking, and much conversation, he had endeavoured to
strip himself of as many real prejudices as he could; I say
real ones, because under the notion of prejudices, he knew to
what dangerous heights some men have proceeded. Thus
prepared, he thought the numerous and gross corruptions in
religion and learning might furnish matter for a satire that
would be useful and diverting. He resolved to proceed in
a manner that should be altogether new, the world having
been already too long nauseated with endless repetitions
upon every subject. The abuses in religion, he proposed to
set forth in the allegory of the coats and the three brothers,
which was to make up the body of the discourse: those in
learning he chose to introduce by way of digressions. He
was then a young gentleman much in the world,[1] and wrote
to the taste of those who were like himself; therefore, in
order to allure them, he gave a liberty to his pen which might

[1] Swift resided at Moor-park in 1696.

not suit with maturer years or graver characters, and which he could have easily corrected with a very few blots, had he been master of his papers for a year or two before their publication.

Not that he would have governed his judgment by the ill-placed cavils of the sour, the envious, the stupid and the tasteless, which he mentions with disdain. He acknowledges there are several youthful sallies, which from the grave and the wise may deserve a rebuke. But he desires to be answerable no further than he is guilty, and that his faults may not be multiplied by the ignorant, the unnatural, and uncharitable applications of those who have neither candour to suppose good meanings, nor palate to distinguish true ones. After which, he will forfeit his life if any one opinion can be fairly deduced from that book which is contrary to religion or morality.

Why should any clergyman of our church be angry to see the follies of fanaticism and superstition exposed, though in the most ridiculous manner; since that is perhaps the most probable way to cure them, or at least to hinder them from further spreading? Besides, though it was not intended for their perusal, it rallies nothing but what they preach against. It contains nothing to provoke them, by the least scurrility upon their persons or their functions. It celebrates the Church of England, as the most perfect of all others in discipline and doctrine; it advances no opinion they reject, nor condemns any they receive. If the clergy's resentment lay upon their hands, in my humble opinion they might have found more proper objects to employ them on; *nondum tibi defuit hostis :* I mean those heavy, illiterate scribblers, prostitute in their reputations, vicious in their lives, and ruined in their fortunes, who, to the shame of good sense as well as piety, are greedily read, merely upon the strength of bold, false, impious assertions, mixed with unmannerly reflections upon the priesthood, and openly intended against all religion: in short, full of such principles as are kindly received, because they are levelled to remove those terrors that religion tells men will be the consequence of immoral lives. Nothing like which is to be met with in this discourse, though some of them are pleased so freely to censure it. And I wish there were no other instance of what I have too frequently observed, that many of that reverend body are not always very nice in distinguishing between their enemies and their friends.

Had the author's intentions met with a more candid interpretation from some, whom out of respect he forbears to name, he might have been encouraged to an examination of books written by some of those authors above described, whose errors, ignorance, dulness, and villainy, he thinks he could have detected and exposed in such a manner, that the persons who are most conceived to be affected by them would soon lay them aside and be ashamed; but he has now given over those thoughts, since the weightiest men in the weightiest stations are pleased to think it a more dangerous point to laugh at those corruptions in religion, which they themselves must disapprove, than to endeavour pulling up those very foundations wherein all christians have agreed.

He thinks it no fair proceeding, that any person should offer determinately to fix a name upon the author of this discourse, who hath all along concealed himself from most of his nearest friends: yet several have gone a step farther, and pronounced another book [1] to have been the work of the same hand with this, which the author directly affirms to be a thorough mistake; he having as yet never so much as read that discourse: a plain instance how little truth there often is in general surmises, or in conjectures drawn from a similitude of style or way of thinking.

Had the author written a book to expose the abuses in law or in physic, he believes the learned professors in either faculty would have been so far from resenting it as to have given him thanks for his pains; especially if he had made an honourable reservation for the true practice of either science: but religion, they tell us, ought not to be ridiculed, and they tell us truth: yet surely the corruptions in it may; for we are taught by the tritest maxim in the world, that Religion being the best of things, its corruptions are likely to be the worst.

There is one thing which the judicious reader cannot but have observed, that some of those passages in this discourse which appear most liable to objection, are what they call parodies, where the author personates the style and manner of

[1] The celebrated Letter on Enthusiasm published in 1708.

other writers, whom he has a mind to expose. I shall produce one instance of a passage in which Dryden, L'Estrange, and some others I shall not name, are levelled at, who, having spent their lives in faction and apostacies, and all manner of vice, pretended to be sufferers for loyalty and religion. So Dryden tells us, in one of his prefaces, of *his merits and sufferings*, and thanks God that he *possesses his soul in patience*;[1] in other places he talks at the same rate; and L'Estrange often uses the like style; and I believe the reader may find more persons to give that passage an application: but this is enough to direct those who may have overlooked the author's intention.

There are three or four other passages which prejudiced or ignorant readers have drawn by great force to hint at ill meanings; as if they glanced at some tenets in religion. In answer to all which, the author solemnly protests he is entirely innocent; and never had it once in his thoughts, that anything he said, would in the least be capable of such interpretations, which he will engage to deduce full as fairly from the most innocent book in the world. And it will be obvious to every reader, that this was not any part of his scheme or design, the abuses he notes being such as all Church-of-England men agree in; nor was it proper for his subject to meddle with other points, than such as have been perpetually controverted since the Reformation.

To instance only in that passage about the three wooden machines mentioned in the introduction: in the original manuscript there was a description of a fourth, which those who had the papers in their power, blotted out, as having something in it of satire, that I suppose they thought was too particular; and therefore they were forced to change it to the number three, whence some have endeavoured to squeeze out a dangerous meaning, that was never thought on. And, indeed, the conceit was half spoiled by changing the numbers; that of four being much more cabalistic, and, therefore, better exposing the pretended virtue of numbers, a superstition there intended to be ridiculed.

Another thing to be observed is, that there generally runs

---

[1] In *The Tale of a Tub* Dryden is repeatedly referred to with great disrespect, not only as a translator and original author, but a mean spirited sycophant of the great.

an irony through the thread of the whole book, which the man of taste will observe and distinguish; and which will render some objections that have been made very weak and insignificant.

This Apology being chiefly intended for the satisfaction of future readers, it may be thought unnecessary to take any notice of such treatises as have been written against the ensuing discourse, which are already sunk into waste paper and oblivion, after the usual fate of common answerers to books which are allowed to have any merit: they are indeed like annuals, that grow about a young tree, and seem to vie with it for a summer, but fall and die with the leaves in autumn, and are never heard of more. When Dr. Eachard wrote his book about the contempt of the clergy, numbers of these answerers immediately started up, whose memory, if he had not kept alive by his replies, it would now be utterly unknown that he was ever answered at all. There is indeed an exception, when any great genius thinks it worth his while to expose a foolish piece; so we still read Marvell's answer to Parker [1] with pleasure, though the book it answers be sunk long ago: so the Earl of Orrery's remarks will be read with delight, when the dissertation he exposes will neither be sought nor found: [2] but these are no enterprises for common hands, nor to be hoped for above once or twice in an age. Men would be more cautious of losing their time in such an undertaking, if they did but consider that to answer a book effectually requires more pains and skill, more wit, learning and judgment, than were employed in the writing of it. And the author assures those gentlemen who have given themselves that trouble with him, that his discourse is the product of the study, the observation, and the invention of several years; that he often blotted out much more than he left, and if his papers had not been a long time out of his possession, they must have still undergone more severe corrections: and do they think such a building is to be battered with dirt-pellets, however envenomed the mouths may be that dis-

[1] Parker, afterwards Bishop of Oxford, wrote many treatises against the Dissenters, with insolence and contempt, says Burnet, that enraged them beyond measure; for which he was chastised by Andrew Marvell, under-secretary to Milton, in a little book called the *Rehearsal Transposed*.

[2] Boyle's *Remarks upon Bentley's Dissertation on the Epistles of Phalaris*.

charge them? He has seen the productions but of two answerers, one of which at first appeared as from an unknown hand, but since avowed by a person,[1] who, upon some occasions, has discovered no ill vein of humour. It is a pity any occasion should put him under a necessity of being so hasty in his productions, which, otherwise, might be entertaining. But there were other reasons obvious enough for his miscarriage in this; he wrote against the conviction of his talent, and entered upon one of the wrongest attempts in nature to turn into ridicule, by a week's labour, a work which had cost so much time and met with so much success in ridiculing others: the manner how he handled his subject I have now forgot, having just looked it over, when it first came out, as others did, merely for the sake of the title.

The other answer is from a person of a graver character, and is made up of half invective, and half annotation;[2] in the latter of which he has generally succeeded well enough. And the project at that time was not amiss to draw in readers to his pamphlet, several having appeared desirous that there might be some explication of the more difficult passages. Neither can he be altogether blamed for offering at the invective part, because it is agreed on all hands, that the author had given him sufficient provocation. The great objection is against his manner of treating it, very unsuitable to one of his function. It was determined by a fair majority, that this answerer had, in a way not to be pardoned, drawn his pen against a certain great man then alive, and universally reverenced for every good quality that could possibly enter into the composition of the most accomplished person; it was observed how he was pleased, and affected to have that noble writer called his adversary; and it was a point of satire well directed; for I have been told Sir William Temple was sufficiently mortified at the term. All the men of wit and politeness were immediately up in arms through indignation, which prevailed over their contempt, by the consequences they apprehended from such an example; and it grew Porsenna's case *idem trecenti juravimus*. In short, things were ripe for a general insurrection, till my Lord Orrery had

---

[1] Author of an *Account of Denmark*, a *Dissertation on Samplers*, and other burlesque pieces.
[2] Wotton's *Defence of his Reflections upon Ancient and Modern Learning*.

a little laid the spirit, and settled the ferment.   But his lordship being principally engaged with another antagonist,[1] it was thought necessary, in order to quiet the minds of men, that this opposer should receive a reprimand, which partly occasioned that discourse of the Battle of the Books; and the author was further at the pains to insert one or two remarks on him in the body of the book.

This answerer has been pleased to find fault with about a dozen passages, which the author will not be at the trouble of defending, further than by assuring the reader, that for the greater part, the reflector is entirely mistaken, and forces interpretations which never once entered into the writer's head, nor will (he is sure) into that of any reader of taste and candour; he allows two or three at most, there produced, to have been delivered unwarily: for which he desires to plead the excuse offered already, of his youth, and frankness of speech, and his papers being out of his power at the time they were published.

But this answerer insists, and says, what he chiefly dislikes, is the design: what that was, I have already told, and I believe there is not a person in England who can understand that book, that ever imagined it to be anything else, but to expose the abuses and corruptions in learning and religion.

But it would be good to know what design this reflector was serving, when he concludes his pamphlet with a caution to the reader to beware of thinking the author's wit was entirely his own: surely this must have had some allay of personal animosity at least, mixed with the design of serving the public, by so useful a discovery; and it indeed touches the author in a tender point; who insists upon it, that through the whole book he has not borrowed one single hint from any writer in the world; and he thought of all criticisms, that would never have been one.   He conceived, it was never disputed to be an original, whatever faults it might have.   However, this answerer produces three instances to prove this author's wit is not his own in many places.   The first is, that the names of Peter, Martin, and Jack, are borrowed from a letter of the late Duke of Buckingham.[2]   Whatever wit is contained in those three names, the author is content to give it up, and desires his readers will subtract as much as they placed upon

---

[1] Bentley, concerning Phalaris and Æsop.   [2] Villiers.

that account; at the same time protesting solemnly, that he never once heard of that letter, except in this passage of the answerer: so that the names were not borrowed, as he affirms, though they should happen to be the same; which, however, is odd enough, and what he hardly believes: that of Jack being not quite so obvious as the other two. The second instance to show the author's wit is not his own is Peter's banter (as he calls it in his Alsatia phrase)[1] upon transubstantiation, which is taken from the same duke's conference with an Irish priest, where a cork is turned into a horse. This the author confesses to have seen about ten years after his book was written, and a year or two after it was published. Nay, the answerer overthrows this himself; for he allows the Tale was written in 1697; and I think that pamplet was not printed in many years after. It was necessary that corruption should have some allegory as well as the rest; and the author invented the properest he could, without inquiring what other people had written; and the commonest reader will find, there is not the least resemblance between the two stories.—The third instance is in these words; " I have been assured, that the battle in St. James's Library is, *mutatis mutandis*, taken out of a French book, entitled, *Combat des Livres*, if I mis-remember not." In which passage there are two clauses observable; " I have been assured;" and, " if I mis-remember not." I desire first to know whether, if that conjecture proves an utter falsehood, those two clauses will be a sufficient excuse for this worthy critic? The matter is a trifle; but, would he venture to pronounce at this rate upon one of greater moment? I know nothing more contemptible in a writer than the character of a plagiary, which he here fixes at a venture; and this not for a passage, but a whole discourse, taken out from another book, only *mutatis mutandis*. The author is as much in the dark about this as the answerer; and will imitate him by an affirmation at random; that if there be a word of truth in this reflection, he is a paltry, imitating pedant; and the answerer is a person of wit, manners, and truth. He takes his boldness, from never having seen any such treatise in his life, nor heard of it before; and he is sure it is impossible for two writers, of different times and countries, to agree in their thoughts after such a manner,

[1] Banter was a word to which Swift had an especial aversion.

that two continued discourses shall be the same, only *mutatis mutandis*. Neither will he insist upon the mistake in the title; but let the answerer and his friend produce any book they please, he defies them to show one single particular where the judicious reader will affirm he has been obliged for the smallest hint; giving only allowance for the accidental encountering of a single thought, which he knows may sometimes happen; though he has never yet found it in that discourse, nor has heard it objected by anybody else.

So that if ever any design was unfortunately executed it must be that of this answerer, who, when he would have it observed that the author's wit is none of his own, is able to produce but three instances—two of them mere trifles, and all three manifestly false. If this be the way these gentlemen deal with the world in those criticisms, where we have not leisure to defeat them, their readers had need be cautious how they rely upon their credit; and whether this proceeding can be reconciled to humanity or truth, let those who think it worth their while determine.

It is agreed this answerer would have succeeded much better if he had stuck wholly to his business as a commentator upon the *Tale of a Tub*, wherein it cannot be denied that he hath been of some service to the public, and hath given very fair conjectures towards clearing up some difficult passages; but it is the frequent error of those men (otherwise very commendable for their labours), to make excursions beyond their talent and their office by pretending to point out the beauties and the faults, which is no part of their trade—which they always fail in—which the world never expected from them, nor gave them any thanks for endeavouring at. The part of Minellius, or Farnaby,[1] would have fallen in with his genius, and might have been serviceable to many readers, who cannot enter into the abstruser parts of that discourse; but *optat ephippia bos piger ;* the dull, unwieldy, ill-shaped ox, would needs put on the furniture of a horse, not considering he was born to labour, to plough the ground for the sake of superior beings, and that he has neither the shape, mettle, nor speed, of the noble animal he would affect to personate.

It is another pattern of this answerer's fair dealing to give

[1] Low commentators, who wrote notes upon classic authors for the use of schoolboys.

us hints that the author is dead, and yet to lay the suspicion upon somebody, I know not who, in the country; to which can only be returned, that he is absolutely mistaken in all his conjectures; and surely conjectures are, at best, too light a pretence to allow a man to assign a name in public. He condemns a book, and consequently the author, of whom he is utterly ignorant; yet at the same time he fixes in print what he thinks a disadvantageous character upon those who never deserved it. A man who receives a buffet in the dark, may be allowed to be vexed; but it is an odd kind of revenge, to go to cuffs in broad day with the first he meets and lay the last night's injury at his door. And thus much for the discreet, candid, pious, and ingenious answerer.

How the author came to be without his papers is a story not proper to be told, and of very little use, being a private fact; of which the reader would believe as little, or as much, as he thought good. He had, however, a blotted copy by him, which he intended to have written over with many alterations; and this the publishers were well aware of, having put it into the bookseller's preface that they apprehended a surreptitious copy, which was to be altered, etc. This, though not regarded by readers, was a real truth, only the surreptitious copy was rather that which was printed; and they made all the haste they could, which, indeed, was needless, the author not being at all prepared; but he has been told the bookseller was in much pain, having given a good sum of money for the copy.

In the author's original copy there were not so many chasms as appear in the book, and why some of them were left he knows not. Had the publication been trusted to him, he would have made several corrections of passages, against which nothing has been ever objected: he would likewise have altered a few of those that seem with any reason to be excepted against; but, to deal freely, the greatest number he should have left untouched, as never suspecting it possible any wrong interpretations could be made of them.

The author observes, at the end of the book, there is a discourse called a *Fragment*, which he more wondered to see in print than all the rest, having been a most inperfect sketch, with the addition of a few loose hints, which he once lent a gentleman who had designed a discourse on somewhat the same subject; he never thought of it afterwards, and it was a sufficient surprise to see it pieced up together wholly out of the method and scheme he had intended, for it was the ground-work of a much larger discourse, and he was sorry to observe the materials so foolishly employed.

There is one further objection made by those who have answered this book, as well as by some others, that Peter is frequently made to repeat oaths and curses. Every reader observes, it was necessary to know that Peter did swear and curse. The oaths are not printed out, but only supposed; and the idea of an oath is not immoral, like the idea of a profane or immodest speech. A man may laugh at the Popish folly of cursing people to hell, and imagine them swearing, without any crime; but lewd words, or dangerous opinions, though printed by halves, fill the reader's mind with ill ideas; and of these the author cannot be accused. For the judicious reader will find that the severest strokes of satire in his book are levelled against the modern custom of employing wit upon those topics; of which there is a remarkable instance in the 112th and 113th pages, as well as in several others, though perhaps once or twice expressed in too free a manner, excusable only for the reasons already alleged. Some overtures have been made by a third hand to the bookseller for the author's altering those pages which he thought might require it; but it seems the bookseller will not hear of any such thing, being apprehensive it might spoil the sale of the book.

The author cannot conclude this apology without making this one reflection: that, as wit is the noblest and most useful gift of human nature, so humour is the most agreeable; and where these two enter far into the composition of any work, they will render it always acceptable to the world. Now, the great part of those who have no share or taste of either, but by their pride, pedantry, and ill manners, lay themselves bare to the lashes of both, think the blow is weak, because they are insensible; and, where wit has any mixture of raillery, it is but calling it banter, and the work is done. This polite word of theirs was first borrowed from the bullies in Whitefriars, then fell among the footmen, and at last retired to the pedants; by whom it is applied as properly to the production of wit as if I should apply it to Sir Isaac

Newton's mathematics. But, if this bantering, as they call it, be so despisable a thing, whence comes it to pass they have such a perpetual itch toward it themselves? To instance only in the answerer already mentioned: it is grievous to see him, in some of his writings, at every turn going out of his way to be waggish to tell us of a cow that pricked up her tail; and in his answer to this discourse, he says, it is all a farce and a ladle; with other passages equally shining. One may say of these *impedimenta literarum*, that wit owes them a shame; and they cannot take wiser counsel than to keep out of harm's way, or, at least, not to come till they are sure they are called.

To conclude: with those allowances above required this book should be read; after which, the author conceives few things will remain which may not be excused in a young writer. He wrote only to the men of wit and taste; and he thinks he is not mistaken in his accounts when he says they have been all of his side enough to give him the vanity of telling his name; wherein the world, with all its wise con-jectures, is yet very much in the dark; which circumstance is no disagreeable amusement either to the public or himself.

The author is informed that the bookseller has prevailed on several gentlemen to write some explanatory notes, for the goodness of which he is not to answer, having never seen any of them, nor intending it, till they appear in print; when it is not unlikely he may have the pleasure to find twenty meanings which never entered into his imagination.

June 3, 1709.

POSTSCRIPT.—Since the writing of this, which was about a year ago, a prostitute bookseller has published a foolish paper, under the name of *Notes on the Tale of a Tub*, with some account of the author: and, with an insolence which I suppose is punishable by law, has presumed to assign certain names. It will be enough for the author to assure the world, that the writer of that paper is utterly wrong in all his conjectures upon that affair. The author further asserts that the whole work is entirely of one hand, which every reader of judgment will easily discover; the gentleman who gave the copy to the bookseller, being a friend of the author, and using no other liberties besides that of expunging certain passages, where now the chasms appear under the name of *desiderata*. But, if any person will prove his claim to three lines in the whole book, let him step forth and tell his name and titles; upon which, the bookseller shall have orders to prefix them to the next edition, and the claimant shall from henceforward be acknowledged the undisputed author.

Treatises written by the same author, most of them mentioned in the following Discourses; which will be speedily published.

A Character of the present Set of Wits in this Island.

A panegyrical Essay upon the Number Three.

A Dissertation upon the principal Productions of Grub Street.

Lectures upon a Dissection of Human Nature.

A Panegyric upon the World.

An analytical Discourse upon Zeal, *histori-theo-physiologically* considered.

A general History of Ears.

A modest Defence of the Proceedings of the Rabble in all ages.

A Description of the Kingdom of Absurdities.

A Voyage into England, by a Person of Quality in *terra australis incognita*, translated from the Original.

A critical Essay upon the Art of Canting, philosophically, physically, and musically considered.

THE BOOKSELLER'S DEDICATION

TO THE RIGHT HONOURABLE JOHN LORD SOMERS

MY LORD,—Although the author has written a large dedication, yet that being addressed to a prince, whom I am never
likely to have the honour of being known to; a person
besides, as far as I can observe, not at all regarded, or thought
on by any of our present writers; and being wholly free
from that slavery which booksellers usually lie under, to the
caprice of authors; I think it a wise piece of presumption
to inscribe these papers to your lordship and to implore your
lordship's protection of them. God and your lordship know
their faults and their merits; for, as to my own particular,
I am altogether a stranger to the matter; and though everybody else should be equally ignorant, I do not fear the sale of
the book, at all the worse, upon that score. Your lordship's
name on the front in capital letters will at any time get off
one edition: neither would I desire any other help to grow
an alderman, than a patent for the sole privilege of dedicating
to your lordship.

I should now in right of a dedicator, give your lordship
a list of your own virtues, and at the same time, be very
unwilling to offend your modesty; but chiefly, I should
celebrate your liberality towards men of great parts and
small fortunes, and give you broad hints that I mean myself.
And I was just going on, in the usual method, to peruse a
hundred or two of dedications, and transcribe an abstract
to be applied to your lordship; but I was diverted by a
certain accident: for upon the covers of these papers I
casually observed written in large letters the two following
words, DETUR DIGNISSIMO; which, for aught I knew,
might contain some important meaning. But it unluckily
fell out, that none of the authors I employ understood Latin;
(though I have them often in pay to translate out of that
language); I was therefore compelled to have recourse to
the curate of our parish, who englished it thus, "Let it be
given to the worthiest:" and his comment was, that the
author meant his work should be dedicated to the sublimest
genius of the age for wit, learning, judgment, eloquence,

and wisdom. I called at a poet's chamber (who works for my shop) in an alley hard by, showed him the translation, and desired his opinion who it was that the author could mean: he told me, after some consideration, that vanity was a thing he abhorred; but by the description, he thought himself to be the person aimed at; and at the same time, he very kindly offered his own assistance gratis towards penning a dedication to himself. I desired him, however, to give a second guess; Why then, said he, it must be I, or my Lord Somers. From thence I went to several other wits of my acquaintance, with no small hazard and weariness to my person, from a prodigious number of dark, winding stairs; but found them all in the same story, both of your lordship and themselves. Now, your lordship is to understand, that this proceeding was not of my own invention; for I have somewhere heard it is a maxim, that those to whom everybody allows the second place, have an undoubted title to the first.

This infallibly convinced me that your lordship was the person intended by the author. But being very unacquainted in the style and form of dedications I employed those wits aforesaid to furnish me with hints and materials, towards a panegyric upon your lordship's virtues.

In two days they brought me ten sheets of paper, filled up on every side. They swore to me, that they had ransacked whatever could be found in the characters of Socrates, Aristides, Epaminondas, Cato, Tully, Atticus, and other hard names, which I cannot now recollect. However, I have reason to believe, they imposed upon my ignorance; because, when I came to read over their collections, there was not a syllable there, but what I and everybody else knew as well as themselves: therefore I grievously suspect a cheat; and that these authors of mine stole and transcribed every word, from the universal report of mankind. So that I look upon myself as fifty shillings out of pocket, to no manner of purpose.

If by altering the title I could make the same materials serve for another dedication (as my betters have done), it would help to make up my loss; but I have made several persons dip here and there in those papers, and before they read three lines, they have all assured me plainly, that they cannot possibly be applied to any person besides your lordship.

I expected indeed, to have heard of your lordship's bravery at the head of an army; of your undaunted courage in mounting a breach, or scaling a wall; or to have had your pedigree traced in a lineal descent from the house of *Austria;* or, of your wonderful talent at dress and dancing; or, your profound knowledge in *algebra, metaphysics,* and the *oriental* tongues. But to ply the world with an old beaten story of your wit, and eloquence, and learning, and wisdom, and justice, and politeness, and candour, and evenness of temper in all scenes of life; of that great discernment in discovering, and readiness in favouring deserving men; with forty other common topics; I confess, I have neither conscience nor countenance to do it. Because there is no virtue, either of a public or a private life, which some circumstances of your own have not often produced upon the stage of the world; and those few, which, for want of occasions to exert them, might otherwise have passed unseen, or unobserved, by your friends, your enemies have at length brought to light.

It is true, I should be very loth the bright example of your lordship's virtues should be lost to after-ages, both for their sake and your own; but chiefly because they will be so very necessary to adorn the history of a late reign;[1] and that is another reason why I would forbear to make a recital of them here; because I have been told by wise men, that as dedications have run for some years past, a good historian will not be apt to have recourse thither in search of characters.

There is one point, wherein I think we dedicators would do well to change our measures; I mean, instead of running on so far upon the praise of our patrons' liberality, to spend a word or two in admiring their patience. I can put no greater compliment on your lordship's, than by giving you so ample an occasion to exercise it at present.—Though perhaps I shall not be apt to reckon much merit to your lordship upon that score, who having been formerly used to tedious harangues and sometimes to as little purpose, will be the readier to pardon this; especially when it is offered by one, who is, with all respect and veneration, my lord, your lordship's most obedient and most faithful servant,

THE BOOKSELLER.

[1] King William's, whose memory he defended in the House of Lords.

THE BOOKSELLER TO THE READER

IT is now six years since these papers came first to my hand, which seems to have been about a tewlvemonth after they were written; for the author tells us in his preface to the first treatise, that he has calculated it for the year 1697, and in several passages of that discourse, as well as the second, it appears they were written about that time.

As to the author, I can give no manner of satisfaction; however I am credibly informed, that this publication is without his knowledge; for he concludes the copy is lost, having lent it to a person, since dead, and being never in possession of it after: so that, whether the work received his last hand, or whether he intended to fill up the defective places, is likely to remain a secret.

If I should go about to tell the reader, by what accident I became master of these papers, it would, in this unbelieving age, pass for little more than the cant or jargon of the trade. I therefore gladly spare both him and myself so unnecessary a trouble. There yet remains a difficult question, why I published them no sooner. I forbore upon two accounts; first, because I thought I had better work upon my own hands; and secondly, because I was not without some hope of hearing from the author, and receiving his directions. But I have been lately alarmed with intelligence of a surreptitious copy, which a certain great wit had new polished and refined, or, as our present writers express themselves, fitted to the humour of the age: as they have already done, with great felicity, to Don Quixote, Boccalini, La Bruyere, and other authors. However, I thought it fairer dealing to offer the whole work in its naturals. If any gentleman will please to furnish me with a key, in order to explain the more difficult parts, I shall very gratefully acknowledge the favour, and print it by itself.

THE EPISTLE DEDICATORY

TO HIS ROYAL HIGHNESS PRINCE POSTERITY [1]

SIR,—I here present your highness with the fruits of a very few leisure hours, stolen from the short intervals of a world of business, and of an employment quite alien from such amusements as this the poor production of that refuse of time, which has laid heavy upon my hands during a long prorogation of parliament, a great dearth of foreign news, and a tedious fit of rainy weather; for which, and other reasons, it cannot choose extremely to deserve such a patronage as that of your highness, whose numberless virtues, in so few years, make the world look upon you as the future example to all princes; for although your highness is hardly got clear of infancy, yet has the universal learned world already resolved upon appealing to your future dictates, with the lowest and most resigned submission; fate having decreed you sole arbiter of the productions of human wit, in this polite and most accomplished age. Methinks the number of appellants were enough to shock and startle any judge, of a genius less unlimited than yours; but in order to prevent such glorious trials, the person, it seems, to whose care the education of your highness is committed, has resolved (as I am told) to keep you in almost a universal ignorance of our studies, which it is your inherent birth-right to inspect.

It is amazing to me that this person should have the assurance, in the face of the sun, to go about persuading your highness that our age is almost wholly illiterate, and has hardly produced one writer upon any subject. I know very well, that when your highness shall come to riper years, and have gone through the learning of antiquity, you will be too curious to neglect inquiring into the authors of the very age before you: and to think that this insolent, in the account he is preparing for your view, designs to reduce them to a

[1] It is the usual style of decried writers to appeal to Posterity, who is here represented as a prince in his nonage, and Time as his governor.

number so insignificant as I am ashamed to mention; it moves my zeal and my spleen for the honour and interest of our vast flourishing body, as well as of myself, for whom, I know by long experience, he has professed, and still continues, a peculiar malice.

It is not unlikely that, when your highness will one day peruse what I am now writing, you may be ready to expostulate with your governor upon the credit of what I here affirm, and command him to show you some of our productions. To which he will answer (for I am well informed of his designs), by asking your highness where they are? and what is become of them? and pretend it a demonstration that there never were any, because they are not then to be found. Not to be found! who has mislaid them? are they sunk in the abyss of things? it is certain, that in their own nature, they were light enough to swim upon the surface for all eternity. Therefore the fault is in him, who tied weights so heavy to their heels as to depress them to the centre. Is their very essence destroyed? who has annihilated them? were they drowned by purges, or martyred by pipes? who administered them to the posteriors of ——? But, that it may no longer be a doubt with your highness, who is to be the author of this universal ruin, I beseech you to observe that large and terrible scythe which your governor affects to bear continually about him. Be pleased to remark the length and strength, the sharpness and hardness, of his nails and teeth; consider his baneful, abominable breath, enemy to life and matter, infectious and corrupting: and then reflect whether it be possible for any mortal ink and paper of this generation to make a suitable resistance. O! that your highness would one day resolve to disarm this usurping *maître du palais*[1] of his furious engines, and bring your empire *hors de page*.[2]

It were needless to recount the several methods of tyranny and destruction, which your governor is pleased to practise upon this occasion. His inveterate malice is such to the writings of our age, that of several thousands produced

[1] Comptroller. The kingdom of France had a race of kings which they call *les roys faineans* (from their doing nothing), who lived lazily in their apartments, while the kingdom was administered by the Mayor de Palais.—H.

[2] Out of guardianship.

yearly from this renowned city, before the next revolution of the sun, there is not one to be heard of: Unhappy infants! many of them barbarously destroyed, before they have so much as learnt their mother tongue to beg for pity. Some he stifles in their cradles; others he frights into convulsions, whereof they suddenly die; some he flays alive; others he tears limb from limb. Great numbers are offered to Moloch; and the rest, tainted by his breath, die of a languishing consumption.

But the concern I have most at heart, is for our corporation of poets; from whom I am preparing a petition to your highness, to be subscribed with the names of one hundred and thirty-six of the first rate; but whose immortal productions are never likely to reach your eyes, though each of them is now an humble and earnest apellant for the laurel, and has large comely volumes ready to show, for a support to his pretensions. The never-dying works of these illustrious persons, your governor, sir, has devoted to unavoidable death; and your highness is to be made believe, that our age has never arrived at the honour to produce one single poet.

We confess Immortality to be a great and powerful goddess; but in vain we offer up to her our devotions and our sacrifices, if your highness's governor, who has usurped the priesthood, must, by an unparalleled ambition and avarice, wholly intercept and devour them.

To affirm that our age is altogether unlearned, and devoid of writers in any kind, seems to be an assertion so bold and so false, that I have been some time thinking the contrary may almost be proved by uncontrollable demonstration. It is true, indeed, that although their numbers be vast, and their productions numerous in proportion, yet are they hurried so hastily off the scene, that they escape our memory, and elude our sight. When I first thought of this address, I had prepared a copious list of titles to present your highness, as an undisputed argument for what I affirm. The originals were posted fresh upon all gates and corners of streets; but, returning in a very few hours to take a review, they were all torn down, and fresh ones in their places. I inquired after them among readers and booksellers; but I inquired in vain; the memorial of them was lost among men; their places were no more to be found; and I was laughed to scorn for a clown and a pedant, without all taste and refinement, little versed in the course of present affairs, and that knew nothing of what had passed in the best companies of court and town. So that I can only avow in general to your highness, that we do abound in learning and wit; but to fix upon particulars, is a task too slippery for my slender abilities. If I should venture in a windy day to affirm to your highness, that there is a large cloud near the horizon, in the form of a bear, another in the zenith, with the head of an ass; a third to the westward, with claws like a dragon; and your highness should in a few minutes think fit to examine the truth, it is certain they would all be changed in figure and position: new ones would arise, and all we could agree upon would be, that clouds there were, but that I was grossly mistaken in the zoography and topography of them.

But your governor perhaps may still insist, and put the question,—What is then become of those immense bales of paper, which must needs have been employed in such numbers of books? can these also be wholly annihilate, and so of a sudden, as I pretend? What shall I say in return of so invidious an objection? it ill befits the distance between your highness and me, to send you for ocular conviction to a jakes, or an oven; to the windows of a bawdy-house, or to a sordid lantern. Books, like men their authors, have no more than one way of coming into the world, but there are ten thousand to go out of it, and return no more.

I profess to your highness, in the integrity of my heart, that what I am going to say is literally true this minute I am writing: what revolutions may happen before it shall be ready for your perusal, I can by no means warrant: however, I beg you to accept it as a specimen of our learning, our politeness, and our wit. I do therefore affirm, upon the word of a sincere man, that there is now actually in being a certain poet, called John Dryden, whose translation of Virgil was lately printed in a large folio, well bound, and, if diligent search were made, for aught I know, is yet to be seen. There is another, called Nahum Tate, who is ready to make oath that he has caused many reams of verse to be published, whereof both himself and his bookseller (if lawfully required) can still produce authentic copies, and therefore wonders why the world is pleased to make such a secret of it. There is a third, known by the name of Tom Durfey, a poet of a vast comprehension, a universal genius, and most profound learning. There are also one Mr. Rymer, and one Mr. Dennis, most profound critics. There is a person styled Dr. Bentley, who has written near a thousand pages of immense erudition, giving a full and true account of a certain squabble, of wonderful importance, between himself and a bookseller: he is a writer of infinite wit and humour; no man rallies with a better grace, and in more sprightly turns. Further, I avow to your highness, that with these eyes I have beheld the person of William Wotton, B.D., who has written a good sizeable volume against a friend of your governor [1] (from whom, alas! he must therefore look for little favour), in a most gentlemanly style, adorned with the utmost politeness and civility; replete with discoveries equally valuable for their novelty and use; and embellished with traits of wit, so poignant and so apposite, that he is a worthy yokemate to his forementioned friend.

Why should I go upon further particulars, which might fill a volume with the just eulogies of my contemporary brethren? I shall bequeath this piece of justice to a larger work, wherein I intend to write a character of the present set of wits in our nation: their persons I shall describe particularly and at length, their genius and understandings in miniature.

In the meantime I do here make bold to present your highness with a faithful abstract, drawn from the universal body of all arts and sciences, intended wholly for your service and instruction: nor do I doubt in the least, but your highness will peruse it as carefully, and make as considerable improvements, as other young princes have already done, by the many volumes of late years written for a help to their studies. [2]

That your highness may advance in wisdom and virtue, as well as years, and at last outshine all your royal ancestors, shall be the daily prayer of,

> Sir, your highness's most devoted, etc.

December, 1697.

[1] Sir William Temple, with whom Wotton was engaged in the controversy concerning ancient and modern learning.

[2] There were innumerable books printed for the use of the Dauphin of France.

THE AUTHOR'S PREFACE

THE wits of the present age being so very numerous and penetrating, it seems the grandees of church and state begin to fall under horrible apprehensions, lest these gentlemen, during the intervals of a long peace, should find leisure to pick holes in the weak sides of religion and government. To prevent which, there has been much thought employed of late, upon certain projects for taking off the force and edge of those formidable inquirers, from canvassing and reasoning upon such delicate points. They have at length fixed upon one, which will require some time as well as cost to perfect. Meanwhile, the danger hourly increasing, by new levies of wits, all appointed (as there is reason to fear) with pen, ink, and paper, which may, at an hour's warning, be drawn out into pamphlets, and other offensive weapons, ready for immediate execution, it was judged of absolute necessity, that some present expedient be thought on, till the main design can be brought to maturity. To this end, at a grand committee some days ago, this important discovery was made by a certain curious and refined observer—that seamen have a custom, when they meet a whale, to fling him out an empty tub by way of amusement, to divert him from laying violent hands upon the ship. This parable was immediately mythologised; the whale was interpreted to be Hobbes' *Leviathan*, which tosses and plays with all schemes of religion and government, whereof a great many are hollow, and dry, and empty, and noisy, and wooden, and given to rotation: this is the leviathan, whence the terrible wits of our age are said to borrow their weapons. The ship in danger is easily understood to be its old antitype, the commonwealth. But how to analyse the tub, was a matter of difficulty; when, after long inquiry and debate, the literal meaning was preserved; and it was decreed that, in order to prevent these leviathans from tossing and sporting with the commonwealth, which of itself is too apt to fluctuate, they should be diverted from that game by a *Tale of a Tub*. And, my genius being conceived to lie not unhappily that way, I had the honour done me to be engaged in the performance.

This is the sole design in publishing the following treatise, which I hope will serve for an *interim* of some months to employ those unquiet spirits, till the perfecting of that great work; into the secret of which, it is reasonable the courteous reader should have some little light.

It is intended, that a large academy be erected, capable of containing nine thousand seven hundred forty and three persons; which, by modest computation, is reckoned to be pretty near the current number of wits in this island. These are to be disposed into the several schools of this academy, and there pursue those studies to which their genius most inclines them. The undertaker himself will publish his proposals with all convenient speed; to which I shall refer the curious reader for a more particular account, mentioning at present only a few of the principal schools. There is, first, a large pæderastic school, with French and Italian masters. There is also the spelling school, a very spacious building: the school of looking-glasses: the school of swearing: the school of critics: the school of salivation: the school of hobby-horses: the school of poetry: the school of tops: the school of spleen: the school of gaming: with many others, too tedious to recount. No person to be admitted member into any of these schools without an attestation under two sufficient persons' hands certifying him to be a wit.

But, to return: I am sufficiently instructed in the principal duty of a preface, if my genius were capable of arriving at it. Thrice have I forced my imagination to make the tour of my invention, and thrice it has returned empty; the latter having been wholly drained by the following treatise. Not so my more successful brethren the moderns; who will by no means let slip a preface or dedication, without some notable distinguishing stroke to surprise the reader at the entry, and kindle a wonderful expectation of what is to ensue. Such was that of a most ingenious poet, who, soliciting his brain for something new, compared himself to the hangman, and his patron to the patient: this was *insigne, recens, indictum ore alio*. When I went through that necessary and noble course of study, I had the happiness to observe many such egregious touches, which I shall not injure the authors by transplanting: because I have remarked, that nothing is so very tender as a modern piece of wit, and which is apt to suffer so much in the carriage. Some things are extremely witty to-day, or fasting, or in this place, or at eight o'clock, or over a bottle, or spoke by Mr. What'd'y'call'm, or in a summer's morning: any of the which, by the smallest transposal or misapplication, is utterly annihilate. Thus wit has its walks and purlieus, out of which it may not stray the breadth of a hair, upon peril of being lost. The moderns have artfully fixed this mercury, and reduced it to the circumstances of time, place, and person. Such a jest there is, that will not pass out of Covent Garden; and such a one that is nowhere intelligible but at Hyde Park corner. Now, though it sometimes tenderly affects me to consider, that all the towardly passages I shall deliver in the following treatise, will grow quite out of date and relish with the first shifting of the present scene, yet I must needs subscribe to the justice of this proceeding: because, I cannot imagine why we should be at the expense to furnish wit for succeeding ages, when the former have made no sort of provision for ours: wherein I speak the sentiment of the very newest, and consequently the most orthodox refiners, as well as my own. However, being extremely solicitous that every accomplished person, who has got into the taste of wit calculated for this present month of August, 1697, should descend to the very bottom of all the sublime, throughout this treatise; I hold fit to lay down this general maxim: whatever reader desires to have a thorough comprehension of an author's thoughts, cannot take a better method than by putting himself into the circumstances and postures of life, that the writer was in upon every important passage, as it flowed from his pen: for this will introduce a parity, and strict correspondence of ideas, between the reader and the author. Now, to assist the diligent reader in so delicate an affair, as far as brevity will permit, I have recollected, that the shrewdest pieces of this treatise were conceived in bed in a garret; at other times, for a reason best known to myself, I thought fit to sharpen my invention with hunger; and, in general, the whole work was begun, continued, and ended, under a long course of physic, and a great want of money. Now, I do affirm, it will be absolutely impossible for the candid peruser to go along with me in a great many bright passages, unless, upon the several difficulties emergent, he will please to capacitate and prepare himself by these directions. And this I lay down as my principal *postulatum*.

Because I have professed to be a most devoted servant of all modern forms, I apprehend some curious wit may object against me, for proceeding thus far in a preface, without declaiming, according to the custom, against the multitude of writers, whereof the whole multitude of writers most reasonably complain. I am just come from perusing some hundreds of prefaces, wherein the authors do, at the very beginning, address the gentle reader concerning this enormous grievance. Of these I have preserved a few examples, and shall set them down as near as my memory has been able to retain them.

One begins thus:—For a man to set up for a writer, when the press swarms with, etc.

Another:—The tax upon paper does not lessen the number of scribblers, who daily pester, etc.

Another:—When every little would-be wit takes pen in hand, 'tis in vain to enter the lists, etc.

Another:—To observe what trash the press swarms with, etc.

Another:—Sir, It is merely in obedience to your commands that I venture into the public; for who upon a less consideration would be of a party with such a rabble of scribblers, etc.

Now, I have two words in my own defence against this objection. First, I am far from granting the number of writers a nuisance to our nation, having strenuously maintained the contrary, in several parts of the following discourse. Secondly, I do not well understand the justice of this proceeding; because I observe many of these polite prefaces to be not only from the same hand, but from those who are most voluminous in their several productions. Upon which I shall tell the reader a short tale.

A mountebank, in Leicester Fields, had drawn a huge assembly about him. Among the rest, a fat unwieldy fellow, half stifled in the press, would be every fit crying out, " Lord! what a filthy crowd is here! pray, good people, give way a little. Bless me! what a devil has raked this rabble together! z—ds? what squeezing is this! honest friend, remove your elbow." At last a weaver, that stood next him, could hold no longer. " A plague confound you (said he) for an over-grown sloven; and who, in the devil's name, I wonder, helps to make up the crowd half so much as yourself? Don't you consider, with a pox, that you take up more room with that carcass than any five here? Is not the place as free for us as for you? bring your own guts to a reasonable compass, and be d—n'd, and then I'll engage we shall have room enough for us all."

There are certain common privileges of a writer, the benefit whereof, I hope, there will be no reason to doubt; particularly, that where I am not understood, it shall be concluded, that something very useful and profound is couched underneath: and again, that whatever word or sentence is printed in a different character, shall be judged to contain something extraordinary either of wit or sublime.

As for the liberty I have thought fit to take of praising myself, upon some occasions or none, I am sure it will need no excuse, if a multitude of great examples be allowed sufficient authority: for it is here to be noted, that praise was originally a pension paid by the world; but the moderns, finding the trouble and charge too great in collecting it, have lately bought out the fee-simple; since which time the right of presentation is wholly in ourselves. For this reason it is, that when an author makes his own eulogy, he uses a certain form to declare and insist upon his title, which is commonly in these or the like words, " I speak without vanity; " which I think plainly shows it to be a matter of right and justice. Now I do here once for all declare, that in every encounter of this nature through the following treatise, the form aforesaid is implied; which I mention, to save the trouble of repeating it on so many occasions.

It is a great ease to my conscience, that I have written so elaborate and useful a discourse, without one grain of satire intermixed; which is the sole point wherein I have taken leave to dissent from the famous originals of our age and country. I have observed some satirists to use the public much at the rate that pedants do a naughty boy, ready horsed for discipline: first, expostulate the case, then plead the necessity of the rod from great provocations, and conclude every period with a lash. Now, if I know anything of mankind, these gentlemen might very well spare their reproof and correction: for there is not, through all nature, another so callous and insensible a member as the world's posteriors, whether you apply to it the toe or the birch. Besides, most of our late satirists seem to lie under a sort of mistake; that because nettles have the prerogative to sting, therefore all other weeds must do so too. I make not this comparison out of the least design to detract from these worthy writers; for it is well known among mythologists, that weeds have the pre-eminence over all other vegetables; and therefore the first monarch of this island, whose taste and judgment were so acute and refined, did very wisely root out the roses from the collar of the order, and plant the thistles in their stead, as the nobler flower of the two. For which reason it is conjectured by profounder antiquaries, that the satirical itch, so prevalent in this part of our island, was first brought among us from beyond the Tweed. Here may it long flourish and abound: may it survive and neglect the scorn of the world, with as much ease and contempt as the world is insensible to the lashes of it. May their own dulness, or that of their party, be no discouragement for the authors to proceed; but let them remember, it is with wits as with razors, which are never so apt to cut those they are employed on as when they have lost their edge. Besides, those whose teeth are too rotten to bite, are best, of all others, qualified to revenge that defect with their breath.

I am not like other men, to envy or undervalue the talents I cannot reach; for which reason I must needs bear a true honour to this large eminent sect of our British writers. And I hope this little panegyric will not be offensive to their ears, since it has the advantage of being only designed for themselves. Indeed, nature herself has taken order, that fame and honour should be purchased at a better pennyworth by satire than by any other productions of the brain; the world being soonest provoked to praise by lashes, as men are to love. There is a problem in an ancient author, why dedications, and other bundles of flattery, run all upon stale musty topics, without the smallest tincture of anything new; not only to the torment and nauseating of the Christian reader, but, if not suddenly prevented, to the universal spreading of that pestilential disease, the lethargy, in this island: whereas there is very little satire, which has not something in it untouched before. The defects of the former are usually imputed to the want of invention among those who are dealers in that kind; but, I think, with a great deal of injustice, the solution being easy and natural; for the materials of panegyric, being very few in number, have been long since exhausted. For, as health is but one thing and has been always the same, whereas diseases are by thousands, beside new and daily additions; so, all the virtues that have been ever in mankind, are to be counted upon a few fingers; but their follies and vices are innumerable, and time adds hourly to the heap. Now the utmost a poor poet can do, is to get by heart a list of the cardinal virtues, and deal them with his utmost liberality to his hero or his patron: he may ring the changes as far as it will go, and vary his phrase till he has talked round; but the reader quickly finds it is all pork, with a little variety of sauce. For there is no inventing terms of art beyond our ideas; and, when our ideas are exhausted terms of art must be so too.

But though the matter for panegyric were as fruitful as the topics of satire, yet would it not be hard to find out a sufficient reason why the latter will be always better received than the first. For, this being bestowed only upon one, or a few persons at a time, is sure to raise envy, and consequently ill words from the rest, who have no share in the blessing; but satire, being levelled at all, is never resented for an offence by any, since every individual person makes bold to understand it of others, and very wisely removes his particular part of the burden upon the shoulders of the world, which are broad enough, and able to bear it. To this purpose, I have sometimes reflected upon the difference between Athens and England, with respect to the point before us. In the Attic commonwealth, it was the privilege and birth-right of every citizen and poet to rail aloud, and in public, or to expose upon the stage, by name, any person they pleased, though of the greatest figure, whether a Creon, an Hyperbolus, an Alcibiades, or a Demosthenes; but, on the other side, the least reflecting word let fall against the people in general, was immediately caught up, and revenged upon the authors, however considerable for their quality or their merits. Whereas in England it is just the reverse of all this. Here, you may securely display your utmost rhetoric against mankind, in the face of the world; tell them, " That all are gone astray; that there is none that doth good, no not one; that we live in the very dregs of time; that knavery and atheism are epidemic as the pox; that honesty is fled with Astræa;" with any other common-places, equally new and eloquent, which are furnished by the *splendida bilis.* [Horace, Spleen.] And when you have done the whole audience, far from being offended, shall return you thanks as a deliverer of precious and useful truths. Nay, further; it is but to venture your lungs, and you may preach in Covent Garden against foppery and fornication, and something else: against pride and dissimulation, and bribery, at Whitehall: you may expose rapine and injustice in the inns of court chapel: and in a city pulpit, be as fierce as you please against avarice, hypocrisy, and extortion. 'Tis but a ball bandied to and fro, and every man carries a racket about him, to strike it from himself, among the rest of the company. But, on the other side, whoever should mistake the nature of things so far as to drop but a single hint in public, how such a one starved half the fleet, and half poisoned the rest: how such a one, from a true principle of love and honour, pays no debts but for wenches and play: how such a one has got a clap, and runs out of his estate: how Paris, bribed by Juno and Venus, loth to offend either party, slept out the whole cause on the bench: or, how such an orator makes long speeches in the senate, with much thought, little sense, and to no purpose; whoever, I say, should venture to be thus particular, must expect to be imprisoned for *scandalum magnatum;* to have challenges sent him; to be sued for defamation; and to be brought before the bar of the house.

But I forget that I am expatiating on a subject wherein I have no concern, having neither a talent nor an inclination for satire. On the other side, I am so entirely satisfied with the whole present procedure of human things, that I have been some years preparing materials towards " A panegyric upon the World;" to which I intended to add a second part, entitled, " A modest defence of the Proceedings of the Rabble in all Ages." Both these I had thoughts to publish, by way of appendix to the following treatise; but finding my commonplace book fill much slower than I had reason to expect, I have chosen to defer them to another occasion. Besides, I have been unhappily prevented in that design by a certain domestic misfortune; in the particulars whereof, though it would be very seasonable, and much in the modern way, to inform the gentle reader, and would also be of great assistance towards extending this preface into the size now in vogue, which by rule ought to be large in proportion as the subsequent volume is small; yet I shall now dismiss our impatient reader from any further attendance at the porch, and, having duly prepared his mind by a preliminary discourse, shall gladly introduce him to the sublime mysteries that ensue.

August, 1697.

A TALE OF A TUB [1]

SECTION I

THE INTRODUCTION

WHOEVER has an ambition to be heard in a crowd, must press, and squeeze, and thrust, and climb, with indefatigable pains, till he has exalted himself to a certain degree of altitude above them. Now in all assemblies, though you wedge them ever so close, we may observe this peculiar property, that over their heads there is room enough, but how to reach it is the difficult point; it being as hard to get quit of number as of hell;

> ——evadere ad auras,
> Hoc opus, hic labor est.[2]—VIRGIL.

To this end, the philosopher's way, in all ages, has been by erecting certain edifices in the air: but, whatever practice and reputation these kind of structures have formerly possessed, or may still continue in, not excepting even that of Socrates, when he was suspended in a basket to help contemplation,[3] I think, with due submission, they seem to labour under two inconveniences. First, That the foundations being laid too high, they have been often out of sight, and ever out of hearing. Secondly, That the materials, being very transitory, have suffered much from inclemencies of air, especially in these north-west regions.

Therefore, towards the just performance of this great work, there remain but three methods that I can think of; whereof the wisdom of our ancestors being highly sensible, has, to

---

[1] Democritus, dum ridet, philosophatur.—B.

[2] But to return, and view the cheerful skies;
In this the task and mighty labour lies.—DRYDEN.

[3] See the *Clouds* of Aristophanes.

encourage all aspiring adventurers, thought fit to erect three wooden machines for the use of those orators who desire to talk much without interruption. These are, the pulpit, the ladder, and the stage itinerant. For as to the bar, though it be compounded of the same matter, and designed for the same use, it cannot, however, be well allowed the honour of a fourth, by reason of its level or inferior situation exposing it to perpetual interruption from collaterals. Neither can the bench itself, though raised to a prominency, put in a better claim, whatever its advocates insist on. For, if they please to look into the original design of its erection, and the circumstances or adjuncts subservient to that design, they will soon acknowledge the present practice exactly correspondent to the primitive institution, and both to answer the etymology of the name, which in the Phœnician tongue is a word of great signification, importing, if literally interpreted, the place of sleep; but in common acceptation, a seat well bolstered and cushioned, for the repose of old and gouty limbs: *senes ut in otia tuta recedant.* Fortune being indebted to them this part of retaliation, that, as formerly they have long talked while others slept; so now they may sleep as long while others talk.

But if no other argument could occur to exclude the bench and the bar from the list of oratorial machines, it were sufficient that the admission of them would overthrow a number, which I was resolved to establish, whatever argument it might cost me; in imitation of that prudent method observed by many other philosophers and great clerks, whose chief art in division has been to grow fond of some proper mystical number, which their imaginations have rendered sacred, to a degree, that they force common reason to find room for it, in every part of nature; reducing, including, and adjusting every genus and species within that compass, by coupling some against their wills, and banishing others at any rate. Now, among all the rest, the profound number THREE is that which has most employed my sublimest speculations, nor ever without wonderful delight. There is now in the press, and will be published next term, a panegyrical essay of mine upon this number; wherein I have, by most convincing proofs, not only reduced the senses and the elements under its banner, but brought over several deserters from its two great rivals, SEVEN and NINE; the two climacterics.[1]

Now, the first of these oratorial machines, in place as well as dignity, is the pulpit. Of pulpits there are in this island several sorts; but I esteem only that made of timber from the *sylva Caledonia* [Scotland], which agrees very well with our climate. If it be upon its decay, it is the better both for conveyance of sound, and for other reasons to be mentioned by and by. The degree of perfection in shape and size I take to consist in being extremely narrow, with little ornament; and, best of all, without cover, (for, by ancient rule, it ought to be the only uncovered vessel in every assembly, where it is rightfully used,) by which means, from its near resemblance to a pillory, it will ever have a mighty influence on human ears.

Of ladders I need say nothing: it is observed by foreigners themselves, to the honour of our country, that we excel all nations in our practice and understanding of this machine. The ascending orators do not only oblige their audience in the agreeable delivery, but the whole world in the early publication of their speeches; which I look upon as the choicest treasury of our British eloquence, and whereof, I am informed, that worthy citizen and bookseller, Mr. John Dunton, hath made a faithful and painful collection, which he shortly designs to publish, in twelve volumes in folio, illustrated with copper-plates. A work highly useful and curious, and altogether worthy of such a hand.[2]

The last engine of orators is the stage itinerant,[3] erected with much sagacity, *sub Jove pluvio, in triviis et quadriviis.*[4] It is the great seminary of the two former, and its orators are sometimes preferred to the one, and sometimes to the other, in proportion to their deservings; there being a strict and perpetual intercourse between all three.

[1] The numbers *seven* and *nine* were supposed to have a certain inherent and fatal power annexed to them, especially in computing the years of human life. More's *Vulgar Errors.*—B.

[2] Mr. John Dunton, a broken bookseller. He published his own memoirs under the title *Life and Errors*, in which he characterises every bookseller, publisher, stationer, and printer in London; and brings up the rear with the character of 17 bookbinders.

[3] The mountebank's stage, whose orators the author determines either to the gallows, or a conventicle.—H.

[4] In the open air, and in streets where the greatest resort is.—H.

From this accurate deduction it is manifest, that for obtaining attention in public there is of necessity required a superior position of place. But, although this point be generally granted, yet the cause is little agreed in; and it seems to me that very few philosophers have fallen into a true, natural solution of this phenomenon. The deepest account, and the most fairly digested of any I have yet met with, is this; that air being a heavy body, and therefore, according to the system of Epicurus [Lucretius, lib. 2.], continually descending, must needs be more so when loaded and pressed down by words; which are also bodies of much weight and gravity, as it is manifest from those deep impressions they make and leave upon us; and therefore must be delivered from a due altitude, or else they will neither carry a good aim, nor fall down with a sufficient force.

> Corpoream quoque enim vocem constare fatendum est,
> Et sonitum, quoniam possunt impellere sensus.[1]
>
> LUCR. Lib. 4.

And I am the readier to favour this conjecture, from a common observation, that in the several assemblies of these orators nature itself has instructed the hearers to stand with their mouths open, and erected parallel to the horizon, so as they may be intersected by a perpendicular line from the zenith to the centre of the earth. In which position, if the audience be well compact, every one carries home a share, and little or nothing is lost.

I confess there is something yet more refined, in the contrivance and structure of our modern theatres. For, first, the pit is sunk below the stage, with due regard to the institution above deduced; that, whatever weighty matter shall be delivered thence, whether it be lead or gold, may fall plump into the jaws of certain critics, as I think they are called, which stand ready opened to devour them. Then, the boxes are built round, and raised to a level with the scene, in deference to the ladies; because, that large portion of wit, laid out in raising pruriences and protuberances, is observed to run much upon a line, and ever in a circle. The whining passions, and little starved conceits, are gently wafted up by their own extreme levity, to the middle region, and there fix and are

---

[1] 'Tis certain then, that voice that thus can wound,
Is all material; body every sound.

frozen by the frigid understandings of the inhabitants. Bombastry and buffoonery, by nature lofty and light, soar highest of all, and would be lost in the roof, if the prudent architect had not, with much foresight, contrived for them a fourth place, called the twelve-penny gallery, and there planted a suitable colony, who greedily intercept them in their passage.

Now this physico-logical scheme of oratorial receptacles or machines contains a great mystery; being a type, a sign, an emblem, a shadow, a symbol, bearing analogy to the spacious commonwealth of writers, and to those methods by which they must exalt themselves to a certain eminency above the inferior world. By the pulpit are adumbrated the writings of our modern saints in Great Britain, as they have spiritualised and refined them, from the dross and grossness of sense and human reason. The matter, as we have said, is of rotten wood; and that upon two considerations; because it is the quality of rotten wood to give light in the dark: and secondly, because its cavities are full of worms; which is a type with a pair of handles, having a respect to the two principal qualifications of the orator, and the two different fates attending upon his works.

The ladder is an adequate symbol of *faction* and of poetry, to both of which so noble a number of authors are indebted for their fame. Of faction, because [1] . . . (*Hiatus in MS.*) . . . Of *poetry*, because its orators do *perorare* with a song; and because, climbing up by slow degrees, fate is sure to turn them off, before they can reach within many steps of the top: and because it is a preferment attained by transferring of propriety, and a confounding of *meum* and *tuum*.

Under the stage itinerant are couched those productions designed for the pleasure and delight of mortal man; such as, Six-penny-worth of Wit, Westminster Drolleries, Delightful Tales, Complete Jesters, and the like; by which the writers of and for *Grub Street* have in these latter ages so nobly

---

[1] Here is pretended a defect in the manuscript; and this is very frequent with our author, when he thinks he cannot say anything worth reading, or when he has no mind to enter on the subject, or when it is a matter of little moment, or perhaps to amuse his reader, or with some satirical intention.—H. Thus a former commentator; but it is obvious that the gap is left to infer the danger of describing the factious partizan's progress to that consummation which is the subject of discussion.—S.

triumphed over Time; have clipped his wings, pared his nails, filed his teeth, turned back his hour-glass, blunted his scythe, and drawn the hobnails out of his shoes. It is under this class I have presumed to list my present treatise, being just come from having the honour conferred upon me to be adopted a member of that illustrious fraternity.

Now, I am not unaware how the productions of the Grub Street brotherhood have of late years fallen under many prejudices, nor how it has been the perpetual employment of two junior start-up societies to ridicule them and their authors, as unworthy their established post in the common-wealth of wit and learning. Their own consciences will easily inform them whom I mean; nor has the world been so negligent a looker-on as not to observe the continual efforts made by the societies of Gresham [1] and of Will's [2] to edify a name and reputation upon the ruin of OURS. And this is yet a more feeling grief to us, upon the regards of tenderness as well as of justice, when we reflect on their proceedings not only as unjust, but as ungrateful, undutiful, and unnatural. For how can it be forgot by the world or themselves, to say nothing of our own records, which are full and clear in the point, that they both are seminaries not only of our planting, but our watering too? I am informed, our two rivals have lately made an offer to enter into the lists with united forces, and challenge us to a comparison of books, both as to weight and number. In return to which, with licence from our president, I humbly offer two answers: first, we say, the proposal is like that which Archimedes made upon a smaller affair,[3] including an impossibility in the practice; for where can they find scales of capacity enough for the first; or an arithmetician of capacity enough for the second? Secondly, we are ready to accept the challenge; but with this condition, that a third indifferent person be assigned, to whose impartial judgment it should be left to decide which society each book, treatise, or pamphlet, do most properly belong to. This point, God knows, is very far from being fixed at present; for we are ready to produce a catalogue of some thousands,

[1] Gresham College was the place where the Royal Society then met.
[2] Will's coffee-house, in Covent Garden, formerly the place where the poets usually met.
[3] *Viz.* About moving the earth.—Original.

which in all common justice ought to be entitled to our fraternity, but by the revolted and new-fangled writers, most prefidiously ascribed to the others. Upon all which, we think it very unbecoming our prudence that the determination should be remitted to the authors themselves; when our adversaries, by briguing and caballing, have caused so universal a defection from us, that the greatest part of our society has already deserted to them, and our nearest friends begin to stand aloof, as if they were half ashamed to own us.

This is the utmost I am authorised to say upon so ungrateful and melancholy a subject; because we are extremely unwilling to inflame a controversy whose continuance may be so fatal to the interests of us all, desiring much rather that things be amicably composed; and we shall so far advance on our side as to be ready to receive the two prodigals with open arms whenever they shall think fit to return from their husks and their harlots; which, I think, from the present course of their studies,[1] they most properly may be said to be engaged in; and, like an indulgent parent, continue to them our affection and our blessing.

But the greatest maim given to that general reception which the writings of our society have formerly received (next to the transitory state of all sublunary things) has been a superficial vein among many readers of the present age, who will by no means be persuaded to inspect beyond the surface and the rind of things; whereas, wisdom is a fox, who, after long hunting, will at last cost you the pains to dig out; it is a cheese, which, by how much the richer, has the thicker, the homelier, and the coarser coat; and whereof, to a judicious palate, the maggots are the best: it is a sack-posset, wherein the deeper you go, you will find it the sweeter. Wisdom is a hen, whose cackling we must value and consider, because it is attended with an egg; but then lastly, it is a nut, which, unless you choose with judgment, may cost you a tooth, and pay you with nothing but a worm. In consequence of these momentous truths, the grubæan ages have always chosen to convey their precepts and their arts shut up within the vehicles of types and fables; which having been perhaps more careful and curious in adorning than was altgoether necessary, it has fared with these vehicles, after the usual

---

[1] Virtuoso experiments, and modern comedies.—Original.

fate of coaches over-finely painted and gilt, that the transitory gazers have so dazzled their eyes and filled their imaginations with the outward lustre, as neither to regard or consider the person or the parts of the owner within. A misfortune we undergo with somewhat less reluctancy, because it has been common to us with Pythagoras, Æsop, Socrates, and other of our predecessors.

However, that neither the world nor ourselves may any longer suffer by such misunderstandings, I have been prevailed on, after much importunity from my friends, to travel in a complete and laborious dissertation upon the prime productions of our society; which, beside their beautiful externals, for the gratification of superficial readers, have darkly and deeply couched under them the most finished and refined systems of all sciences and arts; as I do not doubt to lay open, by untwisting or unwinding, and either to draw up by exantlation, or display by incision.

This great work was entered upon some years ago, by one of our most eminent members: he began with the *History of Reynard the Fox,*[1] but neither lived to publish his essay nor to proceed farther in so useful an attempt; which is very much to be lamented, because the discovery he made and communicated with his friends is now universally received; nor do I think any of the learned will dispute that famous treatise to be a complete body of civil knowledge, and the revelation, or rather the apocalypse, of all state arcana. But the progress I have made is much greater, having already finished my annotations upon several dozens; from some of which I shall impart a few hints to the candid reader, as far as will be necessary to the conclusion at which I aim.

The first piece I have handled is that of *Tom Thumb*, whose author was a Pythagorean philosopher. This dark treatise contains the whole scheme of the Metempsychosis, deducing the progress of the soul through all her stages.

The next is *Dr. Faustus*, penned by Artephius, an author *bonæ notæ*, and an *adeptus;* he published it in the nine-hundred-eighty-fourth year of his age;[2] this writer proceeds

---

[1] Translated into English, and printed by Caxton.

[2] The chemists say of him in their books that he prolonged his life to a thousand years, and then died voluntarily.—H.

wholly by reincrudation, or in the *via humida;* and the marriage between Faustus and Helen does most conspicuously dilucidate the fermenting of the male and female dragon.

Whittington and his Cat is the work of that mysterious rabbi, Jehuda Hannasi, containing a defence of the gemara of the Jerusalem misna,[1] and its just preference to that of Babylon, contrary to the vulgar opinion.

The Hind and Panther. This is the masterpiece of a famous writer now living, intended for a complete abstract of sixteen thousand school-men, from Scotus to Bellarmin.

Tommy Pots.[2] Another piece, supposed by the same hand, by way of supplement to the former.

The Wise Men of Gotham, cum appendice. This is a treatise of immense erudition, being the great original and fountain of those arguments bandied about both in France and England for a just defence of the moderns' learning and wit, against the presumption, the pride and ignorance of the ancients. This unknown author has so exhausted the subject, that a penetrating reader will easily discover whatever has been written since upon that dispute to be little more than repetition. An abstract of this treatise has been lately published by a worthy member of our society.

These notices may serve to give the learned reader an idea, as well as a taste, of what the whole work is likely to produce; wherein I have now altogether circumscribed my thoughts and my studies; and, if I can bring it to a perfection before I die, shall reckon I have well employed the poor remains of an unfortunate life. This, indeed, is more than I can justly expect, from a quill worn to the pith in the service of the state, in *pros* and *cons* upon Popish plots, and meal-tubs,[3] and exclusion bills, and passive obedience, and addresses of lives and fortunes, and prerogative, and property,[4] and liberty of conscience, and letters to a friend; from an understanding and a conscience threadbare and ragged with

---

[1] The gemara is the decision, explanation, or interpretation of the Jewish rabbis; and the misna is properly the code or body of the Jewish civil or common law.—H.

[2] A popular ballad.

[3] In king Charles the Second's time there was an account of a presbyterian plot, found in a tub, which then made much noise.—H.

[4] First edition—*popery*.

perpetual turning; from a head broken in a hundred places by the malignants of the opposite factions; and from a body spent with poxes ill cured, by trusting to bawds and surgeons, who, as it afterwards appeared, were professed enemies to me and the government, and revenged their party's quarrel upon my nose and shins. Fourscore and eleven pamphlets have I written under three reigns, and for the service of six-and-thirty factions. But, finding the state has no farther occasion for me and my ink, I retire willingly to draw it out into speculations more becoming a philosopher; having, to my unspeakable comfort, passed a long life with a conscience void of offence.

But to return. I am assured, from the reader's candour, that the brief specimen I have given will easily clear all the rest of our society's productions from an aspersion grown, as it is manifest, out of envy and ignorance; that they are of little farther use or value to mankind beyond the common entertainments of their wit and their style; for these I am sure have never yet been disputed by our keenest adversaries; in both which, as well as the more profound and mystical part, I have, throughout this treatise, closely followed the most applauded originals. And to render all complete, I have, with much thought and application of mind, so ordered, that the chief title prefixed to it, I mean that under which I design it shall pass in the common conversations of court and town, is modelled exactly after the manner peculiar to our society.

I confess to have been somewhat liberal in the business of titles, having observed the humour of multiplying them to bear great vogue among certain writers, whom I exceedingly reverence. And indeed it seems not unreasonable that books, the children of the brain, should have the honour to be christened with variety of names as well as other infants of quality. Our famous Dryden has ventured to proceed a point farther, endeavouring to introduce also a multiplicity of godfathers; which is an improvement of much more advantage upon a very obvious account. It is a pity this admirable invention has not been better cultivated, so as to grow by this time into general imitation, when such an authority serves it for a precedent. Nor have my endeavours been wanting to second so useful an example; but it seems there is an unhappy expense usually annexed to the calling of a godfather, which was clearly out of my head, as it is very reasonable to believe. Where the pinch lay I cannot certainly affirm; but having employed a world of thoughts and pains to split my treatise into forty sections, and having entreated forty lords of my acquaintance that they would do me the honour to stand, they all made it a matter of conscience, and sent me their excuses.

SECTION II

ONCE upon a time there was a man who had three sons by one wife,[1] and all at a birth, neither could the midwife tell certainly which was the eldest. Their father died while they were young; and upon his death-bed, calling the lads to him, spoke thus:

" Sons, because I have purchased no estate, nor was born to any, I have long considered of some good legacies to bequeath you; and at last, with much care, as well as expense, have provided each of you (here they are) a new coat.[2] Now, you are to understand that these coats have two virtues contained in them; one is, that with good wearing they will last you fresh and sound as long as you live; the other is, that they will grow in the same proportion with your bodies, lengthening and widening of themselves, so as to be always fit.[3] Here; let me see them on you before I die. So; very well; pray, children, wear them clean, and brush them often.[4] You will find in my will, here it is,[5] full instructions in every particular concerning the wearing and management of your coats; wherein you must be very exact, to avoid the penalties I have appointed for every transgression or neglect, upon which your future fortunes will entirely depend. I have also commanded in my will that you should live together in

[1] By these three sons, Peter, Martin, and Jack, Popery, the Church of England, and Protestant dissenters are designed.—W.
[2] The Christian Religion.—B.
[3] *i.e.* Admits of decent ceremonies according to times and places.—B.
[4] Keep up to the purity of religion.—B.
[5] The Bible.—B.

one house like brethren and friends, for then you will be sure
to thrive, and not otherwise."

Here the story says, this good father died, and the three
sons went all together to seek their fortunes.

I shall not trouble you with recounting what adventures
they met for the first seven years, any farther than by taking
notice that they carefully observed their father's will, and
kept their coats in very good order: that they travelled
through several countries, encountered a reasonable quantity
of giants, and slew certain dragons.

Being now arrived at the proper age for producing themselves, they came up to town, and fell in love with the ladies,
but especially three, who about that time were in chief
reputation; the Duchess d'Argent, Madame de Grands
Titres, and the Countess d'Orgueil.[1] On their first appearance our three adventurers met with a very bad reception;
and soon with great sagacity guessing out the reason, they
quickly began to improve in the good qualities of the town;
they wrote, and rallied, and rhymed, and sung, and said,
and said nothing; they drank, and fought, and whored, and
slept, and swore, and took snuff; they went to new plays on
the first night, haunted the chocolate-houses, beat the watch,
lay on bulks, and got claps; they bilked hackney-coachmen,
ran in debt with shopkeepers, and lay with their wives; they
killed bailiffs, kicked fiddlers down stairs, eat at Locket's,[2]
loitered at Will's,[3] they talked of the drawing-room, and
never came there; dined with lords they never saw; whispered a duchess, and spoke never a word; exposed the
scrawls of their laundress for billets-doux of quality; came
ever just from court, and were never seen in it; attended the
levee *sub dio ;* got a list of peers by heart in one company,
and with great familiarity retailed them in another. Above
all, they constantly attended those committees of senators
who are silent in the house and loud in the coffee-house;
while they nightly adjourn to chew the cud of politics, and
are encompassed with a ring of disciples, who lie in wait to
catch up their droppings. The three brothers had acquired
forty other qualifications of the like stamp, too tedious to

---

[1] Their mistresses signify: covetousness, ambition, and pride; the
three vices that the ancient fathers inveighed against.—W.
[2] A noted tavern.   [3] See p. 48, Note 2.

recount, and by consequence were justly reckoned the most accomplished persons in the town; but all would not suffice, and the ladies aforesaid continued still inflexible. To clear up which difficulty I must, with the reader's good leave and patience, have recourse to some points of weight, which the authors of that age have not sufficiently illustrated.

For about this time it happened a sect arose [1] whose tenets obtained and spread very far, especially in the *grand monde*, and among everybody of good fashion. They worshipped a sort of idol,[2] who, as their doctrine delivered, did daily create men by a kind of manufactory operation. This idol they placed in the highest part of the house, on an altar erected about three foot; he was shown in the posture of a Persian emperor, sitting on a superficies, with his legs interwoven under him. This god had a goose for his ensign; whence it is that some learned men pretend to deduce his original from Jupiter Capitolinus. At his left hand, beneath the altar, hell seemed to open and catch at the animals the idol was creating; to prevent which, certain of his priests hourly flung in pieces of the uninformed mass, or substance, and sometimes whole limbs already enlivened, which that horrid gulf insatiably swallowed, terrible to behold. The goose was also held a subaltern divinity or *deus minorum gentium,* before whose shrine was sacrificed that creature whose hourly food is human gore, and who is in so great renown abroad for being the delight and favourite of the Ægyptian Cercopithecus.[3] Millions of these animals were cruelly slaughtered every day to appease the hunger of that consuming deity. The chief idol was also worshipped as the inventor of the yard and needle; whether as the god of seamen, or on account of certain other mystical attributes, has not been sufficiently cleared.

The worshippers of this deity had also a system of their belief, which seemed to turn upon the following fundamentals. They held the universe to be a large suit of clothes, which invests everything; that the earth is invested by the air; the air is invested by the stars; and the stars are invested by

[1] This is an occasional satire upon dress and fashion in order to introduce what follows.—H.
[2] By this idol is meant a tailor.
[3] The Egyptians worshipped a monkey.—H.

the *primum mobile*. Look on this globe of earth, you will find it to be a very complete and fashionable dress. What is that which some call land but a fine coat faced with green? or the sea, but a waistcoat of water-tabby? Proceed to the particular works of the creation, you will find how curious journeyman Nature has been to trim up the vegetable beaux; observe how sparkish a periwig adorns the head of a beech, and what a fine doublet of white satin is worn by the birch. To conclude from all, what is man himself but a micro-coat,[1] or rather a complete suit of clothes with all its trimmings? As to his body there can be no dispute; but examine even the acquirements of his mind, you will find them all contribute in their order towards furnishing out an exact dress: to instance no more; is not religion a cloak, honesty a pair of shoes worn out in the dirt, self-love a surtout, vanity a shirt, and conscience a pair of breeches, which, though a cover for lewdness as well as nastiness, is easily slipt down for the service of both?[2]

These postulata being admitted, it will follow in due course of reasoning that those beings, which the world calls improperly suits of clothes, are in reality the most refined species of animals; or, to proceed higher, that they are rational creatures or men. For, is it not manifest that they live, and move, and talk, and perform all other offices of human life? are not beauty, and wit, and mien, and breeding, their inseparable proprieties? in short, we see nothing but them, hear nothing but them. Is it not they who walk the streets, fill up parliament-, coffee-, play-, bawdy-houses? It is true, indeed, that these animals, which are vulgarly called suits of clothes, or dresses, do, according to certain compositions, receive different appellations. If one of them be trimmed up with a gold chain, and a red gown, and a white rod, and a great horse, it is called a lord-mayor: if certain ermines and furs be placed in a certain position, we style them a judge; and so an apt conjunction of lawn and black satin we entitle a bishop.

Others of these professors, though agreeing in the main system, were yet more refined upon certain branches of it;

---

[1] Alluding to the word microcosm, or a little world, as man has been called by philosophers.—H.
[2] A satire upon the fanatics.—B.

and held that man was an animal compounded of two dresses, the natural and celestial suit, which were the body and the soul: that the soul was the outward, and the body the inward clothing; that the latter was *ex traduce ;* but the former of daily creation and circumfusion; this last they proved by scripture, because in them we live, and move, and have our being; as likewise by philosophy, because they are all in all, and all in every part. Besides, said they, separate these two and you will find the body to be only a senseless unsavoury carcase: by all which it is manifest that the outward dress must needs be the soul.

To this system of religion were tagged several subaltern doctrines, which were entertained with great vogue: as particularly the faculties of the mind were deduced by the learned among them in this manner; embroidery was sheer wit, gold fringe was agreeable conversation, gold lace was repartee, a huge long periwig was humour, and a coat full of powder was very good raillery—all which required abundance of *finesse* and *delicatesse* to manage with advantage, as well as a strict observance after times and fashions.

I have, with much pains and reading, collected out of ancient authors this short summary of a body of philosophy and divinity, which seems to have been composed by a vein and race of thinking very different from any other systems either ancient or modern. And it was not merely to entertain or satisfy the reader's curiosity, but rather to give him light into several circumstances of the following story; that, knowing the state of dispositions and opinions in an age so remote, he may better comprehend those great events which were the issue of them. I advise, therefore, the courteous reader to peruse with a world of application, again and again, whatever I have written upon this matter. And so leaving these broken ends, I carefully gather up the chief thread of my story and proceed.

These opinions, therefore, were so universal, as well as the practices of them, among the refined part of court and town, that our three brother adventurers, as their circumstances then stood, were strangely at a loss. For, on the one side, the three ladies they addressed themselves to, whom we have named already, were ever at the very top of the fashion, and abhorred all that were below it but the breadth of a hair.

On the other side, their father's will was very precise; and it was the main precept in it, with the greatest penalties annexed, not to add to or diminish from their coats one thread, without a positive command in the will. Now, the coats their father had left them were, it is true, of very good cloth, and besides so neatly sewn, you would swear they were all of a piece; but at the same time very plain, and with little or no ornament: and it happened that before they were a month in town great shoulder-knots came up [1]—straight all the world was shoulder-knots—no approaching the ladies' *ruelles* without the *quota* of shoulder-knots. That fellow, cries one, has no soul; where is his shoulder-knot? Our three brethren soon discovered their want by sad experience, meeting in their walks with forty mortifications and indignities. If they went to the playhouse the door-keeper showed them into the twelvepenny gallery; if they called a boat, says a waterman, " I am first sculler; " if they stepped to the Rose to take a bottle, the drawer would cry, " Friend, we sell no ale; " if they went to visit a lady, a footmen met them at the door with " Pray send up your message." In this unhappy case they went immediately to consult their father's will, read it over and over, but not a word of the shoulder-knot. What should they do?—what temper should they find?—obedience was absolutely necessary, and yet shoulder-knots appeared extremely requisite. After much thought one of the brothers, who happened to be more book-learned than the other two, said he had found an expedient. It is true, said he, there is nothing here in this will, *totidem verbis*, making mention of shoulder-knots: but I dare conjecture we may find them *inclusive*, or *totidem syllabis*. This distinction was immediately approved by all, and so they fell again to examine; but their evil star had so directed the matter that the first syllable was not to be found in the whole writings. Upon which disappointment, he who found the former evasion took heart, and said, " Brothers, there are yet hopes; for though we cannot find them *totidem verbis*, nor *totidem syllabis*, I dare engage we shall make them out

---

[1] The first part of the Tale is the history of Peter, thereby Popery is exposed; everybody knows the Papists have made great additions to Christianity: accordingly Peter begins his pranks with adding a shoulder-knot to his coat.—W.

tertio modo or *totidem literis*. This discovery was also highly commended, upon which they fell once more to the scrutiny, and soon picked out S,H,O,U,L,D,E,R; when the same planet, enemy to their repose, had wonderfully contrived that a K was not to be found. Here was a weighty difficulty! but the distinguishing brother, for whom we shall hereafter find a name, now his hand was in, proved by a very good argument that K was a modern, illegitimate letter, unknown to the learned ages, nor anywhere to be found in ancient manuscripts. It is true, said he, the word Calendæ hath in Q. V. C.[1] been sometimes written with a K, but erroneously; for in the best copies it has been ever spelt with a C. And, by consequence, it was a gross mistake in our language to spell knot with a K; but that from henceforward he would take care it should be written with a C.[2] Upon this all farther difficulty vanished—shoulder-knots were made clearly out to be *jure paterno*, and our three gentlemen swaggered with as large and as flaunting ones as the best. But, as human happiness is of a very short duration, so in those days were human fashions, upon which it entirely depends. Shoulder-knots had their time, and we must now imagine them in their decline; for a certain lord came just from Paris, with fifty yards of gold lace upon his coat, exactly trimmed after the court fashion of that month. In two days all mankind appeared closed up in bars of gold lace:[3] whoever durst peep abroad without his complement of gold lace was as scandalous as a —, and as ill received among the women: what should our three knights do in this momentous affair? they had sufficiently strained a point already in the affair of shoulder-knots: upon recourse to the will, nothing appeared there but *altum silentium*. That of the shoulder-knots was a loose, flying, circumstantial point; but this of gold lace seemed too considerable an alteration without better warrant; it did *aliquo modo essentiæ adhærere*, and therefore required a positive precept. But about this time it fell out that the learned brother aforesaid had read *Aristotelis dialectica*, and especially that wonderful piece *de interpretatione*, which has the faculty of teaching its readers to find out a meaning in everything

---

[1] Quibusdam veteribus codicibus; some ancient manuscripts.
[2] The schoolmen are here ridiculed.—B.
[3] Probably new methods of forcing and perverting scripture.—H.

but itself; like commentators on the Revelations, who proceed prophets without understanding a syllable of the text. Brothers, said he, you are to be informed that of wills *duo sunt genera*, nuncupatory [1] and scriptory: that in the scriptory will here before us there is no precept or mention about gold lace, *conceditur :* but *si idem affirmetur de nuncupatorio, negatur.* For, brothers, if you remember, we heard a fellow say when we were boys that he heard my father's man say that he would advise his sons to get gold lace on their coats as soon as ever they could procure money to buy it. By G—! that is very true, cries the other; [2] I remember it perfectly well, said the third. And so without more ado they got the largest gold lace in the parish, and walked about as fine as lords.

A while after there came up all in fashion a pretty sort of flame-coloured satin [3] for linings; and the mercer brought a pattern of it immediately to our three gentlemen; An please your worships, said he, my lord Conway and Sir John Walters had linings out of this very piece last night: it takes wonderfully, and I shall not have a remnant left enough to make my wife a pincushion by to-morrow morning at ten o'clock. Upon this they fell again to rummage the will, because the present case also required a positive precept—the lining being held by orthodox writers to be of the essence of the coat. After a long search they could fix upon nothing to the matter in hand, except a short advice of their father in the will to take care of fire and put out their candles before they went to sleep.[4] This, though a good deal for the purpose, and helping very far towards self-conviction, yet not seeming wholly of force to establish a command (being resolved to avoid further scruple as well as future occasion for scandal), says he that was the scholar, I remember to have read in wills of a codicil annexed, which is indeed a part of the will, and what it contains has equal authority with the rest. Now, I have been considering of this same will here

---

[1] By this is meant tradition, allowed by the Papists to have equal authority with the Scripture.—H.

[2] When the papists cannot find anything which they want in scripture they go to oral tradition.—W.

[3] The fire of purgatory; and praying for the dead is set forth as linings.—B.

[4] That is, to take care of hell, and, in order to do that, to subdue their lusts.—H.

before us, and I cannot reckon it to be complete for want of such a codicil: I will therefore fasten one in its proper place very dexterously—I have had it by me some time—it was written by a dog-keeper of my grandfather's, and talks a great deal, as good luck would have it, of this very flame-coloured satin. The project was immediately approved by the other two; an old parchment scroll was tagged on according to art in the form of a codicil annexed, and the satin bought and worn.

Next winter a player, hired for the purpose by the corporation of fringe-makers, acted his part in a new comedy, all covered with silver fringe,[1] and, according to the laudable custom, gave rise to that fashion. Upon which the brothers, consulting their father's will, to their great astonishment found these words; *item*, I charge and command [2] my said three sons to wear no sort of silver fringe upon or about their said coats, etc., with a penalty, in case of disobedience, too long here to insert. However, after some pause, the brother so often mentioned for his erudition, who was well skilled in criticisms, had found in a certain author, which he said should be nameless, that the same word which in the will is called fringe does also signify a broomstick:[3] and doubtless ought to have the same interpretation in this paragraph. This another of the brothers disliked, because of that epithet silver, which could not he humbly conceived in propriety of speech be reasonably applied to a broomstick: but it was replied upon him that this epithet was understood in a mythological and allegorical sense. However, he objected again why their father should forbid them to wear a broomstick on their coats—a caution that seemed unnatural and impertinent; upon which he was taken up short, as one that spoke irreverently of a mystery, which doubtless was very useful and significant, but ought not to be over-curiously pried into or nicely reasoned upon. And, in short, their father's authority being now considerably sunk, this expedient was allowed to serve as a lawful dispensation for wearing their full proportion of silver fringe.

[1] Introducing the pomps and habits of temporal grandeur positively prohibited in the gospel.
[2] A prohibition of idolatry.—B.
[3] Glosses and interpretations of Scripture.—W.

A while after was revived an old fashion, long antiquated, of embroidery with Indian figures of men, women, and children.[1] Here they remembered but too well how their father had always abhorred this fashion; that he made several paragraphs on purpose, importing his utter detestation of it, and bestowing his everlasting curse to his sons whenever they should wear it. For all this, in a few days they appeared higher in the fashion than anybody else in the town. But they solved the matter by saying that these figures were not at all the same with those that were formerly worn and were meant in the will. Besides, they did not wear them in the sense as forbidden by their father; but as they were a commendable custom, and of great use to the public.[2] That these rigorous clauses in the will did therefore require some allowance and a favourable interpretation, and ought to be understood *cum grano salis*.

But fashions perpetually altering in that age, the scholastic brother grew weary of searching farther evasions, and solving everlasting contradictions. Resolved, therefore, at all hazards, to comply with the modes of the world, they concerted matters together, and agreed unanimously to lock up their father's will in a strong box,[3] brought out of Greece or Italy,[4] I have forgotten which, and trouble themselves no farther to examine it, but only refer to its authority whenever they thought fit. In consequence whereof, a while after it grew a general mode to wear an infinite number of points, most of them tagged with silver:[5] upon which the scholar pronounced, *ex cathedrâ*,[6] that points were absolutely *jure paterno*, as they might very well remember. It is true, indeed, the fashion prescribed somewhat more than were directly named in the will; however, that they, as heirs-general of their father, had power to make and add certain clauses[7] for public emolument, though not deducible,

[1] Images of Saints, etc.—H.

[2] The excuse made for the worship of images by the Church of Rome, that they were help to devotional recollection.

[3] The papists forbade the use of scripture in the vulgar tongue: therefore Peter locks up his father's will in a strong box.—W.

[4] New Testament written in Greek; and the vulgar Latin, the authentic edition of Bible in the Church of Rome is in the language of old Italy.—W.

[5] Gainful rites of the church of Rome.—B.

[6] The popes in their decretals and bulls.—W.

[7] Alluding to the abuse of power in the Roman Church.—B.

totidem verbis, from the letter of the will, or else *multa absurda sequerentur*. This was understood for canonical, and therefore, on the following Sunday, they came to church all covered with points.

The learned brother, so often mentioned, was reckoned the best scholar in all that or the next street to it, insomuch as, having run something behindhand in the world, he obtained the favour of a certain lord [1] to receive him into his house, and to teach his children. A while after the lord died, and he, by long practice upon his father's will, found the way of contriving a deed of conveyance [2] of that house to himself and his heirs; upon which he took possession, turned the young squires out, and received his brothers in their stead.

SECTION III

A DIGRESSION CONCERNING CRITICS

ALTHOUGH I have been hitherto as cautious as I could, upon all occasions, most nicely to follow the rules and methods of writing laid down by the example of our illustrious moderns; yet has the unhappy shortness of my memory led me into an error, from which I must immediately extricate myself, before I can decently pursue my principal subject. I confess with shame it was an unpardonable omission to proceed so far as I have already done before I had performed the due discourses, expostulatory, supplicatory, or deprecatory, with my good lords the critics. Towards some atonement for this grievous neglect, I do here make bold humbly to present them with a short account of themselves and their art, by looking into the original and pedigree of the word, as it is generally understood among us; and very briefly considering the ancient and present state thereof.

By the word critic, at this day so frequent in all conversations, there have sometimes been distinguished three very different species of mortal men, according as I have read in

---

[1] Constantine the Great.—H.
[2] Pope's challenge of temporal sovereignty.—B.

ancient books and pamphlets. For first, by this term were understood such persons as invented or drew up rules for themselves and the world, by observing which a careful reader might be able to pronounce upon the productions of the learned, form his taste to a true relish of the sublime and the admirable, and divide every beauty of matter or of style from the corruption that apes it: in their common perusal of books singling out the errors and defects, the nauseous, the fulsome, the dull, and the impertinent, with the caution of a man that walks through Edinburgh streets in a morning, who is indeed as careful as he can to watch diligently and spy out the filth in his way; not that he is curious to observe the colour and complexion of the ordure, or take its dimensions, much less to be paddling in or tasting it; but only with a design to come out as cleanly as he may. These men seem, though very erroneously, to have understood the appellation of critic in a literal sense; that one principal part of his office was to praise and acquit; and that a critic, who sets up to read only for an occasion of censure and reproof is a creature as barbarous as a judge who should take up a resolution to hang all men that came before him upon a trial.

Again, by the word critic have been meant the restorers of ancient learning from the worms, and graves, and dust of manuscripts.

Now the races of those two have been for some ages utterly extinct; and besides, to discourse any farther of them would not be at all to my purpose.

The third and noblest sort is that of the TRUE CRITIC, whose original is the most ancient of all. Every true critic is a hero born, descending in a direct line from a celestial stem by Momus and Hybris, who begat Zoilus, who begat Tigellius, who begat Etcætera the elder; who begat Bentley, and Rymer, and Wotton, and Perrault, and Dennis; who begat Etcætera the younger.

And these are the critics from whom the commonwealth of learning has in all ages received such immense benefits, that the gratitude of their admirers placed their origin in Heaven, among those of Hercules, Theseus, Perseus, and other great deservers of mankind. But heroic virtue itself has not been exempt from the obloquy of evil tongues. For it has been objected that those ancient heroes, famous for their combating so many giants, and dragons, and robbers, were in their own persons a greater nuisance to mankind than any of those monsters they subdued; and therefore, to render their obligations more complete, when all other vermin were destroyed, should, in conscience, have concluded with the same justice upon themselves. As Hercules most generously did, and upon that score procured to himself more temples and votaries than the best of his fellows. For these reasons I suppose it is why some have conceived it would be very expedient for the public good of learning that every true critic, as soon as he had finished his task assigned, should immediately deliver himself up to ratsbane, or hemp, or leap from some convenient altitude; and that no man's pretensions to so illustrious a character should by any means be received before that operation were performed.

Now, from this heavenly descent of criticism, and the close analogy it bears to heroic virtue, it is easy to assign the proper employment of a true ancient genuine critic; which is, to travel through this vast world of writings; to pursue and hunt those monstrous faults bred within them; to drag out the lurking errors, like Cacus from his den; to multiply them like Hydra's heads; and rake them together like Augeas's dung: or else drive away a sort of dangerous fowl, who have a perverse inclination to plunder the best branches of the tree of knowledge, like those stymphalian birds that eat up the fruit.

These reasonings will furnish us with an adequate definition of a true critic: that he is discoverer and collector of writers' faults; which may be farther put beyond dispute by the following demonstration; that whoever will examine the writings in all kinds, wherewith this ancient sect has honoured the world, shall immediately find, from the whole thread and tenor of them, that the ideas of the authors have been altogether conversant and taken up with the faults, and blemishes, and oversights, and mistakes of other writers: and, let the subject treated on be whatever it will, their imaginations are so entirely possessed and replete with the defects of other pens, that the very quintessence of what is bad does of necessity distil into their own; by which means the whole appears to be nothing else but an abstract of the criticisms themselves have made.

Having thus briefly considered the original and office of a critic, as the word is understood in its most noble and universal acceptation, I proceed to refute the objections of those who argue from the silence and pretermission of authors; by which they pretend to prove that the very art of criticism, as now exercised, and by me explained, is wholly modern; and consequently that the critics of Great Britain and France have no title to an original so ancient and illustrious as I have deduced. Now, if I can clearly make out, on the contrary, that the ancient writers have particularly described both the person and the office of a true critic, agreeably to the definition laid down by me, their grand objection, from the silence of authors, will fall to the ground.

I confess to have, for a long time, borne a part in this general error: from which I should never have acquitted myself, but through the assistance of our noble moderns! whose most edifying volumes I turn undefatigably over night and day for the improvement of my mind and the good of my country: these have, with unwearied pains, made many useful searches into the weak sides of the ancients, and given us a comprehensive list of them.[1] Besides, they have proved beyond contradiction that the very finest things delivered of old have been long since invented and brought to light by much later pens; and that the noblest discoveries those ancients ever made, of art or of nature, have all been produced by the transcending genius of the present age. Which clearly shows how little merit those ancients can justly pretend to, and takes off that blind admiration paid them by men in a corner who have the unhappiness of conversing too little with present things. Reflecting maturely upon all this, and taking in the whole compass of human nature, I easily concluded that these ancients, highly sensible of their many imperfections, must needs have endeavoured, from some passages in their works, to obviate, soften, or divert the censorious reader, by satire or panegyric upon the true critics, in imitation of their masters the moderns. Now, in the commonplaces of both these I was plentifully instructed by a long course of useful study in prefaces and prologues; and therefore immediately resolved to try what I could discover of

[1] " See Wotton of ancient and modern learning."—Note in 1st Edition.

either by a diligent perusal of the most ancient writers, and especially those who treated of the earliest times. Here I found to my great surprise, that although they all entered, upon occasion, into particular descriptions of the true critic, according as they were governed by their fears or their hopes, yet whatever they touched of that kind was with abundance of caution, adventuring no farther than mythology and hieroglyphic. This, I suppose, gave ground to superficial readers for urging the silence of authors against the antiquity of the true critic, though the types are so opposite, and the applications so necessary and natural, that it is not easy to conceive how any reader of a modern eye and taste could overlook them. I shall venture from a great number to produce a few, which, I am very confident, will put this question beyond dispute.

It well deserves considering that these ancient writers, in treating enigmatically upon this subject, have generally fixed upon the very same hieroglyph, varying only the story, according to their affections or their wit. For first; Pausanias is of opinion that the perfection of writing correct was entirely owing to the institution of critics; and that he can possibly mean no other than the true critic is, I think, manifest enough from the following description. He says, they were a race of men who delighted to nibble at the superfluities and excrescencies of books, which the learned at length observing, took warning, of their own accord, to lop the luxuriant, the rotten, the dead, the sapless, and the overgrown branches from their works. But now all this he cunningly shades under the following allegory; that the Nauplians in Argos learned the art of pruning their vines, by observing, that when an ASS had browsed upon one of them, it thrived the better and bore fairer fruit. But Herodotus, holding the very same hieroglyph, speaks much plainer, and almost *in terminis*. He has been so bold as to tax the true critics of ignorance and malice; telling us openly, for I think nothing can be plainer, that in the western part of Lybia there were ASSES with horns: upon which relation Ctesias [1] yet refines, mentioning the very same animal about India, adding that, whereas all other ASSES wanted a gall, these horned ones were so redundant in that part, that their flesh was not to be eaten, because of its extreme bitterness.

[1] *Vide excerpta ex eo apud Photium.*   Note, 1st Edition.

Now, the reason why those ancient writers treated this subject only by types and figures was, because they durst not make open attacks against a party so potent and so terrible as the critics of those ages were; whose very voice was so dreadful that a legion of authors would tremble and drop their pens at the sound; for so Herodotus tells us expressly in another place, how a vast army of Scythians was put to flight in a panic terror by the braying of an ASS. From hence it is conjectured by certain profound philologers that the great awe and reverence paid to a true critic by the writers of Britain have been derived to us from those our Scythian ancestors. In short, this dread was so universal, that in process of time those authors who had a mind to publish their sentiments more freely, in describing the true critics of their several ages, were forced to leave off the use of the former hieroglyph, as too nearly approaching the proto-type, and invented other terms instead thereof, that were more cautious and mystical: so, Diodorus, speaking to the same purpose, ventures no farther than to say that in the mountains of Helicon there grows a certain weed which bears a flower of so damned a scent as to poison those who offer to smell to it. Lucretius gives exactly the same relation:

> Est etiam in magnis Heliconis montibus arbos,
> Floris odore hominem tetro consueta necare.[1]—Lib. 6.

But Ctesias, whom we lately quoted, has been a great deal bolder; he had been used with much severity by the true critics of his own age, and therefore could not forbear to leave behind him at least one deep mark of his vengeance against the whole tribe. His meaning is so near the surface, that I wonder how it possibly came to be overlooked by those who deny the antiquity of the true critics. For, pretending to make a description of many strange animals about India, he has set down these remarkable words: Among the rest, says he, there is a serpent that wants teeth, and consequently cannot bite; but if its vomit, to which it is much addicted, happens to fall upon anything, a certain rottenness or corruption ensues: these serpents are generally found among the mountains where jewels grow, and they frequently emit a

[1] Near Helicon, and round the learned hill,
Grow trees whose blossoms with their odour kill.

poisonous juice: whereof whoever drinks, that person's brains fly out of his nostrils.

There was also among the ancients a sort of critics, not distinguished in species from the former, but in growth or degree, who seem to have been only the tyros or junior scholars; yet, because of their differing employments, they are frequently mentioned as a sect by themselves. The usual exercise of these younger students was to attend constantly at theatres, and learn to spy out the worst parts of the play, whereof they were obliged carefully to take note, and render a rational account to their tutors. Fleshed at these smaller sports, like young wolves, they grew up in time to be nimble and strong enough for hunting down large game. For it has been observed, both among ancients and moderns, that a true critic has one quality in common with a whore and an alderman, never to change his title or his nature; that a grey critic has been certainly a green one, the perfections and acquirements of his age being only the improved talents of his youth; like hemp, which some naturalists inform us is bad for suffocations, though taken but in the seed. I esteem the invention, or at least the refinement of prologues, to have been owing to these younger proficients, of whom Terence makes frequent and honourable mention, under the name of *malevoli*.

Now, it is certain the institution of the true critics was of absolute necessity to the commonwealth of learning. For all human actions seem to be divided, like Themistocles and his company; one man can fiddle, and another can make a small town a great city; and he that cannot do either one or the other deserves to be kicked out of the creation. The avoiding of which penalty has doubtless given the first birth to the nation of critics; and withal, an occasion for their secret detractors to report that a true critic is a sort of mechanic, set up with a stock and tools for his trade at as little expense as a tailor; and that there is much analogy between the utensils and abilities of both: that the tailor's hell is the type of a critic's commonplace-book, and his wit and learning held forth by the goose; that it requires at least as many of these to the making up of one scholar, as of the others to the composition of a man; that the valour of both is equal, and their weapons nearly of a size. Much may be said in answer to those invidious reflections; and I can positively affirm the first to be a falsehood: for, on the contrary, nothing is more certain than that it requires greater layings out to be free of the critic's company than of any other you can name. For as, to be a true beggar, it will cost the richest candidate every groat he is worth; so, before one can commence a true critic, it will cost a man all the good qualities of his mind; which, perhaps for a less purchase, would be thought but an indifferent bargain.

Having thus amply proved the antiquity of criticism, and described the primitive state of it, I shall now examine the present condition of this empire, and show how well it agrees with its ancient self. A certain author, whose works have many ages since been entirely lost, does, in his fifth book and eighth chapter, say of critics that their writings are the mirrors of learning. This I understand in a literal sense, and suppose our author must mean, that whoever designs to be a perfect writer must inspect into the books of critics, and correct his invention there, as in a mirror. Now, whoever considers that the mirrors of the ancients were made of brass, and *sine mercurio*, may presently apply the two principal qualifications of a true modern critic, and consequently must needs conclude that these have always been, and must be for ever, the same. For brass is an emblem of duration, and, when it is skilfully burnished, will cast reflection from its own superficies, without any assistance of mercury from behind. All the other talents of a critic will not require a particular mention, being included or easily deducible to these. However, I shall conclude with three maxims, which may serve both as characteristics to distinguish a true modern critic from a pretender, and will be also of admirable use to those worthy spirits who engage in so useful and honourable an art.

The first is, that criticism, contrary to all other faculties of the intellect, is ever held the truest and best when it is the very first result of the critic's mind; as fowlers reckon the first aim for the surest, and seldom fail of missing the mark if they stay not for a second. Secondly, the true critics are known by their talent of swarming about the noblest writers, to which they are carried merely by instinct, as a rat to the best cheese, or as a wasp to the fairest fruit. So when the king is on horseback, he is sure to be the dirtiest person of the company; and they that make their court best are such as bespatter him most.

Lastly, a true critic, in the perusal of a book, is like a dog at a feast, whose thoughts and stomach are wholly set upon what the guests fling away, and consequently is apt to snarl most when there are the fewest bones.

Thus much, I think, is sufficient to serve by way of address to my patrons, the true modern critics; and may very well atone for my past silence, as well as that which I am likely to observe for the future. I hope I have deserved so well of their whole body as to meet with generous and tender usage at their hands. Supported by which expectations, I go on boldly to pursue those adventures already so happily begun.

SECTION IV

I HAVE now, with much pains and study, conducted the reader to a period where he must expect to hear of great revolutions. For no sooner had our learned brother, so often mentioned, got a warm house of his own over his head than he began to look big and to take mightily upon him; insomuch that unless the gentle reader, out of his great candour, will please a little to exalt his idea, I am afraid he will henceforth hardly know the hero of the play when he happens to meet him; his part, his dress, and his mien being so much altered.

He told his brothers he would have them to know that he was their elder, and consequently his father's sole heir; nay, a while after, he would not allow them to call him brother, but *Mr.* PETER [the pope], and then he must be styled *Father* PETER; and sometimes, *My Lord* PETER. To support this grandeur, which he soon began to consider could not be maintained without a better *fonde* than what he was born to,[1] after much thought, he cast about at last to turn projector and virtuoso, wherein he so well succeeded, that many famous discoveries, projects, and machines, which bear great vogue and practice at present in the world, are owing

[1] The pope's pretension to supremacy.—B.

entirely to lord PETER'S invention. I will deduce the best
account I have been able to collect of the chief among them,
without considering much the order they came out in;
because I think authors are not well agreed as to that point.

I hope, when this treatise of mine shall be translated into
foreign languages (as I may without vanity affirm that the
labour of collecting, the faithfulness in recounting, and the
great usefulness of the matter to the public, will amply
deserve that justice), that the worthy members of the several
academies abroad, especially those of France and Italy, will
favourably accept these humble offers for the advancement of
universal knowledge. I do also advertise the most reverend
fathers, the Eastern missionaries, that I have, purely for their
sakes, made use of such words and phrases as will best admit
an easy turn into any of the oriental languages, especially the
Chinese. And so I proceed with great content of mind, upon
reflecting how much emolument this whole globe of the earth
is likely to reap by my labours.

The first undertaking of lord Peter was, to purchase a large
continent [purgatory], lately said to have been discovered in
terra australis incognita. This tract of land he bought at a
very great pennyworth from the discoverers themselves
(though some pretended to doubt whether they had ever been
there), and then retailed it into several cantons to certain
dealers, who carried over colonies, but were all shipwrecked
in the voyage. Upon which lord Peter sold the said continent
to other customers again, and again, and again, and again,
with the same success.[1]

The second project I shall mention was his sovereign
remedy for the worms,[2] especially those in the spleen. The
patient was to eat nothing after supper for three nights:[3] as
soon as he went to bed he was carefully to lie on one side, and
when he grew weary to turn upon the other; he must also
duly confine his two eyes to the same object; and by no means
break wind at both ends together without manifest occasion.
These prescriptions diligently observed, the worms would void
insensibly by perspiration, ascending through the brain.[4]

[1] The imaginary place between heaven and hell.—B.
[2] Penance and absolution are played upon under the notion of a
sovereign remedy.—W.
[3] Here the author ridicules the penances of the Church of Rome.—H.
[4] The application of relics to physical cures.—B.

A third invention was the erecting of a whispering-office [1] for the public good and ease of all such as are hypochondriacal or troubled with the colic; as likewise of all eavesdroppers, physicians, midwives, small politicians, friends fallen out, repeating poets, lovers happy or in despair, bawds, privy-counsellors, pages, parasites, and buffoons; in short, of all such as are in danger of bursting with too much wind. An ass's head was placed so conveniently that the party affected might easily with his mouth accost either of the animal's ears; to which he was to apply close for a certain space, and by a fugitive faculty, peculiar to the ears of that animal, receive immediate benefit, either by eructation, or expiration, or evomitation.

Another very beneficial project of lord Peter's was, an office of insurance for tobacco-pipes,[2] martyrs of the modern zeal, volumes of poetry, shadows, ——, and rivers; that these, nor any of these, shall receive damage by fire. Whence our friendly societies may plainly find themselves to be only transcribers from this original; though the one and the other have been of great benefit to the undertakers, as well as of equal to the public.

Lord PETER was also held the original author of puppets and raree-shows [ceremonies and processions]; the great usefulness whereof being so generally known, I shall not enlarge farther upon this particular.

But another discovery, for which he was much renowned, was his famous universal pickle.[3] For, having remarked how your common pickle in use among housewives was of no farther benefit than to preserve dead flesh and certain kinds of vegetables, Peter, with great cost as well as art, had contrived a pickle proper for houses, gardens, towns, men, women, children, and cattle; wherein he could preserve them as sound as insects in amber. Now, this pickle, to the taste, the smell, and the sight, appeared exactly the same with what is in common service for beef, and butter, and herrings, and has been often that way applied with great success; but, for its many sovereign virtues, was a quite different thing.

---

[1] The author ridicules auricular confession; and the priest who takes it is described by the ass's head.—W.
[2] Office of indulgences.—S.
[3] Holy water he calls a universal pickle.—W.

For Peter would put in a certain quantity of his powder pimperlimpimp,[1] after which it never failed of success. The operation was performed by spargefaction,[2] in a proper time of the moon. The patient who was to be pickled, if it were a house, would infallibly be preserved from all spiders, rats, and weasels; if the party affected were a dog, he should be exempt from mange, and madness, and hunger. It also infallibly took away all scabs, and lice, and scalled heads from children, never hindering the patient from any duty, either at bed or board.

But of all Peter's rarities he most valued a certain set of bulls [papal], whose race was by great fortune preserved in a lineal descent from those that guarded the golden fleece. Though some, who pretended to observe them curiously, doubted the breed had not been kept entirely chaste, because they had degenerated from their ancestors in some qualities, and had acquired others very extraordinary, by a foreign mixture. The bulls of Colchis are recorded to have brazen feet; but whether it happened by ill pasture and running, by an allay from intervention of other parents, from stolen intrigues; whether a weakness in their progenitors had impaired the seminal virtue, or by a decline necessary through a long course of time, the originals of nature being depraved in these latter sinful ages of the world; whatever was the cause, it is certain that lord Peter's bulls were extremely vitiated by the rust of time in the metal of their feet, which was now sunk into common lead.[3] However, the terrible roaring peculiar to their lineage was preserved; as likewise that faculty of breathing out fire from their nostrils,[4] which, notwithstanding many of their detractors took to be a feat of art, to be nothing so terrible as it appeared, proceeding only from their usual course of diet, which was of squibs and crackers. [Fulminations of the pope.] However, they had two peculiar marks, which extremely distinguished them from the bulls of Jason, and which I have not met together

[1] And because holy water differs only in consecration from common water, he tells us that his pickle by the powder of pimperlimpimp receives new virtues.—W.

[2] Sprinkling.

[3] Alludes to the leaden seal at the bottom of the popish bulls.—B.

[4] These passages, and many others, no doubt, must be construed as antichristian by the Church of Rome.—Orrery.

in the description of any other monster beside that in Horace:

Varias inducere plumas :—and *Atrum desinat in piscem.*

For these had fishes' tails,[1] yet upon occasion could outfly any bird in the air. Peter put these bulls upon several employs. Sometimes he would set them a-roaring to fright naughty boys,[2] and make them quiet. Sometimes he would send them out upon errands of great importance; where, it is wonderful to recount (and perhaps the cautious reader may think much to believe it), an *appetitus sensibilis* deriving itself through the whole family from their noble ancestors, guardians of the golden fleece, they continued so extremely fond of gold, that if Peter sent them abroad, though it were only upon a compliment, they would roar, and spit, and belch, and piss, and fart, and snivel out fire, and keep a perpetual coil, till you flung them a bit of gold; but then, *pulveris exigui jactu,* they would grow calm and quiet as lambs. In short, whether by secret connivance or encouragement from their master, or out of their own liquorish affection to gold, or both, it is certain they were no better than a sort of sturdy, swaggering beggars; and where they could not prevail to get an alms, would make women miscarry, and children fall into fits, who to this very day usually call sprights and hobgoblins by the name of bull-beggars.[3] They grew at last so very troublesome to the neighbourhood, that some gentlemen of the north-west got a parcel of right English bull-dogs, and baited them so terribly that they felt it ever after.

I must needs mention one more of lord Peter's projects, which was very extraordinary, and discovered him to be master of a high reach and profound invention. Whenever it happened that any rogue of Newgate was condemned to be hanged, Peter would offer him a pardon for a certain sum of money; which when the poor caitiff had made all shifts to scrape up and send, his lordship would return a piece of paper in this form: [4]

" To all mayors, sheriffs, jailors, constables, bailiffs, hangmen, etc. Whereas we are informed that A.B. remains in

---

[1] Alluding to the expression *sub signo piscatoris.*—B.
[2] That is, kings who incurred his displeasure.—H.
[3] Heretics or schismatics as the pope calls Protestants.—B.
[4] This is a copy of a general pardon, signed *servus servorum.*—H.

the hands of you, or some of you, under the sentence of death. We will and command you, upon sight hereof, to let the said prisoner depart to his own habitation, whether he stands condemned for murder, sodomy, rape, sacrilege, incest, treason, blasphemy, etc., for which this shall be your sufficient warrant; and if you fail hereof, G— d—mn you and yours to all eternity. And so we bid you heartily farewell. Your most humble man's man,

" Emperor PETER."

The wretches, trusting to this, lost their lives and money too.

I desire of those whom the learned among posterity will appoint for commentators upon this elaborate treatise, that they will proceed with great caution upon certain dark points, wherein all who are not *verè adepti* may be in danger to form rash and hasty conclusions, especially in some mysterious paragraphs, where certain *arcana* are joined for brevity sake, which in the operation must be divided. And I am certain that future sons of art will return large thanks to my memory for so grateful, so useful an *innuendo*.

It will be no difficult part to persuade the reader that so many worthy discoveries met with great success in the world; though I may justly assure him that I have related much the smallest number; my design having been only to single out such as will be of most benefit for public imitation, or which best served to give some idea of the reach and wit of the inventor. And therefore it need not be wondered at if by this time lord Peter was become exceeding rich: but, alas! he had kept his brain so long and so violently upon the rack, that at last it shook itself, and began to turn round for a little ease. In short, what with pride, projects, and knavery, poor Peter was grown distracted, and conceived the strangest imaginations in the world. In the height of his fits, as it is usual with those who run mad out of pride, he would call himself God Almighty,[1] and sometimes monarch of the universe. I have seen him (says my author) take three old high-crowned hats,[2] and clap them all on his head three story

---

[1] The pope is not only allowed to be the vicar of Christ, but by several divines is called God upon earth, and other blasphemous titles.—H.

[2] The triple mitre or crown.—B.

high, with a huge bunch of keys at his girdle,[1] and an angling-rod in his hand. In which guise, whoever went to take him by the hand in the way of salutation, Peter with much grace, like a well-educated spaniel, would present them with his foot, and if they refused his civility, then he would raise it as high as their chaps, and gave them a damned kick on the mouth, which has ever since been called a salute. Whoever walked by without paying him their compliments, having a wonderful strong breath, he would blow their hats off into the dirt. Meantime his affairs at home went upside down, and his two brothers had a wretched time; where his first *boutade* [2] was to kick both their wives one morning out of doors, and his own too; and in their stead gave orders to pick up the first three strollers that could be met with in the streets.[3] A while after he nailed up the cellar-door, and would not allow his brothers a drop of drink to their victuals.[4] Dining one day at an alderman's in the city, Peter observed him expatiating, after the manner of his brethren, in the praises of his sirloin of beef. " Beef," said the sage magistrate, " is the king of meat; beef comprehends in it the quintessence of partridge, and quail, and venison, and pheasant, and plum-pudding, and custard." When Peter came home he would needs take the fancy of cooking up this doctrine into use, and apply the precept, in default of a sirloin, to his brown loaf. " Bread," says he, " dear brothers, is the staff of life; in which bread is contained, inclusive, the quintessence of beef, mutton, veal, venison, partridge, plum-pudding, and custard; and, to render all complete, there is intermingled a due quantity of water, whose crudities are also corrected by yeast or barm, through which means it becomes a wholesome fermented liquor, diffused through the mass of the bread." Upon the strength of these conclusions, next day at dinner was the brown loaf served up in all the formality of a city feast. " Come, brothers," said Peter, " fall to, and spare not; here is excellent good mutton;[5] or hold, now my hand is in, I will help you." At which word, in much ceremony, with fork and knife, he carves out two

[1] The keys of the church.—H.
[2] A sudden jerk, or lash of a horse.—H.
[3] Divorced the married priests and allowed concubines.—B.
[4] The pope's refusing the cup to the laity.—H.
[5] Transubstantiation.

good slices of a loaf, and presents each on a plate to his brothers. The elder of the two, not suddenly entering into lord Peter's conceit, began with very civil language to examine the mystery. "My lord," said he, " I doubt, with great submission, there may be some mistake."—" What," says Peter, " you are pleasant; come then, let us hear this jest your head is so big with."—" None in the world, my lord; but, unless I am very much deceived, your lordship was pleased a while ago to let fall a word about mutton, and I would be glad to see it with all my heart."—" How," said Peter, appearing in great surprise, " I do not comprehend this at all." Upon which the younger interposing to set the business aright, " My lord," said he, " my brother, I suppose, is hungry, and longs for the mutton your lordship has promised us to dinner."—" Pray," said Peter, " take me along with you; either you are both mad, or disposed to be merrier than I approve of; if you there do not like your piece I will carve you another; though I should take that to be the choice bit of the whole shoulder."—" What then, my lord," replied the first, " it seems this is a shoulder of mutton all this while?" —" Pray, sir," says Peter, " eat your victuals, and leave off your impertinence, if you please, for I am not disposed to relish it at present: " but the other could not forbear, being over-provoked at the affected seriousness of Peter's countenance: " By G—, my lord," said he, " I can only say, that to my eyes, and fingers, and teeth, and nose, it seems to be nothing but a crust of bread." Upon which the second put in his word: " I never saw a piece of mutton in my life so nearly resembling a slice from a twelvepenny loaf."—" Look ye, gentlemen," cries Peter, in a rage; " to convince you what a couple of blind, positive, ignorant, wilful puppies you are, I will use but this plain argument: by G—, it is true, good, natural mutton as any in Leadenhall Market; and G— confound you both eternally if you offer to believe otherwise." Such a thundering proof as this left no farther room for objection; the two unbelievers began to gather and pocket up their mistake as hastily as they could. " Why, truly," said the first, " upon more mature consideration—"—" Ay," says the other, interrupting him, " now I have thought better on the thing, your lordship seems to have a great deal of reason."—" Very well," said Peter; " here, boy, fill me a

beer-glass of claret; here's to you both with all my heart."
The two brethren, much delighted to see him so readily appeased, returned their most humble thanks, and said they
would be glad to pledge his lordship. "That you shall,"
said Peter; "I am not a person to refuse you anything that
is reasonable: wine, moderately taken, is a cordial; here is
a glass a-piece for you; it is true natural juice from the grape,
none of your damned vintner's brewings." Having spoke
thus, he presented to each of them another large dry crust,
bidding them drink it off, and not be bashful, for it would do
them no hurt. The two brothers, after having performed
the usual office in such delicate conjunctures, of staring a
sufficient period at lord Peter and each other, and finding
how matters were likely to go, resolved not to enter on a new
dispute, but let him carry the point as he pleased; for he
was now got into one of his mad fits, and to argue or expostulate farther would only serve to render him a hundred times
more untractable.

I have chosen to relate this worthy matter in all its circumstances, because it gave a principal occasion to that great
and famous rupture [the Reformation] which happened about
the same time among these brethren, and was never afterwards made up. But of that I shall treat at large in another
section.

However, it is certain that lord Peter, even in his lucid
intervals, was very lewdly given in his common conversation,
extremely wilful and positive, and would at any time rather
argue to the death than allow himself once to be in an error.
Besides, he had an abominable faculty of telling huge pal-
pable lies upon all occasions; and not only swearing to the
truth, but cursing the whole company to hell if they pretended to make the least scruple of believing him. One time
he swore he had a cow [1] at home which gave as much milk
at a meal as would fill three thousand churches; and, what
was yet more extraordinary, would never turn sour. Another
time he was telling of an old sign-post,[2] that belonged to his
father, with nails and timber enough in it to build sixteen
large men of war. Talking one day of Chinese waggons,

[1] The ridiculous multiplying of the Virgin Mary's milk among the
papists.—W.
[2] By the sign-post is meant the cross of our blessed Saviour.

which were made so light as to sail over mountains, " Z—ds,"
said Peter, " where's the wonder of that? By G—, I saw a
large house of lime and stone [1] travel over sea and land
(granting that it stopped sometimes to bait) above two
thousand German leagues." And that which was the good
of it, he would swear desperately all the while that he never
told a lie in his life; and at every word, " By G—, gentlemen,
I tell you nothing but the truth; and the d—l broil them
eternally that will not believe me."

In short, Peter grew so scandalous, that all the neighbourhood began in plain words to say he was no better than a
knave. And his two brothers, long weary of his ill-usage,
resolved at last to leave him; but first they humbly desired
a copy of their father's will, which had now lain by neglected
time out of mind. Instead of granting this request he called
them damned sons of whores, rogues, traitors, and the rest
of the vile names he could muster up. However, while he
was abroad one day upon his projects, the two youngsters
watched their opportunity, made a shift to come at the will,
and took a *copia vera*,[2] by which they presently saw how
grossly they had been abused; their father having left them
equal heirs, and strictly commanded that whatever they got
should lie in common among them all. Pursuant to which
their next enterprise was to break open the cellar-door, and
get a little good drink,[3] to spirit and comfort their hearts.
In copying the will they had met another precept against
whoring, divorce, and separate maintenance; upon which
their next work was to discard their concubines, and send for
their wives.[4] While all this was in agitation there enters a
solicitor from Newgate, desiring lord Peter would please procure a pardon for a thief that was to be hanged to-morrow.[5]
But the two brothers told him he was a coxcomb to seek
pardons from a fellow who deserved to be hanged much better
than his client; and discovered all the method of that imposture in the same form I delivered it a while ago, advising
the solicitor to put his friend upon obtaining a pardon from

---

[1] The chapel of Loretto, which is said to have travelled from the
Holy Land to Italy.—H.
[2] Translated the Scriptures into the vulgar tongues.—H.
[3] Administered the cup to the laity.—H.
[4] Allowed marriages of priests.—H.
[5] Beginning of the Reformation.—B.

the king.[1] In the midst of all this clutter and revolution, in comes Peter with a file of dragoons at his heels,[2] and gathering from all hands what was in the wind, he and his gang, after several millions of scurrilities and curses, not very important here to repeat, by main force very fairly kicked them both out of doors [out of the church], and would never let them come under his roof from that day to this.

SECTION V

A DIGRESSION IN THE MODERN KIND

WE, whom the world is pleased to honour with the title of modern authors, should never have been able to compass our great design of an everlasting remembrance and never-dying fame, if our endeavours had not been so highly serviceable to the general good of mankind. This, O universe! is the adventurous attempt of me thy secretary;

> ——Quemvis perferre laborem
> Suadet, et inducit noctes vigilare serenas.

To this end I have some time since, with a world of pains and art, dissected the carcase of human nature, and read many useful lectures upon the several parts, both containing and contained: till at last it smelt so strong I could preserve it no longer. Upon which I have been at a great expense to fit up all the bones with exact contexture and in due symmetry; so that I am ready to show a very complete anatomy thereof to all curious gentlemen and others. But not to digress farther in the midst of a digression, as I have known some authors enclose digressions in one another like a nest of boxes, I do affirm that, having carefully cut up human nature, I have found a very strange, new, and important discovery, that the public good of mankind is performed by two ways, instruction and diversion. And I have farther proved, in my said several readings (which perhaps the world may one

---

[1] Directed penitents not to trust to pardons and absolutions procured for money.—H.

[2] By Peter's dragoons is meant the civil power.—H.

day see, if I can prevail on any friend to steal a copy, or on certain gentlemen of my admirers to be very importunate), that as mankind is now disposed, he receives much greater advantage by being diverted than instructed; his epidemical diseases being fastidiosity, amorphy, and oscitation; whereas in the present universal empire of wit and learning, there seems but little matter left for instruction. However, in compliance with a lesson of great age and authority, I have attempted carrying the point in all its heights; and accordingly, throughout this divine treatise, have skilfully kneaded up both together, with a layer of *utile* and a layer of *dulce*.

When I consider how exceedingly our illustrious moderns have eclipsed the weak glimmering lights of the ancients, and turned them out of the road of all fashionable commerce, to a degree that our choice town wits, of most refined accomplishments, are in grave dispute whether there have been ever any ancients or not; in which point we are likely to receive wonderful satisfaction from the most useful labours and lucubrations of that worthy modern, Dr. Bentley: I say, when I consider all this, I cannot but bewail that no famous modern has ever yet attempted a universal system, in a small portable volume, of all things that are to be known, or believed, or imagined, or practised in life. I am, however, forced to acknowledge, that such an enterprise was thought on some time ago by a great philosopher of O. Brazile.[1] The method he proposed was, by a certain curious receipt, a nostrum, which, after his untimely death, I found among his papers; and do here, out of my great affection to the modern learned, present them with it, not doubting it may one day encourage some worthy undertaker.

You take fair correct copies, well bound in calf-skin and lettered at the back, of all modern bodies of arts and sciences whatsoever, and in what language you please. These you distil *in balneo Mariæ*, infusing quintessence of poppy Q. S., together with three pints of Lethe, to be had from the apothecaries. You cleanse away carefully the *sordes* and *caput mortuum*, letting all that is volatile evaporate. You preserve only the first running, which is again to be distilled

---

[1] An enchanted island, supposed to be seen at certain times by the inhabitants of the Isle of Arran and called by them " O Brazil." [Hy-Breasil, that is Breasil's Island, was often put down on old maps.—*Ed.*]

seventeen times, till what remains will amount to about two drams. This you keep in a glass phial, hermetically sealed, for one-and-twenty days. Then you begin your catholic treatise, taking every morning fasting, first shaking the phial, three drops of this elixir, snuffing it strongly up your nose. It will dilate itself about the brain (where there is any) in fourteen minutes, and you immediately perceive in your head an infinite number of abstracts, summaries, compendiums, extracts, collections, medullas, *excerpta quædams, florilegias*, and the like, all disposed into great order, and reducible upon paper.

I must needs own it was by the assistance of this arcanum that I, though otherwise *impar*, have adventured upon so daring an attempt, never achieved or undertaken before, but by a certain author called Homer; in whom, though otherwise a person not without some abilities, and, for an ancient, of a tolerable genius, I have discovered many gross errors which are not to be forgiven his very ashes, if by chance any of them are left. For whereas we are assured he designed his work for a complete body of all knowledge, human, divine, political, and mechanic, it is manifest he has wholly neglected some, and been very imperfect in the rest. For first of all, as eminent a cabalist as his disciples would represent him, his account of the *opus magnum* is extremely poor and deficient; he seems to have read but very superficially either Sendivogus, Behmen, or Anthroposophia Theomagica.[1] He is also quite mistaken about the *sphæra pyroplastica*, a neglect not to be atoned for; and if the reader will admit so severe a censure, *vix crederem autorem hunc unquam audivisse ignis vocem.* His failings are not less prominent in several parts of the mechanics. For, having read his writings with the utmost application usual among modern wits, I could never yet discover the least direction about the structure of that useful instrument, a save-all; for want of which, if the moderns had not lent their assistance, we might yet have wandered in the dark. But I have still behind a fault far more notorious to tax this author

---

[1] A treatise written by a Welsh gentleman of Cambridge; his name, Vaughan, as appears by the answer written to it by the learned Dr. Henry More. [Swift is referring to Thomas Vaughan, brother of Henry Vaughan, the Silurist.—*Ed.*]

with; I mean his gross ignorance in the common laws of this realm, and in the doctrine as well as discipline of the Church of England. A defect indeed, for which both he and all the ancients stand most justly censured by my worthy and ingenious friend Mr. Wotton, Bachelor of Divinity, in his incomparable *Treatise of Ancient and Modern Learning*: a book never to be sufficiently valued, whether we consider the happy turns and flowings of the author's wit, the great usefulness of his sublime discoveries upon the subject of flies and spittle, or the laborious eloquence of his style. And I cannot forbear doing that author the justice of my public acknowledgments for the great helps and liftings I had out of his incomparable piece, while I was penning this treatise.

But beside these omissions in Homer already mentioned, the curious reader will also observe several defects in that author's writings, for which he is not altogether so accountable. For whereas every branch of knowledge has received such wonderful acquirements since his age, especially within these last three years, or thereabouts, it is almost impossible he could be so very perfect in modern discoveries as his advocates pretend. We freely acknowledge him to be the inventor of the compass, of gunpowder, and the circulation of the blood: but I challenge any of his admirers to show me in all his writings a complete account of the spleen; does he not also leave us wholly to seek in the art of political wagering? What can be more defective and unsatisfactory than his long dissertation upon tea? And as to his method of salivation without mercury so much celebrated of late, it is, to my own knowledge and experience, a thing very little to be relied on.

It was to supply such momentous defects that I have been prevailed on, after long solicitation, to take pen in hand; and I dare venture to promise, the judicious reader shall find nothing neglected here that can be of use upon any emergency of life. I am confident to have included and exhausted all that human imagination can rise or fall to. Particularly, I recommend to the perusal of the learned certain discoveries that are wholly untouched by others; whereof I shall only mention, among a great many more, my new help for smatterers, or the art of being deep-learned and shallow-read. A curious invention about mouse-traps. A universal rule of reason, or every man his own carver; together with a most useful engine for catching of owls. All which, the judicious reader will find largely treated on in the several parts of this discourse.

I hold myself obliged to give as much light as is possible into the beauties and excellencies of what I am writing; because it is become the fashion and humour most applauded among the first authors of this polite and learned age, when they would correct the ill-nature of critical, or inform the ignorance of courteous readers. Besides, there have been several famous pieces lately published, both in verse and prose, wherein, if the writers had not been pleased, out of their great humanity and affection to the public, to give us a nice detail of the sublime and the admirable they contain, it is a thousand to one whether we should ever have discovered one grain of either. For my own particular, I cannot deny that whatever I have said upon this occasion had been more proper in a preface, and more agreeable to the mode which usually directs it thither. But I here think fit to lay hold on that great and honourable privilege of being the last writer; I claim an absolute authority in right, as the freshest modern, which gives me a despotic power over all authors before me. In the strength of which title I do utterly disapprove and declare against that pernicious custom of making the preface a bill of fare to the book. For I have always looked upon it as a high point of indiscretion in monster-mongers, and other retailers of strange sights, to hang out a fair large picture over the door, drawn after the life, with a most eloquent description underneath: this has saved me many a three-pence; for my curiosity was fully satisfied, and I never offered to go in, though often invited by the urging and attending orator, with his last moving and standing piece of rhetoric:—Sir, upon my word we are just going to begin. Such is exactly the fate at this time of prefaces, epistles, advertisements, introductions, prolegomenas, apparatuses, to the readers. This expedient was admirable at first; our great Dryden has long carried it as far as it would go, and with incredible success. He has often said to me in confidence, that the world would have never suspected him to be so great a poet, if he had not assured them so frequently in his prefaces that it was impossible they could either doubt or forget it. Perhaps it may be so; however, I much fear his instructions have edified out of their place, and taught men to grow wiser in certain points where he never intended they should; for it is lamentable to behold with what a lazy scorn many of the yawning readers of our age do nowadays twirl over forty or fifty pages of preface and dedication (which is the usual modern stint), as if it were so much Latin. Though it must be also allowed, on the other hand, that a very considerable number is known to proceed critics and wits by reading nothing else. Into which two factions I think all present readers may justly be divided. Now, for myself, I profess to be of the former sort; and therefore, having the modern inclination to expatiate upon the beauty of my own productions, and display the bright parts of my discourse, I thought best to do it in the body of the work; where, as it now lies, it makes a very considerable addition to the bulk of the volume; a circumstance by no means to be neglected by a skilful writer.

Having thus paid my due deference and acknowledgment to an established custom of our newest authors, by a long digression unsought for, and a universal censure unprovoked; by forcing into the light, with much pains and dexterity, my own excellencies and other men's defaults, with great justice to myself and candour to them, I now happily resume my subject, to the infinite satisfaction both of the reader and the author.

SECTION VI

WE left lord Peter in open rupture with his two brethren; both for ever discarded from his house, and resigned to the wide world, with little or nothing to trust to. Which are circumstances that render them proper subjects for the charity of a writer's pen to work on; scenes of misery ever affording the fairest harvest for great adventures. And in this the world may perceive the difference between the integrity of a generous author and that of a common friend.

The latter is observed to adhere closely in prosperity, but on the decline of fortune to drop suddenly off. Whereas the generous author, just on the contrary, finds his hero on the dunghill, from thence by gradual steps raises him to a throne, and then immediately withdraws, expecting not so much as thanks for his pains; in imitation of which example, I have placed lord Peter in a noble house, given him a title to wear and money to spend. There I shall leave him for some time; returning where common charity directs me, to the assistance of his two brothers at their lowest ebb. However, I shall by no means forget my character of an historian to follow the truth step by step, whatever happens, or wherever it may lead me.

The two exiles, so nearly united in fortune and interest, took a lodging together; where, at their first leisure, they began to reflect on the numberless misfortunes and vexations of their life past, and could not tell on the sudden to what failure in their conduct they ought to impute them; when, after some recollection, they called to mind the copy of their father's will, which they had so happily recovered. This was immediately produced, and a firm resolution taken between them to alter whatever was already amiss, and reduce all their future measures to the strictest obedience prescribed therein. The main body of the will (as the reader cannot easily have forgot) consisted in certain admirable rules about the wearing of their coats; in the perusal whereof, the two brothers at every period duly comparing the doctrine with the practice, there was never seen a wider difference between two things; horrible downright transgressions of every point. Upon which they both resolved, without farther delay, to fall immediately upon reducing the whole exactly after their father's model.

But here it is good to stop the hasty reader, ever impatient to see the end of an adventure before we writers can duly prepare him for it. I am to record that these two brothers began to be distinguished at this time by certain names. One of them desired to be called MARTIN,[1] and the other took the appellation of JACK.[2] These two had lived in much friendship and agreement under the tyranny of their brother Peter, as it is the talent of fellow-sufferers to do;

[1] Martin Luther.   [2] John Calvin.

men in misfortune being like men in the dark, to whom all colours are the same: but when they came forward into the world, and began to display themselves to each other and to the light, their complexions appeared extremely different; which the present posture of their affairs gave them sudden opportunity to discover.

But here the severe reader may justly tax me as a writer of short memory, a deficiency to which a true modern cannot but of necessity be a little subject. Because memory, being an employment of the mind upon things past, is a faculty for which the learned in our illustrious age have no manner of occasion, who deal entirely with invention, and strike all things out of themselves, or at least by collision from each other: upon which account we think it highly reasonable to produce our great forgetfulness as an argument unanswerable for our great wit. I ought in method to have informed the reader, about fifty pages ago, of a fancy lord Peter took, and infused into his brothers, to wear on their coats whatever trimmings came up in fashion;[1] never pulling off any as they went out of the mode, but keeping on all together, which amounted in time to a medley the most antic you can possibly conceive; and this to a degree, that upon the time of their falling out there was hardly a thread of the original coat to be seen: but an infinite quantity of lace, and ribbons, and fringe, and embroidery, and points; I mean only those tagged with silver,[2] for the rest fell off. Now this material circumstance, having been forgot in due place, as good fortune has ordered, comes in very properly here when the two brothers are just going to reform their vestures into the primitive state prescribed by their father's will.

They both unanimously entered upon this great work, looking sometimes on their coats; and sometimes on the will. Martin laid the first hand; at one twitch brought off a large handful of points; and, with a second pull, stripped away ten dozen yards of fringe.[3] But when he had gone thus far he demurred a while: he knew very well there yet remained a great deal more to be done; however, the first heat being

---

[1] Multiplication of Romish ceremonies.

[2] Points tagged with silver are those doctrines that promote the greatness and wealth of the Church.—H.

[3] Alluding to the commencement of the Reformation in England by seizing on the Abbey lands.

over, his violence began to cool, and he resolved to proceed more moderately in the rest of the work, having already narrowly escaped a swinging rent, in pulling off the points, which, being tagged with silver (as we have observed before), the judicious workman had, with much sagacity, double sewn, to preserve them from falling.[1] Resolving therefore to rid his coat of a huge quantity of gold lace, he picked up the stitches with much caution, and diligently gleaned out all the loose threads as he went, which proved to be a work of time. Then he fell about the embroidered Indian figures of men, women, and children; against which, as you have heard in its due place, their father's testament was extremely exact and severe: these, with much dexterity and application, were, after a while, quite eradicated or utterly defaced.[2] For the rest, where he observed the embroidery to be worked so close as not to be got away without damaging the cloth, or where it served to hide or strengthen any flaw in the body of the coat, contracted by the perpetual tampering of work-men upon it, he concluded the wisest course was to let it remain, resolving in no case whatsoever that the substance of the stuff should suffer injury; which he thought the best method for serving the true intent and meaning of his father's will. And this is the nearest account I have been able to collect of Martin's proceedings upon this great revolution.

But his brother Jack, whose adventures will be so extra-ordinary as to furnish a great part in the remainder of this discourse, entered upon the matter with other thoughts and a quite different spirit. For the memory of lord Peter's injuries produced a degree of hatred and spite which had a much greater share of inciting him than any regards after his father's commands; since these appeared, at best, only secondary and subservient to the other. However, for this medley of humour he made a shift to find a very plausible name, honouring it with the title of zeal; which is perhaps the most significant word that has been ever yet produced in any language: as I think I have fully proved in my excellent analytical discourse upon that subject; wherein I have deduced a histori-theo-physi-logical account of zeal, showing

---

[1] The dissolution of the monasteries occasioned insurrections during the reign of Edward VI.
[2] The abolition of the worship of saints.

how if first proceeded from a notion into a word, and thence, in a hot summer, ripened into a tangible substance. This work, containing three large volumes in folio, I design very shortly to publish by the modern way of subscription, not doubting but the nobility and gentry of the land will give me all possible encouragement; having had already such a taste of what I am able to perform.

I record, therefore, that brother Jack, brimful of this miraculous compound, reflecting with indignation upon Peter's tyranny, and, farther provoked by the despondency of Martin, prefaced his resolutions to this purpose. "What," said he, "a rogue that locked up his drink, turned away our wives, cheated us of our fortunes; palmed his damned crusts upon us for mutton; and at last kicked us out of doors; must we be in his fashions, with a pox! a rascal, besides, that all the street cries out against." Having thus kindled and inflamed himself as high as possible, and by consequence in a delicate temper for beginning a reformation, he set about the work immediately; and in three minutes made more despatch than Martin had done in as many hours. For, courteous reader, you are given to understand that zeal is never so highly obliged as when you set it a-tearing; and Jack, who doted on that quality in himself, allowed it at this time its full swing. Thus it happened that, stripping down a parcel of gold lace a little too hastily, he rent the main body of his coat from top to bottom; and whereas his talent was not of the happiest in taking up a stitch, he knew no better way than to darn it again with packthread and a skewer.[1] But the matter was yet infinitely worse (I record it with tears) when he proceeded to the embroidery; for, being clumsy by nature, and of temper impatient; withal, beholding millions of stitches that required the nicest hand and sedatest constitution to extricate; in a great rage he tore off the whole piece, cloth and all, and flung it into the kennel,[2] and furiously thus continued his career: "Ah, good brother Martin," said he, "do as I do, for the love of God; strip, tear, pull, rend, flay off all, that we may appear as unlike that

---

[1] The reformers in Scotland left their established clergy in an almost beggarly condition.
[2] The presbyterians, in discarding forms of prayer, and ceremonies, disused those founded in Scripture.

rogue Peter as it is possible; I would not for a hundred pounds carry the least mark about me that might give occasion to the neighbours of suspecting that I was related to such a rascal." But Martin, who at this time happened to be extremely phlegmatic and sedate, begged his brother, of all love, not to damage his coat by any means; for he never would get such another: desired him to consider that it was not their business to form their actions by any reflection upon Peter, but by observing the rules prescribed in their father's will. That he should remember Peter was still their brother, whatever faults or injuries he had committed; and therefore they should by all means avoid such a thought as that of taking measures for good and evil from no other rule than of opposition to him. That it was true, the testament of their good father was very exact in what related to the wearing of their coats; yet it was no less penal and strict in prescribing agreement, and friendship, and affection between them. And therefore, if straining a point were at all dispensible, it would certainly be so rather to the advance of unity than increase of contradiction.

MARTIN had still proceeded as gravely as he began, and doubtless would have delivered an admirable lecture of morality, which might have exceedingly contributed to my reader's repose both of body and mind, the true ultimate end of ethics; but Jack was already gone a flight-shot beyond his patience. And as in scholastic disputes nothing serves to rouse the spleen of him that opposes so much as a kind of pedantic affected calmness in the respondent; disputants being for the most part like unequal scales, where the gravity of one side advances the lightness of the other, and causes it to fly up and kick the beam: so it happened here that the weight of Martin's argument exalted Jack's levity, and made him fly out, and spurn against his brother's moderation. In short, Martin's patience put Jack in a rage; but that which most afflicted him was, to observe his brother's coat so well reduced into the state of innocence; while his own was either wholly rent to his shirt, or those places which had escaped his cruel clutches were still in Peter's livery. So that he looked like a drunken beau, half rifled by bullies; or like a fresh tenant of Newgate, when he has refused the payment of garnish; or like a discovered shoplifter, left to the mercy of Exchange women;[1] or like a bawd in her old velvet petticoat, resigned into the secular hands of the mobile. Like any, or like all of these, a medley of rags, and lace, and rents, and fringes, unfortunate Jack did now appear: he would have been extremely glad to see his coat in the condition of Martin's, but infinitely gladder to find that of Martin in the same predicament with his. However, since neither of these was likely to come to pass, he thought fit to lend the whole business another turn, and to dress up necessity into a virtue. Therefore, after as many of the fox's arguments[2] as he could muster up, for bringing Martin to reason, as he called it; or, as he meant it, into his own ragged, bobtailed condition; and observing he said all to little purpose; what, alas! was left for the forlorn Jack to do, but, after a million of scurrilities against his brother, to run mad with spleen, and spite, and contradiction. To be short, here began a mortal breach between these two. Jack went immediately to new lodgings, and in a few days it was for certain reported that he had run out of his wits. In a short time after he appeared abroad, and confirmed the report by falling into the oddest whimseys that ever a sick brain conceived.

And now the little boys in the streets began to salute him with several names. Sometimes they would call him Jack the bald;[3] sometimes, Jack with a lantern;[4] sometimes, Dutch Jack;[5] sometimes, French Hugh;[6] sometimes, Tom the beggar;[7] and sometimes, Knocking Jack of the north.[8] And it was under one, or some, or all of these appellations, which I leave the learned reader to determine, that he has given rise to the most illustrious and epidemic sect of Æolists; who, with honourable commemoration, do still acknowledge

---

[1] The galleries over the piazzas in the late Royal Exchange were filled with shops, kept chiefly by women, in the manner of the Exeter Change in the Strand, which is no more to be seen, but, in its place Exeter Hall.

[2] The fox in the fable, who, caught in a trap, lost his tail, and used arguments to persuade the rest to cut off theirs.—H.

[3] Calvin, from *caldus*, bald.—H.

[4] All who pretend to inward light.—H.

[5] Jack of Leyden, who gave rise to the anabaptists.—H.

[6] The Huguenots.

[7] The Gueuses, by which name some Protestants in Flanders were called.—H.

[8] John Knox.—H.

the renowned JACK for their author and founder. Of whose
original, as well as principles, I am now advancing to gratify
the world with a very particular account.

Melleo contingens cuncta lepore.

SECTION VII

A DIGRESSION IN PRAISE OF DIGRESSIONS

I HAVE sometimes heard of an Iliad in a nutshell; but it has
been my fortune to have much oftener seen a nutshell in an
Iliad. There is no doubt that human life has received most
wonderful advantages from both; but to which of the two
the world is chiefly indebted I shall leave among the curious
as a problem worthy of their utmost inquiry. For the invention of the latter I think the commonwealth of learning is
chiefly obliged to the great modern improvement of digressions: the late refinements in knowledge running parallel to
those of diet in our nation, which, among men of a judicious
taste, are dressed up in various compounds, consisting in
soups and olios, fricassees and ragouts.

It is true, there is a sort of morose, detracting, ill-bred
people, who pretend utterly to disrelish these polite innova-
tions; and as to the similitude from diet, they allow the
parallel, but are so bold to pronounce the example itself a
corruption and degeneracy of taste. They tell us that the
fashion of jumbling fifty things together in a dish was at
first introduced, in compliance to a depraved and debauched
appetite, as well as to a crazy constitution: and to see a man
hunting through an olio, after the head and brains of a goose,
a widgeon, or a woodcock, is a sign he wants a stomach and
digestion for more substantial victuals. Farther, they affirm
that digressions in a book are like foreign troops in a state,
which argue the nation to want a heart and hands of its own,
and often either subdue the natives, or drive them into the
most unfruitful corners.

But, after all that can be objected by these supercilious
censors, it is manifest the society of writers would quickly

be reduced to a very inconsiderable number if men were put upon making books with the fatal confinement of delivering nothing beyond what is to the purpose. It is acknowledged, that were the case the same among us as with the Greeks and Romans, when learning was in its cradle, to be reared and fed, and clothed by invention, it would be an easy task to fill up volumes upon particular occasions, without farther expatiating from the subjects than by moderate excursions, helping to advance or clear the main design. But with knowledge it has fared as with a numerous army, encamped in a fruitful country, which, for a few days, maintains itself by the product of the soil it is on; till provisions being spent, they are sent to forage many a mile, among friends or enemies, it matters not. Meanwhile, the neighbouring fields, trampled and beaten down, become barren and dry, affording no sustenance but clouds of dust.

The whole course of things being thus entirely changed between us and the ancients, and the moderns wisely sensible of it, we of this age have discovered a shorter and more prudent method to become scholars and wits, without the fatigue of reading or of thinking. The most accomplished way of using books at present is two-fold; either, first, to serve them as some men do lords, learn their titles exactly, and then brag of their acquaintance. Or, secondly, which is indeed the choicer, the profounder, and politer method, to get a thorough insight into the index, by which the whole book is governed and turned, like fishes by the tail. For to enter the palace of learning at the great gate requires an expense of time and forms; therefore men of much haste and little ceremony are content to get in by the back door. For the arts are all in flying march, and therefore more easily subdued by attacking them in the rear. Thus physicians discover the state of the whole body by consulting only what comes from behind. Thus men catch knowledge by throwing their wit into the posteriors of a book, as boys do sparrows with flinging salt upon their tails. Thus human life is best understood by the wise man's rule of regarding the end. Thus are the sciences found, like Hercules's oxen, by tracing them backwards. Thus are old sciences unravelled, like old stockings, by beginning at the foot. Beside all this, the army of the sciences has been of late, with a world of martial discipline, drawn into its close order, so that a view or a muster may be taken of it with abundance of expedition. For this great blessing we are wholly indebted to systems and abstracts, in which the modern fathers of learning, like prudent usurers, spent their sweat for the ease of us their children. For labour is the seed of idleness, and it is the peculiar happiness of our noble age to gather the fruit.

Now, the method of growing wise, learned, and sublime, having become so regular an affair, and so established in all its forms, the number of writers must needs have increased accordingly, and to a pitch that has made it of absolute necessity for them to interfere continually with each other. Besides, it is reckoned that there is not at this present a sufficient quantity of new matter left in nature to furnish and adorn any one particular subject to the extent of a volume. This I am told by a very skilful computer, who has given a full demonstration of it from rules of arithmetic.

This perhaps may be objected against by those who maintain the infinity of matter, and therefore will not allow that any species of it can be exhausted. For answer to which, let us examine the noblest branch of modern wit or invention, planted and cultivated by the present age, and which, of all others, has borne the most and the fairest fruit. For, though some remains of it were left us by the ancients, yet have not any of those, as I remember, been translated or compiled into systems for modern use. Therefore we may affirm, to our own honour, that it has, in some sort, been both invented and brought to perfection by the same hands. What I mean is, that highly celebrated talent among the modern wits of deducing similitudes, allusions, and applications, very surprising, agreeable, and apposite, from the *pudenda* of either sex, together with their proper uses. And truly, having observed how little invention bears any vogue, beside what is derived into these channels, I have sometimes had a thought that the happy genius of our age and country was prophetically held forth by that ancient typical description of the Indian pigmies, whose stature did not exceed above two foot; *sed quorum pudenda crassa, et ad talos usque pertingentia.* Now I have been very curious to inspect the late productions wherein the beauties of this kind have most prominently appeared; and although this vein has bled so freely, and all endeavours have been used in the power of human breath to dilate, extend, and keep it open, like the Scythians, who had a custom, and an instrument, to blow up the privities of their mares, that they might yield the more milk: yet I am under an apprehension it is near growing dry and past all recovery; and that either some new *fonde* of wit should, if possible, be provided, or else that we must even be content with repetition here, as well as upon all other occasions.

This will stand as an incontestable argument that our modern wits are not to reckon upon the infinity of matter for a constant supply. What remains, therefore, but that our last recourse must be had to large indexes and little compendiums? quotations must be plentifully gathered, and booked in alphabet; to this end, though authors need be little consulted, yet critics, and commentators, and lexicons, carefully must. But above all, those judicious collectors of bright parts, and flowers, and observandas, are to be nicely dwelt on by some called the sieves and boulters of learning; though it is left undetermined whether they dealt in pearls or meal; and, consequently, whether we are more to value that which passed through, or what stayed behind.

By these methods, in a few weeks there starts up many a writer capable of managing the profoundest and most universal subjects. For what though his head be empty, provided his commonplace-book be full? and if you will bate him but the circumstances of method, and style, and grammar, and invention; allow him but the common privileges of transcribing from others, and digressing from himself, as often as he shall see occasion; he will desire no more ingredients towards fitting up a treatise that shall make a very comely figure on a bookseller's shelf; there to be preserved neat and clean for a long eternity, adorned with the heraldry of its title fairly inscribed on a label; never to be thumbed or greased by students, nor bound to everlasting chains of darkness in a library: but when the fulness of time is come, shall happily undergo the trial of purgatory, in order to ascend the sky.

Without these allowances, how is it possible we modern wits should ever have an opportunity to introduce our collections, listed under so many thousand heads of a different nature; for want of which the learned world would be deprived of infinite delight, as well as instruction, and we ourselves buried beyond redress in an inglorious and undistinguished oblivion?

From such elements as these I am alive to behold the day wherein the corporation of authors can outvie all its brethren in the guild. A happiness derived to us, with a great many others, from our Scythian ancestors; among whom the number of pens was so infinite, that the Grecian eloquence had no other way of expressing it than by saying that in the regions far to the north it was hardly possible for a man to travel, the very air was so replete with feathers.

The necessity of this digression will easily excuse the length; and I have chosen for it as proper a place as I could readily find. If the judicious reader can assign a fitter, I do here impower him to remove it into any other corner he pleases. And so I return with great alacrity, to pursue a more important concern.

SECTION VIII

THE learned Æolists [1] maintain the original cause of all things to be wind, from which principle this whole universe was at first produced, and into which it must at last be resolved; that the same breath which had kindled and blew up the flame of nature should one day blow it out:—

Quod procul a nobis flectat fortuna gubernas.

This is what the *adepti* understand by their *anima mundi;* that is to say, the spirit, or breath, or wind of the world; for, examine the whole system by the particulars of nature, and you will find it not to be disputed. For whether you please to call the *forma informans* of man by the name of *spiritus, animus, afflatus,* or *anima;* what are all these but several appellations for wind, which is the ruling element in every compound, and into which they all resolve upon their corruption? Farther, what is life itself but, as it is commonly called, the breath of our nostrils? Whence it is very justly

[1] All pretenders to inspiration.—H.

observed by naturalists that wind still continues of great
emolument in certain mysteries not to be named, giving
occasion for those happy epithets of *turgidus* and *inflatus*,
applied either to the *emittent* or *recipient* organs.

By what I have gathered out of ancient records, I find the
compass of their doctrine took in two-and-thirty points,
wherein it would be tedious to be very particular. However,
a few of their most important precepts, deducible from it,
are by no means to be omitted; among which the following
maxim was of much weight; that since wind had the master
share, as well as operation, in every compound, by consequence, those beings must be of chief excellence wherein
that *primordium* appears most prominently to abound; and
therefore man is in the highest perfection of all created things,
as having, by the great bounty of philosophers, been endued
with three distinct *animas* or winds, to which the sage
Æolists, with much liberality, have added a fourth, of equal
necessity as well as ornament with the other three; by this
quartem principium taking in the four corners of the world;
which gave occasion to that renowned *cabalist, Bumbastus*,[1]
of placing the body of a man in due position to the four
cardinal points.

In consequence of this, their next principle was, that man
brings with him into the world a peculiar portion or grain of
wind, which may be called a *quinta essentia*, extracted from
the other four. This quintessence is of a catholic use upon
all emergencies of life, is improvable into all arts and sciences,
and may be wonderfully refined, as well as enlarged, by
certain methods in education. This, when blown up to
its perfection, ought not to be covetously hoarded up,
stifled or hid under a bushel, but freely communicated to
mankind. Upon these reasons, and others of equal weight,
the wise Æolists affirm the gift of belching to be the noblest
act of a rational creature. To cultivate which art, and
render it more serviceable to mankind, they made use of
several methods. At certain seasons of the year you might
behold the priests among them, in vast numbers, with their
mouths gaping wide against a storm.[2]   At other times were

---

[1] One of the names of Paracelsus, called Christophorus Theophrastus
Paracelsus Bumbastus.—H.

[2] Those seditious preachers who blow up seeds of rebellion.—H.

to be seen several hundreds linked together in a circular chain, with every man a pair of bellows applied to his neighbour's breech, by which they blew up each other to the shape and size of a tun; and for that reason, with great propriety of speech, did usually call their bodies their vessels. When, by these and the like performances, they were grown sufficiently replete, they would immediately depart, and disembogue, for the public good, a plentiful share of their acquirements into their disciples' chaps. For we must here observe that all learning was esteemed among them to be compounded from the same principle. Because, first, it is generally affirmed, or confessed, that learning puffeth men up: and, secondly, they proved it by the following syllogism: Words are but wind; and learning is nothing but words; *ergo*, learning is nothing but wind. For this reason, the philosophers among them did, in their schools, deliver to their pupils all their doctrines and opinions by eructation, wherein they had acquired a wonderful eloquence, and of incredible variety. But the great characteristic by which their chief sages were best distinguished was a certain position of countenance, which gave undoubted intelligence to what degree or proportion the spirit agitated the inward mass. For, after certain gripings, the wind and vapours issuing forth, having first, by their turbulence and convulsions within, caused an earthquake in man's little world, distorted the mouth, bloated the cheeks, and given the eyes a terrible kind of relievo; at such junctures all their belches were received for sacred, the sourer the better, and swallowed with infinite consolation by their meagre devotees. And, to render these yet more complete, because the breath of man's life is in his nostrils, therefore the choicest, most edifying, and most enlivening belches, were very wisely conveyed through that vehicle, to give them a tincture as they passed.

Their gods were the four winds, whom they worshipped as the spirits that pervade and enliven the universe, and as those from whom alone all inspiration can properly be said to proceed. However, the chief of these, to whom they performed the adoration of *latria*,[1] was the almighty North,[2] an ancient deity, whom the inhabitants of Megalopolis, in

---

[1] Worship paid only to the supreme Deity.
[2] Presbyterians of the Scottish discipline.

Greece, had likewise in the highest reverence: *omnium deorum Boream maxime celebrant.*[1] This god, though endued with ubiquity, was yet supposed, by the profounder Æolists, to possess one peculiar habitation, or (to speak in form) a *cœlum empyræum*, wherein he was more intimately present. This was situated in a certain region, well known to the ancient Greeks, by them called Σκοτία, or the land of darkness. And although many controversies have arisen upon that matter, yet so much is undisputed, that from a region of the like denomination the most refined Æolists have borrowed their original; whence, in every age, the zealous among their priesthood have brought over their choicest inspiration, fetching it with their own hands from the fountain-head in certain bladders, and disploding it among the sectaries in all nations, who did, and do, and ever will, daily gasp and pant after it.

Now, their mysteries and rites were performed in this manner.[2] It is well known among the learned that the virtuosoes of former ages had a contrivance for carrying and preserving winds in casks or barrels, which was of great assistance upon long sea-voyages: and the loss of so useful an art at present is very much to be lamented; although, I know not how, with great negligence omitted by Pancirolus.[3] It was an invention ascribed to Æolus himself, from whom this sect is denominated; and who, in honour of their founder's memory, have to this day preserved great numbers of those barrels, whereof they fix one in each of their temples, first beating out the top; into this barrel, upon solemn days, the priest enters; where, having before duly prepared himself by the methods already described, a secret funnel is also conveyed from his posteriors to the bottom of the barrel, which admits new supplies of inspiration from a northern chink or cranny. Whereupon, you behold him swell immediately to the shape and size of his vessel. In this posture he disembogues whole tempests upon his auditory, as the spirit from beneath gives him utterance; which, issuing *ex adytis et penetralibus*, is not performed without much pain and

---

[1] Pausan. I. 8.
[2] The original of tub-preaching described.—B.
[3] An author who writ *De Artibus perditis*, etc. Of arts lost and of arts invented.—H.

gripings. And the wind, in breaking forth, deals with his face [1] as it does with that of the sea, first blackening, then wrinkling, and at last bursting it into a foam. It is in this guise the sacred Æolist delivers his oracular belches to his panting disciples; of whom, some are greedily gaping after the sanctified breath; others are all the while hymning out the praises of the winds; and, gently wafted to and fro by their own humming, do thus represent the soft breezes of their deities appeased.

It is from this custom of the priests that some authors maintain these Æolists to have been very ancient in the world. Because the delivery of their mysteries, which I have just now mentioned, appears exactly the same with that of other ancient oracles, whose inspirations were owing to certain subterraneous effluviums of wind, delivered with the same pain to the priest, and much about the same influence on the people. It is true, indeed, that these were frequently managed and directed by female officers, whose organs were understood to be better disposed for the admission of those oracular gusts, as entering and passing up through a receptacle of greater capacity, and causing also a pruriency by the way, such as, with due management, hath been refined from a carnal into a spiritual ecstasy. And, to strengthen this profound conjecture, it is farther insisted, that this custom of female priests [2] is kept up still in certain refined colleges of our modern Æolists, who are agreed to receive their inspiration, derived through the receptacle aforesaid, like their ancestors the sibyls.

And whereas the mind of a man, when he gives the spur and bridle to his thoughts, does never stop, but naturally sallies out into both extremes, of high and low, of good and evil; his first flight of fancy commonly transports him to ideas of what is most perfect, finished, and exalted; till, having soared out of his own reach and sight, not well perceiving how near the frontiers of height and depth border upon each other; with the same course and wing he falls down plumb into the lowest bottom of things; like one who travels the east into the west; or like a straight line drawn

---

[1] An exact description of the changes made in the face by enthusiastic preachers.—H.

[2] Quakers suffer their women to preach and pray.—H.

by its own length into a circle. Whether a tincture of malice in our natures makes us fond of furnishing every bright idea with its reverse; or whether reason, reflecting upon the sum of things, can, like the sun, serve only to enlighten one half of the globe, leaving the other half by necessity under shade and darkness; or whether fancy, flying up to the imagination of what is highest and best, becomes overshot, and spent, and weary, and suddenly falls, like a dead bird of paradise, to the ground; or whether, after all these metaphysical conjectures, I have not entirely missed the true reason; the proposition, however, which has stood me in so much circumstance, is altogether true; that as the most uncivilised parts of mankind have some way or other climbed up into the conception of a god or supreme power, so they have seldom forgot to provide their fears with certain ghastly notions, which, instead of better, have served them pretty tolerably for a devil. And this proceeding seems to be natural enough; for it is with men, whose imaginations are lifted up very high, after the same rate as with those whose bodies are so; that, as they are delighted with the advantage of a nearer contemplation upwards, so they are equally terrified with the dismal prospect of a precipice below. Thus, in the choice of a devil it has been the usual method of mankind to single out some being, either in act or in vision, which was in most antipathy to the god they had framed. Thus also the sect of Æolists possessed themselves with a dread and horror and hatred of two malignant natures, betwixt whom and the deities they adored perpetual enmity was established. The first of these was the chameleon,[1] sworn foe to inspiration, who in scorn devoured large influences of their god, without refunding the smallest blast by eructation. The other was a huge terrible monster, called Moulinavent,[2] who, with four strong arms, waged eternal battle with all their divinities, dexterously turning to avoid their blows, and repay them [3] with interest.

Thus furnished and set out with gods, as well as devils, was the renowned sect of Æolists, which makes at this day so illustrious a figure in the world, and whereof that polite nation of Laplanders are, beyond all doubt, a most authentic

---

[1] The author here, no doubt, means latitudinarians.
[2] A wind-mill.—B.   [3] Infidels.—B.

branch; of whom I therefore cannot, without injustice, here omit to make honourable mention; since they appear to be so closely allied in point of interest, as well as inclinations, with their brother Æolists among us, as not only to buy their winds by wholesale from the same merchants, but also to retail them after the same rate and method, and to customers much alike.

Now, whether this system here delivered was wholly compiled by Jack, or, as some writers believe, rather copied from the original at Delphos, with certain additions and emendations, suited to the times and circumstances, I shall not absolutely determine. This I may affirm, that Jack gave it at least a new turn, and formed it into the same dress and model as it lies deduced by me.

I have long sought after this opportunity of doing justice to a society of men for whom I have a peculiar honour, and whose opinions, as well as practices, have been extremely misrepresented and traduced by the malice or ignorance of their adversaries. For I think it one of the greatest and best of human actions to remove prejudices, and place things in their truest and fairest light, which I therefore boldly undertake, without any regards of my own, besides the conscience, the honour, and the thanks.

SECTION IX

A DIGRESSION CONCERNING THE ORIGINAL, THE USE, AND IMPROVEMENT OF MADNESS IN A COMMONWEALTH

Nor shall it in any ways detract from the just reputation of this famous sect, that its rise and institution are owing to such an author as I have described Jack to be; a person whose intellectuals were overturned, and his brain shaken out of its natural position; which we commonly suppose to be a distemper, and call by the name of madness or phrensy. For if we take a survey of the greatest actions that have been performed in the world under the influence of single men, which are, the establishment of new empires by conquest, the advance and progress of new schemes in philosophy, and the contriving, as well as the propagating, of new religions; we shall find the authors of them all to have been persons whose natural reason had admitted great revolutions, from their diet, their education, the prevalency of some certain temper, together with the particular influence of air and climate. Besides, there is something individual in human minds, that easily kindles at the accidental approach and collision of certain circumstances, which, though of paltry and mean appearance, do often flame out into the greatest emergencies of life. For great turns are not always given by strong hands, but by lucky adaptation, and at proper seasons; and it is of no import where the fire was kindled, if the vapour has once got up into the brain. For the upper region of man is furnished like the middle region of the air; the materials are formed from causes of the widest difference, yet produce at last the same substance and effect. Mists arise from the earth, steams from dunghills, exhalations from the sea, and smoke from fire; yet all clouds are the same in composition as well as consequences, and the fumes issuing from a jakes will furnish as comely and useful a vapour as incense from an altar. Thus far, I suppose, will easily be granted me; and then it will follow that, as the face of nature never produces rain but when it is overcast and disturbed, so human understanding, seated in the brain, must be troubled and overspread by vapours ascending from the lower faculties to water the invention and render it fruitful. Now, although these vapours (as it has been already said) are of as various original as those of the skies, yet the crops they produce differ both in kind and degree, merely according to the soil. I will produce two instances to prove and explain what I am now advancing.

A certain great prince[1] raised a mighty army, filled his coffers with infinite treasures, provided an invincible fleet, and all this without giving the least part of his design to his greatest ministers or his nearest favourites. Immediately the whole world was alarmed; the neighbouring crowns in trembling expectations towards what point the storm would burst; the small politicians everywhere forming profound conjectures. Some believed he had laid a scheme for uni-

[1] Henry the Great of France.—H.

versal monarchy; others, after much insight, determined the matter to be a project for pulling down the pope, and setting up the reformed religion, which had once been his own. Some, again, of a deeper sagacity, sent him into Asia to subdue the Turk and recover Palestine. In the midst of all these projects and preparations, a certain state-surgeon,[1] gathering the nature of the disease by these symptoms, attempted the cure, at one blow performed the operation, broke the bag, and out flew the vapour; nor did anything want to render it a complete remedy, only that the prince unfortunately happened to die in the performance. Now, is the reader exceedingly curious to learn whence this vapour took its rise, which had so long set the nations at a gaze? what secret wheel, what hidden spring, could put into motion so wonderful an engine? It was afterwards discovered that the movement of this whole machine had been directed by an absent female, whose eyes had raised a protuberancy, and, before emission, she was removed into an enemy's country. What should an unhappy prince do in such ticklish circumstances as these? He tried in vain the poet's never-failing receipt of *corpora quæque*; for,

> Idque petit corpus mens unde est saucia amore:
> Unde feritur, eo tendit, gestitque coire.—LUCR.

Having to no purpose used all peaceable endeavours, the collected part of the semen, raised and inflamed, became adust, converted to choler, turned head upon the spinal duct, and ascended to the brain: the very same principle that influences a bully to break the windows of a whore who has jilted him naturally stirs up a great prince to raise mighty armies, and dream of nothing but sieges, battles, and victories.

> ——Teterrima belli
> Causa—

The other instance is what I have read somewhere in a very ancient author, of a mighty king[2] who, for the space of above thirty years, amused himself to take and lose towns; beat armies, and be beaten; drive princes out of their dominions; fright children from their bread and butter; burn, lay waste, plunder, dragoon, massacre subject and

---

[1] Ravillac, who stabbed Henry the Great.—H.
[2] Louis XIV. of France.—H.

stranger, friend and foe, male and female. It is recorded that the philosophers of each country were in grave dispute upon causes, natural, moral, and political, to find out where they should assign an original solution of this phenomenon. At last, the vapour or spirit which animated the hero's brain, being in perpetual circulation, seized upon that region of the human body so renowned for furnishing the *zibeta occidentalis*, and, gathering there into a tumour, left the rest of the world for that time in peace. Of such mighty consequence it is where those exhalations fix, and of so little from whence they proceed. The same spirits which, in their superior progress, would conquer a kingdom, descending upon the anus, conclude in a fistula.

Let us next examine the great introducers of new schemes in philosophy, and search till we can find from what faculty of the soul the disposition arises in mortal man of taking it into his head to advance new systems, with such an eager zeal, in things agreed on all hands impossible to be known: from what seeds this disposition springs, and to what quality of human nature these grand innovators have been indebted for their number of disciples. Because it is plain that several of the chief among them, both ancient and modern, were usually mistaken by their adversaries, and indeed by all except their own followers, to have been persons crazed, or out of their wits; having generally proceeded, in the common course of their words and actions, by a method very different from the vulgar dictates of unrefined reason; agreeing for the most part in their several models with their present undoubted successors in the academy of modern Bedlam, whose merits and principles I shall farther examine in due place. Of this kind were Epicurus, Diogenes, Apollonius, Lucretius, Paracelsus, Des Cartes, and others; who, if they were now in the world, tied fast, and separate from their followers, would, in this our undistinguishing age, incur manifest danger of phlebotomy, and whips, and chains, and dark chambers, and straw. For what man, in the natural state or course of thinking, did ever conceive it in his power to reduce the notions of all mankind exactly to the same length, and breadth, and height of his own? yet this is the first humble and civil design of all innovators in the empire of reason. Epicurus modestly hoped that, one time or other, a certain fortuitous concourse of all men's opinions, after perpetual justlings, the sharp with the smooth, the light and the heavy, the round and the square, would, by certain clinamina, unite in the notions of atoms and void, as these did in the originals of all things. Cartesius reckoned to see, before he died, the sentiments of all philosophers, like so many lesser stars in his romantic system, wrapped and drawn within his own vortex. Now, I would gladly be informed how it is possible to account for such imaginations as these in particular men, without recourse to my phenomenon of vapours ascending from the lower faculties to overshadow the brain, and there distilling into conceptions, for which the narrowness of our mother-tongue has not yet assigned any other name beside that of madness or phrensy. Let us therefore now conjecture how it comes to pass that none of these great prescribers do ever fail providing themselves and their notions with a number of implicit disciples. And I think the reason is easy to be assigned; for there is a peculiar string in the harmony of human understanding, which, in several individuals, is exactly of the same tuning. This, if you can dexterously screw up to its right key, and then strike gently upon it, whenever you have the good fortune to light among those of the same pitch, they will, by a secret necessary sympathy, strike exactly at the same time. And in this one circumstance lies all the skill or luck of the matter; for, if you chance to jar the string among those who are either above or below your own height, instead of subscribing to your doctrine, they will tie you fast, call you mad, and feed you with bread and water. It is therefore a point of the nicest conduct to distinguish and adapt this noble talent with respect to the differences of persons and of times. Cicero understood this very well, who, when writing to a friend in England, with a caution, among other matters, to beware of being cheated by our hackney-coachmen (who, it seems, in those days were as errant rascals as they are now), has these remarkable words: *Est quod gaudeas te in ista loca venisse, ubi aliquid sapere viderere.* For, to speak a bold truth, it is a fatal miscarriage so ill to order affairs as to pass for a fool in one company, when in another you might be treated as a philosopher. Which I desire some certain gentlemen of my acquaintance to lay up in their hearts, as a very seasonable *innuendo.*

This, indeed, was the fatal mistake of that worthy gentlemen, my most ingenious friend, Mr. Wotton; a person, in appearance, ordained for great designs, as well as performances: whether you will consider his notions or his looks, surely no man ever advanced into the public with fitter qualifications of body and mind for the propagation of a new religion. O, had those happy talents, misapplied to vain philosophy, been turned into their proper channels of dreams and visions, where distortion of mind and countenance are of such sovereign use, the base detracting world would not then have dared to report that something is amiss, that his brain has undergone un unlucky shake, which even his brother modernists themselves, like ungrates, do whisper so loud, that it reaches up to the very garret I am now writing in!

Lastly, whosoever pleases to look into the fountains of enthusiasm, from whence, in all ages, have eternally proceeded such fattening streams, will find the spring-head to have been as troubled and muddy as the current: of such great emolument is a tincture of this vapour, which the world calls madness, that without its help the world would not only be deprived of those two great blessings, conquests and systems, but even all mankind would unhappily be reduced to the same belief in things invisible. Now, the former *postulatum* being held, that it is of no import from what originals this vapour proceeds, but either in what angles it strikes and spreads over the understanding, or upon what species of brain it ascends; it will be a very delicate point to cut the feather, and divide the several reasons to a nice and curious reader, how this numerical difference in the brain can produce effects of so vast a difference from the same vapour as to be the sole point of individuation between Alexander the Great, Jack of Leyden, and Monsieur des Cartes. The present argument is the most abstracted that ever I engaged in; it strains my faculties to their highest stretch: and I desire the reader to attend with the utmost propensity; for I now proceed to unravel this knotty point.

There is in mankind a certain . . . . . . (*Hic multa desiderantur*). And this I take to be a clear solution of the matter.

Having therefore so narrowly passed through this intricate difficulty, the reader will, I am sure, agree with me in the conclusion, that if the moderns mean by madness only a disturbance or transposition of the brain, by force of certain vapours issuing up from the lower faculties, then has this madness been the parent of all those mighty revolutions that have happened in empire, philosophy, and in religion. For the brain in its natural position and state of serenity disposes its owner to pass his life in the common forms, without any thoughts of subduing multitudes to his own power, his reasons or his vision; and the more he shapes his understanding by the pattern of human learning, the less he is inclined to form parties after his particular notions, because that instructs him in his private infirmities, as well as in the stubborn ignorance of the people. But when a man's fancy gets astride on his reason; when imagination is at cuffs with the senses; and common understanding, as well as common sense, is kicked out of doors; the first proselyte he makes is himself; and when that is once compassed the difficulty is not so great in bringing over others; a strong delusion always operating from without as vigorously as from within. For cant and vision are to the ear and the eye the same that tickling is to the touch. Those entertainments and pleasures we most value in life are such as dupe and play the wag with the senses. For if we take an examination of what is generally understood by happiness, as it has respect either to the understanding or the senses, we shall find all its properties and adjuncts will herd under this short definition, that it is a perpetual possession of being well deceived. And first with relation to the mind or understanding, it is manifest what mighty advantages fiction has over truth; and the reason is just at our elbow, because imagination can build nobler scenes, and produce more wonderful revolutions, than fortune or nature will be at expense to furnish. Nor is mankind so much to blame in his choice thus determining him, if we consider that the debate merely lies between things past and things conceived: and so the question is only this; whether things that have place in the imagination may not as properly be said to exist as those that are seated in the memory; which may be justly held in the affirmative, and very much to the advantage of the former, since this is acknowledged to be the womb of things, and the other allowed to be no more than the grave. Again, if we take this definition of happiness, and examine it with reference to the senses, it will be acknowledged wonderfully adapt. How fading and insipid do all objects accost us that are not conveyed in the vehicle of delusion! how shrunk is everything as it appears in the glass of nature! so that, if it were not for the assistance of artificial mediums, false lights, refracted angles, varnish and tinsel, there would be a mighty level in the felicity and enjoyments of mortal men. If this were seriously considered by the world, as I have a certain reason to suspect it hardly will, men would no longer reckon among their high points of wisdom the art of exposing weak sides and publishing infirmities; an employment, in my opinion, neither better nor worse than that of unmasking, which, I think, has never been allowed fair usage either in the world or the playhouse.

In the proportion that credulity is a more peaceful possession of the mind than curiosity, so far preferable is that wisdom which converses about the surface to that pretended philosophy which enters into the depth of things, and than comes gravely back with informations and discoveries that in the inside they are good for nothing. The two senses to which all objects first address themselves are the sight and the touch; these never examine farther than the colour, the shape, the size, and whatever other qualities dwell or are drawn by art upon the outward of bodies; and then comes reason officiously with tools for cutting, and opening, and mangling, and piercing, offering to demonstrate that they are not of the same consistence quite through. Now I take all this to be the last degree of perverting nature; one of whose eternal laws it is, to put her best furniture forward. And therefore, in order to save the charges of all such expensive anatomy for the time to come, I do here think fit to inform the reader that in such conclusions as these reason is certainly in the right; and that, in most corporeal beings which have fallen under my cognisance, the outside has been infinitely preferable to the in: whereof I have been farther convinced from some late experiments. Last week I saw a woman flayed, and you will hardly believe how much it altered her person for the worse. Yesterday I ordered the carcase of a beau to be stripped in my presence; when we were all amazed to find so many unsuspected faults under one suit of clothes. Then I laid open his brain, his heart, and his spleen: but I plainly perceived at every operation, that the farther we proceeded we found the defects increase upon us in number and bulk: from all which, I justly formed this conclusion to myself, that whatever philosopher or projector can find out an art to solder and patch up the flaws and imperfections of nature will deserve much better of mankind, and teach us a more useful science, than that so much in present esteem, of widening and exposing them, like him who held anatomy to be the ultimate end of physic. And he whose fortunes and dispositions have placed him in a convenient station to enjoy the fruits of this noble art; he that can, with Epicurus, content his ideas with the films and images that fly off upon his senses from the superficies of things; such a man, truly wise, creams off nature, leaving the sour and the dregs for philosphy and reason to lap up. This is the sublime and refined point of felicity, called the possession of being well deceived; the serene peaceful state of being a fool among knaves.

But to return to madness. It is certain that, according to the system I have above deduced, every species thereof proceeds from a redundancy of vapours; therefore, as some kinds of phrensy give double strength to the sinews, so there are of other species, which add vigour, and life, and spirit to the brain: now, it usually happens that these active spirits, getting possession of the brain, resemble those that haunt other waste and empty dwellings, which, for want of business, either vanish and carry away a piece of the house, or else stay at home and fling it all out of the windows. By which are mystically displayed the two principal branches of madness, and which some philosophers, not considering so well as I, have mistaken to be different in their causes, over hastily assigning the first to deficiency, and the other to redundance.

I think it therefore manifest, from what I have here advanced, that the main point of skill and address is, to furnish employment for this redundancy of vapour, and prudently to adjust the season of it; by which means it may certainly become of cardinal and catholic emolument in a commonwealth. Thus one man, choosing a proper juncture, leaps into a gulf, thence proceeds a hero, and is called the saviour of his country: another achieves the same enterprise,

but, unluckily timing it, has left the brand of madness fixed
as a reproach upon his memory: upon so nice a distinction,
are we taught to repeat the name of Curtius with reverence
and love; that of Empedocles with hatred and contempt.
Thus also it is usually conceived that the elder Brutus only
personated the fool and madman for the good of the public;
but this was nothing else than a redundancy of the same
vapour long misapplied, called by the Latins *ingenium par
negotiis;* or, to translate it as nearly as I can, a sort of phrensy,
never in its right element till you take it up in the business of
the state.

Upon all which, and many other reasons of equal weight,
though not equally curious, I do here gladly embrace an
opportunity I have long sought for of recommending it as a
very noble undertaking to Sir Edward Seymour, Sir Chris-
topher Musgrave, Sir John Bowles, John Howe, Esq., and
other patriots concerned, that they would move for leave to
bring in a bill for appointing commissioners to inspect into
Bedlam and the parts adjacent; who shall be empowered to
send for persons, papers, and records; to examine into the
merits and qualifications of every student and professor; to
observe with utmost exactness their several dispositions and
behaviour; by which means, duly distinguishing and adapting their talents, they might produce admirable instruments
for the several offices in a state,[1] civil and military;
proceeding in such methods as I shall here humbly propose.
And I hope the gentle reader will give some allowance to my
great solicitudes in this important affair, upon account of the
high esteem I have borne that honourable society, whereof
I had some time the happiness to be an unworthy member.

Is any student tearing his straw in piecemeal, swearing and
blaspheming, biting his grate, foaming at the mouth, and
emptying his piss-pot in the spectators' faces? let the right
worshipful the commissioners of inspection give him a
regiment of dragoons, and send him into Flanders among the
rest. Is another eternally talking, sputtering, gaping,
bawling in a sound without period or article? what wonderful talents are here mislaid! let him be furnished immediately
with a green bag and papers, and threepence in his pocket,[2]

[1] Ecclesiastical.—H.
[2] A lawyer's coach-hire, when four went together from any of the
Inns.

and away with him to Westminster Hall. You will find a
third gravely taking the dimensions of his kennel; a person
of foresight and insight, though kept quite in the dark; for
why, like Moses, *ecce cornuta* [1] *erat ejus facies.* He walks duly
in one pace, entreats your penny with due gravity and ceremony; talks much of hard times, and taxes, and the whore of
Babylon; bars up the wooden window of his cell constantly
at eight o'clock; dreams of fire, and shoplifters, and court-
customers, and privileged places. Now, what a figure would
all these acquirements amount to if the owner were sent into
the city among his brethren! Behold a fourth, in much and
deep conversation with himself, biting his thumbs at proper
junctures; his countenance checkered with business and
design; sometimes walking very fast, with his eyes nailed to a
paper that he holds in his hands: a great saver of time, somewhat thick of hearing, very short of sight, but more of
memory: a man ever in haste, a great hatcher and breeder
of business, and excellent at the famous art of whispering
nothing; a huge idolator of monosyllables and procrastina-
tion; so ready to give his word to everybody, that he never
keeps it: one that has forgot the common meaning of words,
but an admirable retainer of the sound: extremely subject
to the looseness, for his occasions are perpetually calling him
away. If you approach his grate in his familiar intervals;
Sir, says he, give me a penny, and I'll sing you a song: but
give me the penny first. (Hence comes the common saying,
and commoner practice, of parting with money for a song).
What a complete system of court skill is here described in
every branch of it, and all utterly lost with wrong application!
Accost the hole of another kennel (first stopping your nose),
you will behold a surly, gloomy, nasty, slovenly mortal,
raking in his own dung, and dabbling in his urine. The best
part of his diet is the reversion of his own ordure, which,
expiring into steams, whirls perpetually about, and at last
reinfunds. His complexion is of a dirty yellow, with a thin
scattered beard, exactly agreeable to that of his diet upon its
first declination; like other insects, who, having their birth
and education in an excrement, from thence borrow their
colour and their smell. The student of this apartment is

[1] Cornatus is either horned or shining, and by this term Moses is
described in the vulgar Latin of the Bible.—H.

very sparing of his words, but somewhat over-liberal of his breath: he holds his hand out ready to receive your penny, and immediately upon receipt withdraws to his former occupations. Now, is it not amazing to think the society of Warwick Lane should have no more concern for the recovery of so useful a member, who, if one may judge from these appearances, would become the greatest ornament to that illustrious body? Another student struts up fiercely to your teeth, puffing with his lips, half squeezing out his eyes, and very graciously holds out his hand to kiss. The keeper desires you not to be afraid of this professor, for he will do you no hurt: to him alone is allowed the liberty of the antechamber, and the orator of the place gives you to understand that this solemn person is a tailor run mad with pride. This considerable student is adorned with many other qualities, upon which at present I shall not farther enlarge.——Hark in your ear—I am strangely mistaken if all his address, his motions, and his airs, would not then be very natural, and in their proper element.

I shall not descend so minutely as to insist upon the vast number of beaux, fiddlers, poets, and politicians, that the world might recover by such a reformation; but what is more material, beside the clear gain redounding to the commonwealth, by so large an acquisition of persons to employ, whose talents and acquirements, if I may be so bold as to affirm it, are now buried, or at least misapplied; it would be a mighty advantage accruing to the public from this inquiry, that all these would very much excel, and arrive at great perfection in their several kinds; which, I think, is manifest from what I have already shown, and shall enforce by this one plain instance; that even I myself, the author of these momentous truths, am a person whose imaginations are hard-mouthed and exceedingly disposed to run away with his reason, which I have observed, from long experience, to be a very light rider, and easily shaken off; upon which account my friends will never trust me alone, without a solemn promise to vent my speculations in this or the like manner, for the universal benefit of human kind; which perhaps the gentle, courteous, and candid reader, brimful of that modern charity and tenderness usually annexed to his office, will be very hardly persuaded to believe.

SECTION X

A FARTHER DIGRESSION

IT is an unanswerable argument of a very refined age, the wonderful civilities that have passed of late years between the nation of authors and that of readers. There can hardly pop out a play, a pamphlet, or a poem, without a preface full of acknowledgment to the world for the general reception and applause they have given it, which the Lord knows where, or when, or how, or from whom it received. In due deference to so laudable a custom, I do here return my humble thanks to his majesty and both houses of parliament, to the lords of the king's most honourable privy-council, to the reverend the judges, to the clergy, and gentry, and yeomanry of this land; but in a more especial manner to my worthy brethren and friends at Will's coffee-house, and Gresham College, and Warwick Lane, and Moorfields, and Scotland Yard, and Westminster Hall, and Guildhall: in short, to all inhabitants and retainers whatsoever, either in court, or church, or camp, or city, or country, for their generous and universal acceptance of this divine treatise. I accept their approbation and good opinion with extreme gratitude, and, to the utmost of my poor capacity, shall take hold of all opportunities to return the obligation.

I am also happy that fate has flung me into so blessed an age for the mutual felicity of booksellers and authors, whom I may safely affirm to be at this day the two only satisfied parties in England. Ask an author how his last piece has succeeded; why, truly, he thanks his stars the world has been very favourable, and he has not the least reason to complain: and yet, by G—, he wrote it in a week, at bits and starts, when he could steal an hour from his urgent affairs; as it is a hundred to one, you may see farther in the preface, to which he refers you; and for the rest to the bookseller. There you go as a customer, and make the same question: he blesses his God the thing takes wonderfully, he is just printing the second edition, and has but three left in his shop. You beat

down the price: " Sir, we shall not differ; " and, in hopes of
your custom another time, lets you have it as reasonable as
you please; and " pray send as many of your acquaintance
as you will, I shall, upon your account, furnish them all at
the same rate."

Now, it is not well enough considered to what accidents and
occasions the world is indebted for the greatest part of those
noble writings which hourly start up to entertain it. If it
were not for a rainy day, a drunken vigil, a fit of the spleen, a
course of physic, a sleepy Sunday, an ill run at dice, a long
tailor's bill, a beggar's purse, a factious head, a hot sun,
costive diet, want of books, and a just contempt of learning:
but for these events, I say, and some others too long to recite
(especially a prudent neglect of taking brimstone inwardly),
I doubt the number of authors and of writings would dwindle
away to a degree most woful to behold. To confirm this
opinion, hear the words of the famous Troglodyte philosopher:
It is certain (said he) some grains of folly are of course
annexed, as part of the composition of human nature, only
the choice is left us, whether we please to wear them inlaid or
embossed: and we need not to go very far to seek how that
is usually determined, when we remember it is with human
faculties as with liquors, the lightest will be ever at the top.

There is in this famous island of Britain a certain paltry
scribbler, very voluminous, whose character the reader
cannot wholly be a stranger to. He deals in a pernicious
kind of writings, called *second parts;* and usually passes
under the name of the author of the first. I easily foresee,
that as soon as I lay down my pen this nimble operator will
have stolen it, and treat me as inhumanly as he has already
done Dr. Blackmore, Lestrange, and many others, who shall
here be nameless; I therefore fly for justice and relief into the
hands of that great rectifier of saddles,[1] and lover of mankind,
Dr. Bentley, begging he will take this enormous grievance into
his most modern consideration: and if it should so happen
that the furniture of an ass, in the shape of second part, must,
for my sins, be clapped by a mistake upon my back, that he
will immediately please, in the presence of the world, to
lighten me of the burden, and take it home to his own house,
till the true beast thinks fit to call for it.

[1] Alluding to the trite phrase, " Place the saddle on the right horse."

In the meantime I do here give this public notice, that my resolutions are to circumscribe within this discourse the whole stock of matter I have been so many years providing. Since my vein is once opened, I am content to exhaust it all at a running, for the peculiar advantage of my dear country, and for the universal benefit of mankind. Therefore, hospitably considering the number of my guests, they shall have my whole entertainment at a meal; and I scorn to set up the leavings in the cupboard. What the guests cannot eat may be given to the poor; and the dogs [1] under the table may gnaw the bones. This I understand for a more generous proceeding than to turn the company's stomach, by inviting them again to-morrow to a scurvy meal of scraps.

If the reader fairly considers the strength of what I have advanced in the foregoing section, I am convinced it will produce a wonderful revolution in his notions and opinions; and he will be abundantly better prepared to receive and to relish the concluding part of this miraculous treatise. Readers may be divided into three classes—the superficial, the ignorant, and the learned: and I have with much felicity fitted my pen to the genius and advantage of each. The superficial reader will be strangely provoked to laughter; which clears the breast and the lungs, is sovereign against the spleen, and the most innocent of all diuretics. The ignorant reader, between whom and the former the distinction is extremely nice, will find himself disposed to stare; which is an admirable remedy for ill eyes, serves to raise and enliven the spirits, and wonderfully helps perspiration. But the reader truly learned, chiefly for whose benefit I wake when others sleep, and sleep when others wake, will here find sufficient matter to employ his speculations for the rest of his life. It were much to be wished, and I do here humbly propose for an experiment, that every prince in Christendom will take seven of the deepest scholars in his dominions, and shut them up close for seven years in seven chambers, with a command to write seven ample commentaries on this comprehensive discourse. I shall venture to affirm that, whatever difference may be found in their several conjectures, they will be all, without the least distortion, manifestly deducible from the text. Meantime, it is my earnest request that so useful an

[1] By dogs, the author means injudicious critics.—H.

undertaking may be entered upon, if their majesties please, with all convenient speed; because I have a strong inclination, before I leave the world, to taste a blessing which we mysterious writers can seldom reach till we have gotten into our graves: whether it is, that fame, being a fruit grafted on the body, can hardly grow, and much less ripen, till the stock is in the earth; or whether she be a bird of prey, and is lured, among the rest, to pursue after the scent of a carcase; or whether she conceives her trumpet sounds best and farthest when she stands on a tomb, by the advantage of a rising ground and the echo of a hollow vault.

It is true, indeed, the republic of dark authors, after they once found out this excellent expedient of dying, have been peculiarly happy in the variety as well as extent of their reputation. For night being the universal mother of things, wise philosophers hold all writings to be fruitful in the proportion that they are dark; and therefore, the true illuminated [1] (that is to say, the darkest of all) have met with such numberless commentators, whose scholastic midwifery has delivered them of meanings that the authors themselves perhaps never conceived, and yet may very justly be allowed the lawful parents of them; the words of such writers being like seed, which, however scattered at random, when they light upon a fruitful ground, will multiply far beyond either the hopes or imagination of the sower.

And therefore, in order to promote so useful a work, I will here take leave to glance a few innuendoes, that may be of great assistance to those sublime spirits who shall be appointed to labour in a universal comment upon this wonderful discourse. And, first,[2] I have couched a very profound mystery in the number of O's multiplied by seven and divided by nine. Also if a devout brother of the rosy cross will pray fervently for sixty-three mornings, with a lively faith, and then transpose certain letters and syllables, according to prescription, in the second and fifth section, they will certainly reveal into a full receipt of the *opus magnum*. Lastly, whoever will be at the pains to calculate the whole number of each letter in this treatise, and sum up the difference exactly between the

---

[1] A name of the Rosicrucians.
[2] This is what the cabalists among the Jews have done with the Bible.—Original.

several numbers, assigning the true natural cause for every such difference, the discoveries in the product will plentifully reward his labour.   But then he must beware of Bythus and Sigé, and be sure not to forget the qualities of Achamoth,[1] *à cujus lacrymis humecta prodit substantia, à risu lucida, à tristitia, et à timore mobilis;* wherein Eugenius Philalethes [2] hath committed an unpardonable mistake.

SECTION XI

AFTER so wide a compass as I have wandered, I do now gladly overtake and close in with my subject, and shall henceforth hold on with it an even pace to the end of my journey, except some beautiful prospect appears within sight of my way; whereof though at present I have neither warning nor expectation, yet upon such an accident, come when it will, I shall beg my reader's favour and company, allowing me to conduct him through it along with myself.   For in writing it is as in travelling; if a man is in haste to be at home (which I acknowledge to be none of my case, having never so little business as when I am there), and his horse be tired with long riding and ill ways, or naturally a jade, I advise him clearly to make the straightest and the commonest road, be it ever so dirty; but then surely we must own such a man to be a scurvy companion at best; he spatters himself and his fellow-travellers at every step; all their thoughts, and wishes, and conversation turn entirely upon the subject of their journey's end; and at every splash, and plunge, and stumble, they heartily wish one another at the devil.

On the other side, when a traveller and his horse are in heart and plight, when his purse is full and the day before him, he takes the road only where it is clean and convenient; entertains his company there as agreeably as he can; but, upon the first occasion, carries them along with him to every delightful scene in view, whether of art, of nature, or of both; and if they chance to refuse, out of stupidity or weariness,

[1] Words quoted from Trenæus.—W.
[2] Vid. *Anima magica abscondita.*—W.

let them jog on by themselves and be d—n'd; he'll overtake them at the next town; at which arriving, he rides furiously through; the men, women, and children, run out to gaze; a hundred noisy curs [1] run barking after him, of which, if he honours the boldest with a lash of his whip, it is rather out of sport than revenge; but should some sourer mongrel dare too near an approach, he receives a salute on the chaps by an accidental stroke from the courser's heels, nor is any ground lost by the blow, which sends him yelping and limping home.

I now proceed to sum up the singular adventures of my renowned Jack; the state of whose dispositions and fortunes the careful reader does, no doubt, most exactly remember, as I last parted with them in the conclusion of a former section. Therefore, his next care must be, from two of the foregoing, to extract a scheme of notions that may best fit his understanding for a true relish of what is to ensue.

JACK had not only calculated the first revolution of his brain so prudently as to give rise to that epidemic sect of Æolists, but succeeding also into a new and strange variety of conceptions, the fruitfulness of his imagination led him into certain notions, which, although in appearance very unaccountable, were not without their mysteries and their meanings, nor wanted followers to countenance and improve them. I shall therefore be extremely careful and exact in recounting such material passages of this nature as I have been able to collect, either from undoubted tradition or indefatigable reading; and shall describe them as graphically as it is possible, and as far as notions of that height and latitude can be brought within the compass of a pen.[2] Nor do I at all question but they will furnish plenty of noble matter for such whose converting imaginations dispose them to reduce all things into types; who can make shadows, no thanks to the sun; and then mould them into substances, no thanks to philosophy; whose peculiar talent lies in fixing tropes and allegories to the letter, and refining what is literal into figure and mystery.

JACK had provided a fair copy of his father's will, engrossed in form upon a large skin of parchment; and resolv-

---

[1] What the author calls the true critics.
[2] The following passage refers to the practice of the fanatics in perverting Scripture.—B.

ing to act the part of a most dutiful son, he became the fondest creature of it imaginable. For although, as I have often told the reader, it consisted wholly in certain plain, easy directions, about the management and wearing of their coats, with legacies, and penalties in case of obedience or neglect, yet he began to entertain a fancy that the matter was deeper and darker, and therefore must needs have a great deal more of mystery at the bottom. " Gentlemen," said he, " I will prove this very skin of parchment to be meat, drink, and cloth, to be the philosopher's stone and the universal medicine." In consequence of which raptures, he resolved to make use of it in the necessary as well as the most paltry occasions of life.[1] He had a way of working it into any shape he pleased; so that it served him for a nightcap when he went to bed, and for an umbrella in rainy weather. He would lap a piece of it about a sore toe, or, when he had fits, burn two inches under his nose; or, if anything lay heavy on his stomach, scrape off and swallow as much of the powder as would lie on a silver penny; they were all infallible remedies. With analogy to these refinements, his common talk and conversation ran wholly in the phrase of his will, and he circumscribed the utmost of his eloquence within that compass, not daring to let slip a syllable without authority from that.[2] Once, at a strange house, he was suddenly taken short upon an urgent juncture, whereon it may not be allowed too particularly to dilate; and being not able to call to mind, with that suddenness the occasion required, an authentic phrase for demanding the way to the back-side, he chose rather, as the most prudent course, to incur the penalty in such cases usually annexed. Neither was it possible for the united rhetoric of mankind to prevail with him to make himself clean again; because, having consulted the will upon this emergency, he met with a passage near the bottom (whether foisted in by the transcriber is not known) which seemed to forbid it.[3]

He made it a part of his religion never to say grace to his

[1] The author lashes those pretenders to purity who place so much merit in using Scripture phrases.—H.

[2] The fanatics pretend that nothing is lawful but what is expressly commanded in Scripture.—B.

[3] Revelations, last chapter, 11th verse.—H.

meat;[1] nor could all the world persuade him, as the common phrase is, to eat his victuals like a Christian.

He bore a strange kind of appetite to snap-dragon,[2] and to the livid snuffs of a burning candle, which he would catch and swallow with an agility wonderful to conceive; and, by this procedure, maintained a perpetual flame in his belly, which, issuing in a glowing steam from both his eyes, as well as his nostrils and his mouth, made his head appear, in a dark night like the skull of an ass, wherein a roguish boy had conveyed a farthing candle, to the terror of his majesty's liege subjects. Therefore, he made use of no other expedient to light himself home, but was wont to say that a wise man was his own lantern.

He would shut his eyes as he walked along the streets,[3] and if he happened to bounce his head against a post, or fall into a kennel, as he seldom missed either to do one or both, he would tell the gibing apprentices who looked on that he submitted with entire resignation as to a trip or a blow of fate, with whom he found, by long experience, how vain it was either to wrestle or to cuff; and whoever durst undertake to do either would be sure to come off with a swinging fall or a bloody nose. "It was ordained," said he, "some few days before the creation, that my nose and this very post should have a rencounter; and therefore nature thought fit to send us both into the world in the same age, and to make us country-men and fellow-citizens. Now, had my eyes been open, it is very likely the business might have been a great deal worse; for how many a confounded slip is daily got by a man with all his foresight about him? Besides, the eyes of the understanding see best when those of the senses are out of the way; and therefore blind men are observed to tread their steps with much more caution, and conduct, and judgment, than those who rely with too much confidence upon the virtue of the visual nerve, which every little accident shakes out of order, and a drop or a film can wholly disconcert; like a lantern among a pack of roaring bullies when they scour the streets, exposing its owner and itself to outward kicks and

---

[1] The slovenly way of receiving the sacrament among the fanatics. —H.

[2] Hot, untimely, blind zeal of enthusiasts (?)—Original.

[3] Absolute predestination burlesqued.—B.

buffets, which both might have escaped if the vanity of appearing would have suffered them to walk in the dark. But farther, if we examine the conduct of these boasted lights, it will prove yet a great deal worse than their fortune. It is true, I have broke my nose against this post, because fortune either forgot, or did not think it convenient, to twitch me by the elbow, and give me notice to avoid it. But let not this encourage either the present age or posterity to trust their noses into the keeping of their eyes, which may prove the fairest way of losing them for good and all. For, O ye eyes, ye blind guides; miserable guardians are ye of our frail noses; ye, I say, who fasten upon the first precipice in view, and then tow our wretched willing bodies after you to the very brink of destruction: and alas! that brink is rotten, our feet slip, and we tumble down prone into a gulf, without one hospitable shrub in the way to break the fall; a fall to which not any nose of mortal make is equal, except that of the giant Laurcalco,[1] who was lord of the silver bridge. Most properly, therefore, O eyes, and with great justice, may you be compared to those foolish lights which conduct men through dirt and darkness, till they fall into a deep pit or a noisome bog."

This I have produced as a scantling of Jack's great eloquence, and the force of his reasoning upon such abstruse matters.

He was, besides, a person of great design and improvement in affairs of devotion, having introduced a new deity, who has since met with a vast number of worshippers; by some called Babel, by others Chaos, who had an ancient temple of Gothic structure upon Salisbury plain, famous for its shrine and celebration by pilgrims.

When he had some roguish trick to play,[2] he would down with his knees, up with his eyes, and fall to prayers, though in the midst of the kennel. Then it was that those who understood his pranks would be sure to get far enough out of his way; and whenever curiosity attracted strangers to laugh or to listen, he would, of a sudden, with one hand, out with his gear and piss full in their eyes, and with the other all bespatter them with mud.

---

[1] Vid. *Don Quixote.*
[2] The villanies and cruelties committed by enthusiasts and fanatics.

In winter he went always loose and unbuttoned,[1] and clad as thin as possible to let in the ambient heat;[2] and in summer lapped himself close and thick to keep it out.

In all revolutions of government[3] he would make his court for the office of hangman general; and in the exercise of that dignity, wherein he was very dexterous, would make use of no other vizard[4] than a long prayer.

He had a tongue so musculous and subtile, that he could twist it up into his nose, and deliver a strange kind of speech from thence.[5] He was also the first in these kingdoms who began to improve the Spanish accomplishment of braying; and having large ears, perpetually exposed and erected, he carried his art to such a perfection, that it was a point of great difficulty to distinguish, either by the view or the sound, between the original and the copy.

He was troubled with a disease reverse to that called the stinging of the tarantula; and would run dog-mad at the noise of music,[6] especially a pair of bagpipes.[7] But he would cure himself again by taking two or three turns in Westminster Hall, or Billingsgate, or in a boarding-school, or the Royal Exchange, or a state coffee-house.

He was a person that feared no colours, but mortally hated all, and, upon that account, bore a cruel aversion against painters, insomuch that, in his paroxysms, as he walked the streets, he would have his pockets loaden with stones to pelt at the signs.[8]

Having, from this manner of living, frequent occasion to wash himself, he would often leap over head and ears into water,[9] though it were in the midst of the winter, but was always observed to come out again much dirtier, if possible, than he went in.

He was the first that ever found out the secret of contriving a soporiferous medicine to be conveyed in at the ears;[10] it was

---

[1] Affected differences in habit and behaviour.—H.

[2] The fanatics opposing reasonable customs.—B.

[3] Severe persecutors, in a form of cant and devotion.—H.

[4] Cromwell and his confederates went, as they called it, to seek the Lord, when they resolved to murder the king.—H.

[5] Their cant and affected tones.—B.

[6] Dissenters' aversion against instrumental music in churches.—W.

[7] Organs.—B.

[8] Defaced the statues and paintings in all the churches in England. —H.

[9] Baptism of adults by plunging.   [10] Fanatic preaching.

a compound of sulphur and balm of Gilead, with a little pilgrim's salve.

He wore a large plaster of artificial caustics on his stomach, with the fervour of which he could set himself a-groaning, like the famous board upon application of a red-hot iron.

He would stand in the turning of a street, and, calling to those who passed by, would cry to one, " Worthy sir, do me the honour of a good slap in the chaps." [1] To another, " Honest friend, pray favour me with a handsome kick on the arse: Madam, shall I entreat a small box on the ear from your ladyship's fair hands? Noble captain, lend a reasonable thwack, for the love of God, with that cane of yours over these poor shoulders." And when he had, by such earnest solicitations, made a shift to procure a basting sufficient to swell up his fancy and his sides, he would return home extremely comforted, and full of terrible accounts of what he had undergone for the public good. " Observe this stroke " (said he, showing his bare shoulders); " a plaguy janizary gave it me this very morning, at seven o'clock, as, with much ado, I was driving off the great Turk. Neighbours, mind, this broken head deserves a plaster; had poor Jack been tender of his noddle, you would have seen the pope and the French king, long before this time of day, among your wives and your warehouses. Dear Christians, the great Mogul was come as far as Whitechapel, and you may thank these poor sides that he hath not (God bless us!) already swallowed up man, woman, and child."

It was highly worth observing the singular effects of that aversion or antipathy which Jack and his brother Peter seemed, even to an affectation, to bear against each other. Peter had lately done some rogueries that forced him to abscond, and he seldom ventured to stir out before night, for fear of bailiffs. Their lodgings were at the two most distant parts of the town from each other; and whenever their occasions or humours called them abroad, they would make choice of the oddest unlikely times, and most uncouth rounds they could invent, that they might be sure to avoid one another; yet, after all this, it was their perpetual fortune to meet. The reason of which is easy enough to apprehend;

[1] The fanatics have always had a way of affecting to run into persecution.—H.

for, the phrensy and the spleen of both having the same foundation, we may look upon them as two pair of compasses, equally extended, and the fixed foot of each remaining in the same centre, which, though moving contrary ways at first, will be sure to encounter somewhere or other in the circumference. Besides, it was among the great misfortunes of Jack to bear a huge personal resemblance with his brother Peter. Their humour and dispositions were not only the same, but there was a close analogy in their shape, their size, and their mien. Insomuch, as nothing was more frequent than for a bailiff to seize Jack by the shoulders, and cry, "Mr. Peter, you are the king's prisoner." Or, at other times, for one of Peter's nearest friends to accost Jack with open arms, "Dear Peter, I am glad to see thee; pray send me one of your best medicines for the worms." This, we may suppose, was a mortifying return of those pains and proceedings Jack had laboured in so long; and finding how directly opposite all his endeavours had answered to the sole end and intention which he had proposed to himself, how could it avoid having terrible effects upon a head and heart so furnished as his? However, the poor remainders of his coat bore all the punishment; the orient sun never entered upon his diurnal progress without missing a piece of it. He hired a tailor to stitch up the collar so close that it was ready to choke him, and squeezed out his eyes at such a rate as one could see nothing but the white. What little was left of the main substance of the coat he rubbed every day for two hours against a rough-cast wall, in order to grind away the remnants of lace and embroidery; but at the same time went on with so much violence that he proceeded a heathen philosopher. Yet, after all he could do of this kind, the success continued still to disappoint his expectation. For, as it is the nature of rags to bear a kind of mock resemblance to finery, there being a sort of fluttering appearance in both which is not to be distinguished at a distance, in the dark, or by short-sighted eyes, so, in those junctures, it fared with Jack and his tatters, that they offered to the first view a ridiculous flaunting, which, assisting the resemblance in person and air, thwarted all his projects of separation, and left so near a similitude between them as frequently deceived the very disciples and followers of both.

(Desunt nonnulla.)

The old Sclavonian proverb said well, that it is with men as with asses; whoever would keep them fast must find a very good hold at their ears. Yet I think we may affirm that it has been verified by repeated experience that—

Effugiet tamen hæc sceleratus vincula Proteus.

It is good, therefore, to read the maxims of our ancestors, with great allowances to times and persons; for, if we look into primitive records, we shall find that no revolutions have been so great or so frequent as those of human ears. In former days there was a curious invention to catch and keep them, which I think we may justly reckon among the *artes perditæ;* and how can it be otherwise, when in the latter centuries the very species is not only diminished to a very lamentable degree, but the poor remainder is also degenerated so far as to mock our skilfullest tenure? For, if the only slitting of one ear in a stag has been found sufficient to propagate the defect through a whole forest, why should we wonder at the greatest consequences from so many loppings and mutilations to which the ears of our fathers, and our own, have been of late so much exposed? It is true, indeed, that while this island of ours was under the dominion of grace, many endeavours were made to improve the growth of ears once more among us. The proportion of largeness was not only looked upon as an ornament of the outward man, but as a type of grace in the inward. Besides, it is held by naturalists that, if there be a protuberancy of parts in the superior region of the body, as in the ears and nose, there must be a parity also in the inferior: and, therefore, in that truly pious age, the males in every assembly, according as they were gifted, appeared very forward in exposing their ears to view, and the regions about them; because Hippocrates tells us that, when the vein behind the ear happens to be cut, a man becomes an eunuch; and the females were nothing backwarder in beholding and edifying by them; whereof those who had already used the means looked about them with great concern, in hopes of conceiving a suitable offspring by such a prospect: others, who stood candidates for benevolence found there a plentiful choice, and were sure to fix upon such as discovered the largest ears, that the breed might not dwindle between them. Lastly, the devouter sisters, who looked upon all extraordinary dilatations of that member as protrusions of zeal, or spiritual excrescences, were sure to honour every head they sat upon as if they had been marks of grace; but especially that of the preacher, whose ears were usually of the prime magnitude; which, upon that account, he was very frequent and exact in exposing with all advantages to the people; in his rhetorical paroxysms turning sometimes to hold forth the one, and sometimes to hold forth the other: from which custom the whole operation of preaching is to this very day, among their professors, styled by the phrase of holding forth.

Such was the progress of the saints for advancing the size of that member; and it is thought the success would have been every way answerable, if, in process of time, a cruel king had not arisen,[1] who raised a bloody persecution against all ears above a certain standard: upon which, some were glad to hide their flourishing sprouts in a black border, others crept wholly under a periwig; some were slit, others cropped, and a great number sliced off to the stumps. But of this more hereafter in my general history of ears, which I design very speedily to bestow upon the public.

From this brief survey of the falling state of ears in the last age, and the small care had to advance their ancient growth in the present, it is manifest how little reason we can have to rely upon a hold so short, so weak, and so slippery, and that whoever desires to catch mankind fast must have recourse to some other methods. Now, he that will examine human nature with circumspection enough may discover several handles, whereof the six senses afford one a-piece, beside a great number that are screwed to the passions, and some few riveted to the intellect. Among these last, curiosity is one, and, of all others, affords the firmest grasp: curiosity, that spur in the side, that bridle in the mouth, that ring in the nose, of a lazy and impatient and a grunting reader. By this handle it is, that an author should seize upon his readers; which as soon as he has once compassed, all resistance and struggling are in vain; and they become his prisoners as close as he pleases, till weariness or dulness force him to let go his gripe.

[1] Charles the Second, at his restoration, turned out all the dissenting teachers that would not conform.—H.

And therefore, I, the author of this miraculous treatise, having hitherto, beyond expectation, maintained, by the aforesaid handle, a firm hold upon my gentle readers, it is with great reluctance that I am at length compelled to remit my grasp; leaving them, in the perusal of what remains, to that natural oscitancy inherent in the tribe. I can only assure thee, courteous reader, for both our comforts, that my concern is altogether equal to thine for my unhappiness in losing, or mislaying among my papers, the remaining part of these memoirs; which consisted of accidents, turns, and adventures, both new, agreeable, and surprising; and therefore calculated, in all due points, to the delicate taste of this our noble age. But, alas! with my utmost endeavours, I have been able only to retain a few of the heads. Under which, there was a full account how Peter got a protection out of the king's bench; and of a reconcilement [1] between Jack and him, upon a design they had, in a certain rainy night, to trepan brother Martin into a spunging-house, and there strip him to the skin. How Martin, with much ado, showed them both a fair pair of heels. How a new warrant came out against Peter; upon which, how Jack left him in the lurch, stole his protection, and made use of it himself. How Jack's tatters came into fashion in court and city; how he got upon a great horse,[2] and eat custard. But the particulars of all these, with several others which have now slid out of my memory, are lost beyond all hopes of recovery. For which misfortune, leaving my readers to condole with each other, as far as they shall find it to agree with their several constitutions, but conjuring them by all the friendship that has passed between us, from the title-page to this, not to proceed so far as to injure their healths for an accident past remedy—I now go on to the ceremonial part of an accomplished writer, and therefore, by a courtly modern, least of all others to be omitted.

[1] In the reign of James the Second the Presbyterians joined the Papists, against the Church of England, and addressed him for repeal of the penal laws and test.

[2] Sir Humphry Edwin, a presbyterian, when Lord Mayor of London went in his formalities to a conventicle.

THE CONCLUSION

GOING too long is a cause of abortion as effectual, though not so frequent, as going too short, and holds true especially in the labours of the brain. Well fare the heart of that noble jesuit [1] who first adventured to confess in print that books must be suited to their several seasons, like dress, and diet, and diversions; and better fare our noble nation for refining upon this among other French modes. I am living fast to see the time when a book that misses its tide shall be neglected, as the moon by day, or like mackerel a week after the season. No man has more nicely observed our climate than the bookseller who bought the copy of this work; he knows to a tittle what subjects will best go off in a dry year, and which it is proper to expose foremost when the weather-glass is fallen to much rain. When he had seen this treatise, and consulted his almanac upon it, he gave me to understand that he had manifestly considered the two principal things, which were, the bulk and the subject, and found it would never take but after a long vacation, and then only in case it should happen to be a hard year for turnips. Upon which I desired to know, considering my urgent necessities, what he thought might be acceptable this month. He looked westward and said, I doubt we shall have a fit of bad weather; however, if you could prepare some pretty little banter, (but not in verse,) or a small treatise upon the ——, it would run like wildfire. But if it hold up, I have already hired an author to write something against Dr. Bentley, which I am sure will turn to account.[2]

At length we agreed upon this expedient; that when a customer comes for one of these, and desires in confidence to know the author, he will tell him very privately as a friend, naming whichever of the wits shall happen to be that week in vogue; and if Durfey's last play shall be in course, I would as lieve he may be the person as Congreve. This I mention,

[1] Père d'Orleans.—Original.

[2] When Dr. Prideaux took his *Connection of the Old and New Testament* to the bookseller, he told him it was a dry subject, and the printing could not be ventured unless he would enliven it with a little humour.—H.

because I am wonderfully well acquainted with the present relish of our courteous readers; and have often observed with singular pleasure, that a fly driven from a honey-pot will immediately, with very good appetite, alight and finish his meal on an excrement.

I have one word to say upon the subject of profound writers, who are grown very numerous of late; and I know very well the judicious world is resolved to list me in that number. I conceive therefore, as to the business of being profound, that it is with writers as with wells—a person with good eyes may see to the bottom of the deepest, provided any water be there; and often when there is nothing in the world at the bottom besides dryness and dirt, though it be but a yard and a half under-ground, it shall pass however for wondrous deep, upon no wiser a reason than because it is wondrous dark.

I am now trying an experiment very frequent among modern authors, which is to write upon nothing; when the subject is utterly exhausted, to let the pen still move on: by some called the ghost of wit, delighting to walk after the death of its body. And to say the truth, there seems to be no part of knowledge in fewer hands than that of discerning when to have done. By the time that an author has written out a book he and his readers are become old acquaintance, and grow very loth to part; so that I have sometimes known it to be in writing as in visiting, where the ceremony of taking leave has employed more time than the whole conversation before. The conclusion of a treatise resembles the conclusion of human life, which has sometimes been compared to the end of a feast, where few are satisfied to depart, *ut plenus vitæ conviva;* for men will sit down after the fullest meal, though it be only to doze or to sleep out the rest of the day, But in this latter I differ extremely from other writers; and shall be too proud if, by all my labours, I can have anyways contributed to the repose of mankind in times so turbulent and unquiet as these.[1] Neither do I think such an employment so very alien from the office of a wit as some would suppose. For, among a very polite nation in Greece, there were the same temples built and consecrated to Sleep and the Muses; between which two deities they believed the strictest friendship was established.

[1] Written before the Peace of Ryswick, signed September 1697.

I have one concluding favour to request of my reader, that he will not expect to be equally diverted and informed by every line or every page of this discourse; but give some allowance to the author's spleen and short fits or intervals of dulness, as well as his own; and lay it seriously to his conscience, whether, if he were walking the streets in dirty weather or a rainy day, he would allow it fair dealing in folks at their ease from a window to criticise his gait and ridicule his dress at such a juncture.

In my disposure of employments of the brain I have thought fit to make invention the master, and to give method and reason the office of its lackeys. The cause of this distribution was, from observing it my peculiar case to be often under a temptation of being witty, upon occasions where I could be neither wise, nor sound, nor anything to the matter in hand. And I am too much a servant of the modern way to neglect any such opportunities, whatever pains or improprieties I may be at to introduce them. For I have observed that, from a laborious collection of seven hundred and thirty-eight flowers and shining hints of the best modern authors, digested with great reading into my book of commonplaces, I have not been able, after five years, to draw, hook, or force into common conversation, any more than a dozen. Of which dozen, the one moiety failed of success by being dropped among unsuitable company; and the other cost me so many strains and traps and ambages to introduce, that I at length resolved to give it over. Now, this disappointment (to discover a secret), I must own, gave me the first hint of setting up for an author; and I have since found among some particular friends, that it is become a very general complaint, and has produced the same effects upon many others. For I have remarked many a towardly word to be wholly neglected or despised in discourse, which has passed very smoothly with some consideration and esteem after its preferment and sanction in print. But now, since by the liberty and encouragement of the press, I am grown absolute master of the occasions and opportunities to expose the talents I have acquired, I already discover that the issues of my *observanda* begin to grow too large for the receipts. Therefore I shall here pause a while, till I find, by feeling the world's pulse and my own, that it will be of absolute necessity for us both to resume my pen.

THE HISTORY OF MARTIN

Giving an account of his departure from Jack, and their setting up
for themselves, on which account they were obliged to travel and
meet many disasters, finding no shelter near Peter's habitation;
Martin succeeds in the north: Peter thunders against Martin for
the loss of the large revenue he used to receive from thence.
Harry Huff sent Martin a challenge to fight, which he received;
Peter rewards Harry for the pretended victory, which encouraged
Harry to huff Peter also. With many other extraordinary adventures of the said Martin in several places with many considerable
persons.

With a digression concerning the nature, usefulness, and necessity of
wars and quarrels.

How Jack and Martin, being parted, set up each for himself.
How they travelled over hills and dales, met many disasters,
suffered much from the good cause, and struggled with
difficulties and wants, not having where to lay their head;
by all which they afterwards proved themselves to be right
father's sons, and Peter to be spurious. Finding no shelter
near Peter's habitation, Martin travelled northwards, and
finding the Thuringians and neighbouring people disposed
to change, he set up his stage first among them; where,
making it his business to cry down Peter's powders, plasters,
salves, and drugs, which he had sold a long time at a dear
rate, allowing Martin none of the profit, though he had been
often employed in recommending and putting them off; the
good people, willing to save their pence, began to hearken
to Martin's speeches. How several great lords took the hint,
and on the same account declared for Martin; particularly
one, who not having enough of one wife wanted to marry a
second; and knowing Peter used not to grant such licences
but at a swinging price, he struck up a bargain with Martin,
whom he found more tractable, and who assured him he had
the same power to allow such things. How most of the other
northern lords, for their own private ends, withdrew themselves and their dependants from Peter's authority, and

closed in with Martin. How Peter, enraged at the loss of such large territories, and consequently of so much revenue, thundered against Martin, and sent out the strongest and most terrible of his bulls to devour him; but this having no effect, and Martin defending himself boldly and dexterously, Peter at last put forth proclamations, declaring Martin and all his adherents rebels and traitors, ordaining and requiring all his loving subjects to take up arms, and to kill, burn, and destroy all and every one of them, promising large rewards, etc., upon which ensued bloody wars and desolation.

How Harry Huff,[1] lord of Albion, one of the greatest bullies of those days, sent a cartel to Martin to fight him on a stage, at cudgels, quarter-staff, back-sword, etc. Hence the origin of that genteel custom of prize-fighting, so well known and practised to this day among those polite islanders, though unknown everywhere else. How Martin, being a bold blustering fellow, accepted the challenge; how they met and fought, to the great diversion of the spectators; and, after giving one another broken heads and many bloody wounds and bruises, how they both drew off victorious; in which their example has been frequently imitated by great clerks and others since that time. How Martin's friends applauded his victory; and how lord Harry's friends complimented him on the same score; and particularly lord Peter, who sent him a fine feather for his cap,[2] to be worn by him and his successors as a perpetual mark for his bold defence of lord Peter's cause. How Harry, flushed with his pretended victory over Martin, began to huff Peter also, and at last downright quarrelled with him about a wench.[3] How some of lord Harry's tenants, ever fond of changes, began to talk kindly of Martin, for which he mauled them soundly; as he did also those that adhered to Peter. How he turned some out of house and hold, others he hanged or burnt, etc.

How Harry Huff, after a good deal of blustering, wenching, and bullying, died, and was succeeded by a good-natured boy,[4] who, giving way to the general bent of his tenants, allowed Martin's notions to spread everywhere and take deep root in Albion. How, after his death, the farm fell into the hands

[1] Henry VIII.'s controversy with Luther in behalf of the pope.
[2] The title of "Defender of the Faith."
[3] Ann Boleyn.   [4] Edward VI.

of a lady who was violently in love with lord Peter.[1] How she purged the whole country with fire and sword, resolved not to leave the name or remembrance of Martin. How Peter triumphed, and set up shops again for selling his own powders, plasters, and salves, which were now called the only true ones, Martin's being all declared counterfeit. How great numbers of Martin's friends left the country, and, travelling up and down in foreign parts, grew acquainted with many of Jack's followers, and took a liking to many of their notions and ways, which they afterwards brought back into Albion, now under another lady,[2] more moderate and more cunning than the former. How she endeavoured to keep friendship both with Peter and Martin, and trimmed for some time between the two, not without countenancing and assisting at the same time many of Jack's followers; but, finding no possibility of reconciling all the three brothers, because each would be master and allow no other salves, powders, or plasters to be used but his own, she discarded all three, and set up a shop for those of her own farm, well furnished with powders, plasters, salves, and all other drugs necessary, all right and true, composed according to receipts made by physicians and apothecaries of her own creating, which they extracted out of Peter's, and Martin's, and Jack's receipt-books, and of this medley or hodgepodge made up a dispensatory of their own; strictly forbidding any other to be used, and particularly Peter's, from which the greatest part of this new dispensatory was stolen. How the lady, farther to confirm this change, wisely imitating her father, degraded Peter from the rank he pretended as eldest brother, and set up herself in his place as head of the family, and ever after wore her father's old cap, with the fine feather he had got from Peter for standing his friend; which has likewise been worn with no small ostentation to this day by all her successors, though declared enemies to Peter. How lady Bess and her physicians, being told of many defects and imperfections in their new medley dispensatory, resolve on a farther alteration, and to purge it from a great deal of Peter's trash that still remained in it, but were prevented by her death. How she was succeeded by a north-country farmer, who pretended great skill in the managing of farms,

[1] Queen Mary.   [2] Queen Elizabeth.

though he could never govern his own poor little farm, nor yet this large new one after he got it. How this new landlord, to show his valour and dexterity, fought against enchanters, weeds, giants, and windmills, and claimed great honour for his victories, though he ofttimes b-sh-t himself when there was no danger. How his successor, no wiser than he, occasioned great disorders by the new methods he took to manage his farms. How he attempted to establish, in his northern farm, the same dispensatory used in the southern, but miscarried because Jack's powders, pills, salves, and plasters, were there in great vogue.

How the author finds himself embarrassed for having introduced into his history a new sect, differing from the three he had undertaken to treat of, and how his inviolable respect to the sacred number *three* obliges him to reduce these four, as he intends to do all other things, to that number;[1] and for that end to drop the former Martin, and to substitute in his place lady Bess's institution, which is to pass under the name of Martin in the sequel of this true history. This weighty point being cleared, the author goes on and describes mighty quarrels and squabbles between Jack and Martin [great civil war] ; how sometimes the one had the better, and sometimes the other, to the great desolation of both farms, till at last both sides concur to hang up the landlord, who pretended to die a martyr for Martin, though he had been true to neither side, and was suspected by many to have a great affection for Peter.

A DIGRESSION ON THE NATURE, USEFULNESS, AND NECESSITY OF WARS AND QUARRELS

THIS being a matter of great consequence, the author intends to treat it methodically and at large in a treatise apart, and here to give only some hints of what his large treatise contains. The state of war natural to all creatures. War is an attempt to take by violence from others a part of what they have and we want. Every man fully sensible of his own merit, and

[1] " A panegyrical Essay upon the number THREE " is among the treatises advertised at the beginning of the *Tale of a Tub.*

finding it not duly regarded by others, has a natural right to take from them all that he thinks due to himself; and every creature, finding its own wants more than those of others, has the same right to take everything its nature requires. Brutes much more modest in their pretensions this way than men; and mean men more than great ones. The higher one raises his pretensions this way, the more bustle he makes about them; and the more success he has, the greater hero. Thus greater souls, in proportion to their superior merit, claim a greater right to take everything from meaner folks. This the true foundation of grandeur and heroism, and of the distinction of degrees among men. War therefore necessary to establish subordination, and to found cities, kingdoms, etc., as also to purge bodies politic of gross humours. Wise princes find it necessary to have wars abroad, to keep peace at home. War, famine, and pestilence, the usual cures for corruptions in bodies politic. A comparison of these three. The author is to write a panegyric on each of them. The greatest part of mankind loves war more than peace. They are but few and mean-spirited that live in peace with all men. The modest and meek of all kinds always a prey to those of more noble or stronger appetites. The inclination to war universal: those that cannot, or dare not, make war in person, employ others to do it for them. This maintains bullies, bravoes, cut-throats, lawyers, soldiers, etc. Most professions would be useless if all were peaceable. Hence brutes want neither smith nor lawyers, magistrates nor joiners, soldiers nor surgeons. Brutes, having but narrow appetites, are incapable of carrying on or perpetuating war against their own species, or of being led out in troops and multitudes to destroy one another. These prerogatives proper to man alone. The excellency of human nature demonstrated by the vast train of appetites, passions, wants, etc., that attend it. This matter to be more fully treated in the author's Panegyric on Mankind.

THE HISTORY OF MARTIN (*continued*)

How Jack, having got rid of the old landlord, set up another to his mind [Cromwell], quarrelled with Martin, and turned him out of doors. How he pillaged all his shops, and abolished the whole dispensatory. How the new landlord laid about him, mauled Peter, worried Martin, and made the whole neighbourhood tremble. How Jack's friends fell out among themselves, split into a thousand parties, turned all things topsyturvy, till everybody grew weary of them; and at last, the blustering landlord dying, Jack was kicked out of doors, a new landlord brought in, and Martin re-established [Restoration]. How this new landlord let Martin do what he pleased, and Martin agreed to everything his pious landlord desired, provided Jack might be kept low. Of several efforts Jack made to raise up his head, but all in vain; till at last the landlord died, and was succeeded by one who was a great friend to Peter, who, to humble Martin, gave Jack some liberty.[1] How Martin grew enraged at this, called in a foreigner, and turned out the landlord; in which Jack concurred with Martin, because this landlord was entirely devoted to Peter, into whose arms he threw himself, and left his country [Revolution]. How the new landlord secured Martin in the full possession of his former rights, but would not allow him to destroy Jack, who had always been his friend. How Jack got up his head in the north, and put himself in possession of a whole canton,[2] to the great discontent of Martin, who, finding also that some of Jack's friends were allowed to live and get their bread in the south parts of the country, grew highly discontent with the new landlord he had called into his assistance. How this landlord kept Martin in order, upon which he fell into a raging fever, and swore he would hang himself or join in with Peter, unless Jack's children were all turned out to starve.[3] Of several attempts made to cure Martin, and make peace between him and Jack, that they might unite against Peter; but all made ineffectual by the great address of a number of

---

[1] Indulgences to sectaries.   [2] Presbytery in Scotland.
[3] Clamour that the Church was in danger.

Peter's friends, that herded among Martin's, and appeared the most zealous for his interest. How Martin, getting abroad in this mad fit, looked so like Peter in his air and dress, and talked so like him, that many of the neighbours could not distinguish the one from the other; especially when Martin went up and down strutting in Peter's armour, which he had borrowed to fight Jack. What remedies were used to cure Martin's distemper. . . .

Here the author being seized with a fit of dulness, (to which he is very subject,) after having read a poetical epistle addressed to . . ., it entirely composed his senses, so that he has not writ a line since.

N.B. Some things that follow after this are not in the MS., but seem to have been written since, to fill up the place of what was not thought convenient then to print.

A PROJECT FOR THE UNIVERSAL BENEFIT
OF MANKIND

THE author, having laboured so long, and done so much, to serve and instruct the public, without any advantage to himself, has at last thought of a project which will tend to the great benefit of all mankind and produce a handsome revenue to the author. He intends to print by subscription, in 96 large volumes in *folio*, an exact description of *Terra Australis incognita*, collected with great care and pains from 999 learned and pious authors of undoubted veracity. The whole work, illustrated with maps and cuts agreeable to the subject, and done by the best masters, will cost but one guinea each volume to subscribers; one guinea to be paid in advance, and afterwards a guinea on receiving each volume, except the last. This work will be of great use for all men, and necessary for all families, because it contains exact accounts of all the provinces, colonies, and mansions of that spacious country, where, by a general doom, all transgressors of the law are to be transported; and every one having this work may choose out the fittest and best place for himself, there being enough for all, so as every one shall be fully satisfied.

The author supposes that one copy of this work will be bought at the public charge, or out of the parish-rates, for every parish-church in the three kingdoms, and in all the dominions thereunto belonging; and that every family that can command ten pounds per annum, even though retrenched from less necessary expenses, will subscribe for one. He does not think of giving out above nine volumes yearly; and considering the number requisite, he intends to print at least 100,000 for the first edition. He is to print proposals against next term, with a specimen, and a curious map of the capital city, with its twelve gates, from a known author, who took an exact survey of it in a dream. Considering the great care and pains of the author, and the usefulness of the work, he hopes every one will be ready, for their own good as well as his, to contribute cheerfully to it, and not grudge him the profit he may have by it, especially if it comes to a third or fourth edition, as he expects it will very soon.

He doubts not but it will be translated into foreign languages by most nations of Europe, as well as of Asia and Africa, being of as great use to all those nations as to his own; for this reason, he designs to procure patents and privileges for securing the whole benefit to himself from all those different princes and states; and hopes to see many millions of this great work printed, in those different countries and languages, before his death.

After this business is pretty well established, he has promised to put a friend on another project, almost as good as this, by establishing insurance-offices everywhere for securing people from shipwreck and several other accidents in their voyage to this country; and these offices shall furnish, at a certain rate, pilots well versed in the route, and that know all the rocks, shelves, quicksands, etc., that such pilgrims and travellers may be exposed to. Of these he knows a great number ready instructed in most countries: but the whole scheme of this matter he is to draw up at large and communicate to his friend.

[Here ends the manuscript.]

A FULL AND TRUE ACCOUNT

OF THE

BATTLE FOUGHT LAST FRIDAY

BETWEEN THE

ANCIENT AND THE MODERN BOOKS
IN SAINT JAMES'S LIBRARY

THE BOOKSELLER TO THE READER

THE following discourse, as it is unquestionably of the same author, so it seems to have been written about the same time, with the former; I mean the year 1697, when the famous dispute was on foot about ancient and modern learning. The controversy took its rise from an essay of Sir William Temple's upon that subject; which was answered by W. Wotton, B.D., with an appendix by Dr. Bentley, endeavouring to destroy the credit of Æsop and Phalaris for authors, whom Sir William Temple had, in the essay before mentioned, highly commended. In that appendix the doctor falls hard upon a new edition of Phalaris, put out by the Honourable Charles Boyle, now Earl of Orrery, to which Mr. Boyle replied at large with great learning and wit; and the doctor voluminously rejoined. In this dispute the town highly resented to see a person of Sir William Temple's character and merits roughly used by the two reverend gentlemen aforesaid, and without any manner of provocation. At length, there appearing no end of the quarrel, our author tells us that the BOOKS in St. James's Library, looking upon themselves as parties principally concerned, took up the controversy, and came to a decisive battle; but the manuscript, by the injury of fortune or weather, being in several places imperfect, we cannot learn to which side the victory fell.

I must warn the reader to beware of applying to persons what is here meant only of books, in the most literal sense. So, when Virgil is mentioned, we are not to understand the person of a famous poet called by that name; but only certain sheets of paper bound up in leather, containing in print the works of the said poet: and so of the rest.

THE PREFACE OF THE AUTHOR

SATIRE is a sort of glass wherein beholders do generally discover everybody's face but their own; which is the chief reason for that kind reception it meets with in the world, and that so very few are offended with it. But, if it should happen otherwise, the danger is not great; and I have learned from experience never to apprehend mischief from those understandings I have been able to provoke: for anger and fury, though they add strength to the sinews of the body, yet are found to relax those of the mind, and to render all its efforts feeble and impotent.

There is a brain that will endure but one scumming; let the owner gather it with discretion, and manage his little stock with husbandry; but, of all things, let him beware of bringing it under the lash of his betters, because that will make it all bubble up into impertinence, and he will find no new supply. Wit without knowledge being a sort of cream, which gathers in a night to the top, and by a skilful hand may be soon whipped into froth; but once scummed away, what appears underneath will be fit for nothing but to be thrown to the hogs.

A FULL AND TRUE ACCOUNT, Etc.

WHOEVER examines, with due circumspection, into the annual records of time, will find it remarked that war is the child of pride, and pride the daughter of riches:—the former of which assertions may be soon granted, but one cannot so easily subscribe to the latter; for pride is nearly related to beggary and want, either by father or mother, and sometimes by both: and, to speak naturally, it very seldom happens among men to fall out when all have enough; invasions usually travelling from north to south, that is to say, from poverty to plenty. The most ancient and natural grounds of quarrels are lust and avarice; which, though we may allow to be brethren, or collateral branches of pride, are certainly the issues of want. For, to speak in the phrase of writers upon politics, we may observe in the republic of dogs, which in its original seems to be an institution of the many, that the whole state is ever in the profoundest peace after a full meal; and that civil broils arise among them when it happens for one great bone to be seized on by some leading dog, who either divides it among the few, and then it falls to an oligarchy, or keeps it to himself, and then it runs up to a tyranny. The same reasoning also holds place among them in those dissensions we behold upon a turgescency in any of their females. For the right of possession lying in common, (it being impossible to establish a property in so delicate a case,) jealousies and suspicions do so abound, that the whole commonwealth of that street is reduced to a manifest state of war, of every citizen against every citizen, till some one of more courage, conduct, or fortune than the rest seizes and enjoys the prize: upon which naturally arises plenty of heart-burning, and envy, and snarling against the happy dog. Again if we look upon any of these republics engaged in a foreign war, either of invasion or defence, we shall find the same reasoning will serve as to the grounds and occasions of each; and that poverty or want, in some degree or other, (whether real or in opinion, which makes no alteration in the case,) has a great share, as well as pride, on the part of the aggressor.

Now, whoever will please to take this scheme, and either reduce or adapt it to an intellectual state or commonwealth of learning, will soon discover the first ground of disagreement between the two great parties at this time in arms, and may form just conclusions upon the merits of either cause. But the issue or events of this war are not so easy to conjecture at; for the present quarrel is so inflamed by the warm heads of either faction, and the pretensions somewhere or other so exorbitant, as not to admit the least overtures of accommodation. This quarrel first began, as I have heard it affirmed by an old dweller in the neighbourhood, about a small spot of ground, lying and being upon one of the two tops of the hill Parnassus; the highest and largest of which had, it seems, been time out of mind in quiet possession of certain tenants, called the Ancients; and the other was held by the Moderns. But these, disliking their present station, sent certain ambassadors to the ancients, complaining of a great nuisance; how the height of that part of Parnassus quite spoiled the prospect of theirs, especially toward the *east;*[1] and therefore, to avoid a war, offered them the choice of this alternative, either that the ancients would please to remove themselves and their effects down to the lower summit, which the moderns would graciously surrender to them, and advance into their place; or else the said ancients will give leave to the moderns to come with shovels and mattocks, and level the said hill as low as they shall think it convenient. To which the ancients made answer, how little they expected such a message as this from a colony whom they had admitted, out of their own free grace, to so near a neighbourhood. That, as to their own seat, they were aborigines of it, and therefore to talk with them of a removal or surrender was a language they did not understand. That if the height of the hill on their sides shortened the prospect of the moderns, it was a disadvantage they could not help; but desired them to consider whether that injury (if it be any) were not largely recompensed by the shade and shelter it afforded them. That as to the levelling or digging down, it was either folly

[1] Sir William Temple affects to trace the progress of arts and science, from east to west.

or ignorance to propose it if they did or did not know how that side of the hill was an entire rock, which would break their tools and hearts, without any damage to itself. That they would therefore advise the moderns rather to raise their own side of the hill than dream of pulling down that of the ancients; to the former of which they would not only give licence, but also largely contribute. All this was rejected by the moderns with much indignation, who still insisted upon one of the two expedients; and so this difference broke out into a long and obstinate war, maintained on the one part by resolution, and by the courage of certain leaders and allies; but, on the other, by the greatness of their number, upon all defeats affording continual recruits. In this quarrel whole rivulets of ink have been exhausted, and the virulence of both parties enormously augmented. Now, it must be here understood that ink is the great missive weapon in all battles of the learned, which, conveyed through a sort of engine called a quill, infinite numbers of these are darted at the enemy by the valiant on each side, with equal skill and violence, as if it were an engagement of *porcupines*. This malignant liquor was compounded, by the engineer who invented it, of two ingredients, which are, gall and copperas; by its bitterness and venom to suit, in some degree, as well as to foment, the genius of the combatants. And as the Grecians, after an engagement, when they could not agree about the victory, were wont to set up trophies on both sides, the beaten party being content to be at the same expense, to keep itself in countenance, (a laudable and ancient custom, happily revived of late in the art of war,) so the learned, after a sharp and bloody dispute, do, on both sides, hang out their trophies too, whichever comes by the worst. These trophies have largely inscribed on them the merits of the cause; a full impartial account of such a *battle*, and how the victory fell clearly to the party that set them up. They are known to the world under several names; as disputes, arguments, rejoinders, brief considerations, answers, replies, remarks, reflections, objections, confutations. For a very few days they are fixed up in all public places, either by themselves or their representatives,[1] for passengers to gaze at; whence the chiefest and largest are removed to certain

[1] Their title-pages.—Original.

magazines they call libraries, there to remain in a quarter purposely assigned them, and thenceforth begin to be called books of controversy.

In these books is wonderfully instilled and preserved the spirit of each warrior while he is alive; and after his death his soul transmigrates thither to inform them. This at least is the more common opinion; but I believe it is with libraries as with other cemeteries; where some philosophers affirm that a certain spirit, which they call *brutum hominis*, hovers over the monument, till the body is corrupted and turns to dust or to worms, but then vanishes or dissolves; so, we may say, a restless spirit haunts over every book, till dust or worms have seized upon it; which to some may happen in a few days, but to others later: and therefore books of controversy, being, of all others, haunted by the most disorderly spirits, have always been confined in a separate lodge from the rest; and for fear of a mutual violence against each other, it was thought prudent by our ancestors to bind them to the peace with strong iron chains. Of which invention the original occasion was this: When the works of Scotus first came out, they were carried to a certain library, and had lodgings appointed them; but this author was no sooner settled than he went to visit his master Aristotle; and there both concerted together to seize Plato by main force, and turn him out from his ancient station among the divines, where he had peaceably dwelt near eight hundred years. The attempt succeeded, and the two usurpers have reigned ever since in his stead: but, to maintain quiet for the future, it was decreed that all *polemics* of the larger size should be held fast with a chain.

By this expedient the public peace of libraries might certainly have been preserved if a new species of controversial books had not arisen of late years, instinct with a more malignant spirit, from the war above mentioned between the learned about the higher summit of *Parnassus*.

When these books were first admitted into the public libraries, I remember to have said, upon occasion, to several persons concerned, how I was sure they would create broils wherever they came, unless a world of care were taken: and therefore I advised that the champions of each side should be coupled together, or otherwise mixed, that, like the blending of contrary poisons, their malignity might be employed among themselves. And it seems I was neither an ill prophet nor an ill counsellor; for it was nothing else but the neglect of this caution which gave occasion to the terrible fight that happened on Friday last between the ancient and modern books in the king's library. Now, because the talk of this battle is so fresh in everybody's mouth, and the expectation of the town so great to be informed in the particulars, I, being possessed of all qualifications requisite in an historian, and retained by neither party, have resolved to comply with the urgent importunity of my friends, by writing down a full impartial account thereof.

The guardian of the regal library,[1] a person of great valour, but chiefly renowned for his humanity, had been a fierce champion for the moderns; and, in an engagement upon Parnassus, had vowed, with his own hands to knock down two of the ancient chiefs, who guarded a small pass on the superior rock; but, endeavouring to climb up, was cruelly obstructed by his own unhappy weight and tendency towards his centre; a quality to which those of the modern party are extremely subject; for, being light-headed, they have, in speculation, a wonderful agility, and conceive nothing too high for them to mount; but, in reducing to practice, discover a mighty pressure about their posteriors and their heels. Having thus failed in his design, the disappointed champion bore a cruel rancour to the ancients; which he resolved to gratify by showing all marks of his favour to the books of their adversaries, and lodging them in the fairest apartments; when, at the same time, whatever book had the boldness to own itself for an advocate of the ancients was buried alive in some obscure corner, and threatened, upon the least displeasure, to be turned out of doors. Besides, it so happened that about this time there was a strange confusion of place among all the books in the library; for which several reasons were assigned. Some imputed it to a great heap of learned dust, which a perverse wind blew off from a shelf of moderns into the keeper's eyes. Others affirmed he had a humour to pick the worms out of the schoolmen, and swallow

---

[1] The honourable Mr. Boyle, in the preface to his edition of Phalaris, says he was refused a MS. by the library keeper, Dr. Bentley; the two ancients were Phalaris and Æsop.

them fresh and fasting; whereof some fell upon his spleen, and some climbed up into his head, to the great perturbation of both. And lastly, others maintained that, by walking much in the dark about the library, he had quite lost the situation of it out of his head; and therefore, in replacing his books, he was apt to mistake, and clap Des Cartes next to Aristotle; poor Plato had got between Hobbes and the Seven Wise Masters, and Virgil was hemmed in with Dryden on one side and Withers on the other.

Meanwhile those books that were advocates for the moderns chose out one from among them to make a progress through the whole library, examine the number and strength of their party, and concert their affairs. This messenger performed all things very industriously, and brought back with him a list of their forces, in all, fifty thousand, consisting chiefly of light-horse, heavy-armed foot, and mercenaries; whereof the foot were in general but sorrily armed and worse clad; their horses large, but extremely out of case and heart; however, some few, by trading among the ancients, had furnished themselves tolerably enough.

While things were in this ferment, discord grew extremely high; hot words passed on both sides, and ill blood was plentifully bred. Here a solitary ancient, squeezed up among a whole shelf of moderns, offered fairly to dispute the case, and to prove by manifest reason that the priority was due to them from long possession, and in regard of their prudence, antiquity, and, above all, their great merits toward the moderns. But these denied the premises, and seemed very much to wonder how the ancients could pretend to insist upon their antiquity, when it was so plain (if they went to that) that the moderns were much the more ancient of the two. As for any obligations they owed to the ancients, they renounced them all. It is true, said they, we are informed some few of our party have been so mean to borrow their subsistence from you; but the rest, infinitely the greater number, (and especially we French and English,) were so far from stooping to so base an example, that there never passed, till this very hour, six words between us. For our horses were of our own breeding, our arms of our own forging, and our clothes of our own cutting out and sewing. Plato was by chance up on the next shelf, and observing those that spoke to be in the ragged plight mentioned a while ago; their jades lean and foundered, their weapons of rotten wood, their armour rusty, and nothing but rags underneath; he laughed aloud, and in his pleasant way swore, by ——, he believed them.

Now, the moderns had not proceeded in their late negotiation with secrecy enough to escape the notice of the enemy. For those advocates who had begun the quarrel, by setting first on foot the dispute of precedency, talked so loud of coming to a battle, that Sir William Temple [1] happened to overhear them, and gave immediate intelligence to the ancients; who thereupon drew up their scattered troops together, resolving to act upon the defensive; upon which, several of the moderns fled over to their party, and among the rest Temple himself. This Temple, having been educated and long conversed among the ancients, was, of all the moderns, their greatest favourite, and became their greatest champion.

Things were at this crisis when a material accident fell out. For upon the highest corner of a large window there dwelt a certain spider, swollen up to the first magnitude by the destruction of infinite numbers of flies, whose spoils lay scattered before the gates of his palace, like human bones before the cave of some giant. The avenues to his castle were guarded with turnpikes and palisadoes, all after the modern way of fortification. After you had passed several courts you came to the centre, wherein you might behold the constable himself in his own lodgings, which had windows fronting to each avenue, and ports to sally out upon all occasions of prey or defence. In this mansion he had for some time dwelt in peace and plenty, without danger to his person by swallows from above, or to his palace by brooms from below: when it was the pleasure of fortune to conduct thither a wandering bee, to whose curiosity a broken pane in the glass had discovered itself, and in he went; where, expatiating a while, he at last happened to alight upon one of the outward walls of the spider's citadel; which, yielding to the unequal weight, sunk down to the very foundation. Thrice he endeavoured to force his passage, and thrice the centre shook. The spider within, feeling the terrible convulsion,

[1] The allies who espoused the cause of ancient learning.

supposed at first that nature was approaching to her final dissolution; or else, that Beelzebub,[1] with all his legions, was come to revenge the death of many thousands of his subjects whom his enemy had slain and devoured. However, he at length valiantly resolved to issue forth and meet his fate. Meanwhile the bee had acquitted himself of his toils, and, posted securely at some distance, was employed in cleansing his wings, and disengaging them from the ragged remnants of the cobweb. By this time the spider was adventured out, when, beholding the chasms, the ruins, and dilapidations of his fortress, he was very near at his wits' end; he stormed and swore like a madman, and swelled till he was ready to burst. At length, casting his eye upon the bee, and wisely gathering causes from events, (for they knew each other by sight,) A plague split you, said he, for a giddy son of a whore; is it you, with a vengeance, that have made this litter here? could not you look before you, and be d—d? do you think I have nothing else to do (in the devil's name) but to mend and repair after your arse?—Good words, friend, said the bee (having now pruned himself, and being disposed to droll): I'll give you my hand and word to come near your kennel no more; I was never in such a confounded pickle since I was born.—Sirrah, replied the spider, if it were not for breaking an old custom in our family, never to stir abroad against an enemy, I should come and teach you better manners.—I pray have patience, said the bee, or you'll spend your substance, and, for aught I see, you may stand in need of it all, toward the repair of your house.—Rogue, rogue, replied the spider, yet methinks you should have more respect to a person whom all the world allows to be so much your betters.—By my troth, said the bee, the comparison will amount to a very good jest; and you will do me a favour to let me know the reasons that all the world is pleased to use in so hopeful a dispute. At this the spider, having swelled himself into the size and posture of a disputant, began his argument in the true spirit of controversy, with resolution to be heartily scurrilous and angry to urge on his own reasons, without the least regard to the answers or objections of his opposite; and fully predetermined in his mind against all conviction.

[1] Supposed to be the tutelar deity of the flies.

Not to disparage myself, said he, by the comparison with such a rascal, what art thou but a vagabond without house or home, without stock or inheritance? born to no possession of your own, but a pair of wings and a drone-pipe. Your livelihood is a universal plunder upon nature; a freebooter over fields and gardens; and, for the sake of stealing, will rob a nettle as easily as a violet. Whereas I am a domestic animal, furnished with a native stock within myself. This large castle (to show my improvements in the mathematics [1]) is all built with my own hands, and the materials extracted altogether out of my own person.

I am glad, answered the bee, to hear you grant at least that I am come honestly by my wings and my voice; for then, it seems, I am obliged to Heaven alone for my flights and my music; and Providence would never have bestowed on me two such gifts, without designing them for the noblest ends. I visit indeed all the flowers and blossoms of the field and garden; but whatever I collect thence enriches myself, without the least injury to their beauty, their smell, or their taste. Now, for you and your skill in architecture and other mathematics, I have little to say: in that building of yours there might, for aught I know, have been labour and method enough; but, by woful experience for us both, it is too plain the materials are naught; and I hope you will henceforth take warning, and consider duration and matter, as well as method and art. You boast indeed of being obliged to no other creature, but of drawing and spinning out all from yourself; that is to say, if we may judge of the liquor in the vessel by what issues out, you possess a good plentiful store of dirt and poison in your breast; and, though I would by no means lessen or disparage your genuine stock of either, yet I doubt you are somewhat obliged, for an increase of both, to a little foreign assistance. Your inherent portion of dirt does not fail of acquisitions, by sweepings exhaled from below; and one insect furnishes you with a share of poison to destroy another. So that, in short, the question comes all to this; whether is the nobler being of the two, that which, by a lazy contemplation of four inches round, by an overweening pride, feeding and engendering on itself, turns all into excre-

---

[1] Urged by those who contended for the excellence of modern learning.

ment and venom, producing nothing at all but flybane and a cobweb; or that which, by a universal range, with long search, much study, true judgment, and distinction of things, brings home honey and wax.

This dispute was managed with such eagerness, clamour, and warmth, that the two parties of books, in arms below, stood silent a while, waiting in suspense what would be the issue; which was not long undetermined: for the bee, grown impatient at so much loss of time, fled straight away to a bed of roses, without looking for a reply, and left the spider, like an orator, collected in himself, and just prepared to burst out.

It happened upon this emergency that Æsop broke silence first. He had been of late most barbarously treated by a strange effect of the regent's humanity, who [1] had torn off his title-page, sorely defaced one half of his leaves, and chained him fast among a shelf of moderns. Where, soon discovering how high the quarrel was likely to proceed, he tried all his arts, and turned himself to a thousand forms. At length, in the borrowed shape of an ass, the regent mistook him for a modern; by which means he had time and opportunity to escape to the ancients, just when the spider and the bee were entering into their contest; to which he gave his attention with a world of pleasure, and, when it was ended, swore in the loudest key that in all his life he had never known two cases so parallel and adapt to each other as that in the window and this upon the shelves. The disputants, said he, have admirably managed the dispute between them, have taken in the full strength of all that is to be said on both sides, and exhausted the substance of every argument *pro* and *con*. It is but to adjust the reasonings of both to the present quarrel, then to compare and apply the labours and fruits of each, as the bee has learnedly deduced them, and we shall find the conclusion fall plain and close upon the moderns and us. For pray, gentlemen, was ever anything so modern as the spider in his air, his turns, and his paradoxes? he argues in the behalf of you his brethren and himself with many boastings of his native stock and great genius; that he spins and spits wholly from himself, and scorns to own any obligation or assistance from without. Then he displays to

[1] Bentley, who denied the antiquity of Æsop.

you his great skill in architecture and improvement in the mathematics. To all this the bee, as an advocate retained by us the ancients, thinks fit to answer, that, if one may judge of the great genius or inventions of the moderns by what they have produced, you will hardly have countenance to bear you out in boasting of either. Erect your schemes with as much method and skill as you please; yet, if the materials be nothing but dirt, spun out of your own entrails (the guts of modern brains), the edifice will conclude at last in a cobweb; the duration of which, like that of other spiders' webs, may be imputed to their being forgotten, or neglected, or hid in a corner. For anything else of genuine that the moderns may pretend to, I cannot recollect; unless it be a large vein of wrangling and satire, much of a nature and substance with the spider's poison; which, however they pretend to spit wholly out of themselves, is improved by the same arts, by feeding upon the insects and vermin of the age. As for us the ancients, we are content, with the bee, to pretend to nothing of our own beyond our wings and our voice: that is to say, our flights and our language. For the rest, whatever we have got has been by infinite labour and search, and ranging through every corner of nature; the difference is, that, instead of dirt and poison, we have rather chosen to fill our hives with honey and wax; thus furnishing mankind with the two noblest of things, which are sweetness and light.

It is wonderful to conceive the tumult arisen among the books upon the close of this long descant of Æsop: both parties took the hint, and heightened their animosities so on a sudden, that they resolved it should come to a battle. Immediately the two main bodies withdrew, under their several ensigns, to the farther parts of the library, and there entered into cabals and consults upon the present emergency. The moderns were in very warm debates upon the choice of their leaders; and nothing less than the fear impending from their enemies could have kept them from mutinies upon this occasion. The difference was greatest among the horse, where every private trooper pretended to the chief command, from Tasso and Milton to Dryden and Withers. The light-horse [1] were commanded by Cowley and Despreaux.[2] There

---

[1] The epic poets were full-armed horsemen; the lyrical bards light-horse.   [2] More commonly known by the name of Boileau.—H.

came the bowmen [1] under their valiant leaders, Des Cartes, Gassendi, and Hobbes; whose strength was such that they could shoot their arrows beyond the atmosphere, never to fall down again, but turn like that of Evander, into meteors; or, like the cannon-ball, into stars. Paracelsus brought a squadron of stinkpot-flingers from the snowy mountains of Rhætia. There came a vast body of dragoons, of different nations, under the leading of Harvey,[2] their great aga: part armed with scythes, the weapons of death; part with lances and long knives, all steeped in poison; part shot bullets of a most malignant nature, and used white powder, which infallibly killed without report. There came several bodies of heavy-armed foot, all mercenaries, under the ensigns of Guicciardini, Davila, Polydore Virgil, Buchanan, Mariana, Camden, and others. The engineers were commanded by Regiomontanus and Wilkins. The rest was a confused multitude, led by Scotus, Aquinas, and Bellarmine; of mighty bulk and stature, but without either arms, courage, or discipline. In the last place came infinite swarms of calones,[3] a disorderly rout led by L'Estrange; rogues and ragamuffins, that follow the camp for nothing but the plunder, all without coats [4] to cover them.

The army of the ancients was much fewer in number; Homer led the horse, and Pinder the lighthorse; Euclid was chief engineer; Plato and Aristotle commanded the bowmen; Herodotus and Livy the foot; Hippocrates the dragoons; the allies, led by Vossius and Temple, brought up the rear.

All things violently tending to a decisive battle, Fame, who much frequented, and had a large apartment formerly assigned her in the regal library, fled up straight to Jupiter, to whom she delivered a faithful account of all that passed between the two parties below; for among the gods she always tells truth. Jove, in great concern, convokes a council in the milky way. The senate assembled, he declares

[1] The philosophers, whether physical or metaphysical.

[2] Harvey, who discovered the circulation of the blood, a discovery much insisted on by the advocates for the moderns, and excepted against as doubtful or erroneous by Sir W. Temple.

[3] Calones. By calling this disorderly rout calones, the author points both his satire and contempt against all sorts of mercenary scribblers. Sir Roger L'Estrange was distinguished by his activity in this dirty warfare in the reigns of Charles II. and James.—H.

[4] These are pamphlets, which are not bound or covered.—H.

the occasion of convening them; a bloody battle just impendent between two mighty armies of ancient and modern creatures, called books, wherein the celestial interest was but too deeply concerned. Momus,[1] the patron of the moderns, made an excellent speech in their favour, which was answered by Pallas, the protectress of the ancients. The assembly was divided in their affections; when Jupiter commanded the book of fate to be laid before him. Immediately were brought by Mercury three large volumes in folio, containing memoirs of all things past, present, and to come. The clasps were of silver double gilt, the covers of celestial turkey leather, and the paper such as here on earth might pass almost for vellum. Jupiter, having silently read the decree, would communicate the import to none, but presently shut up the book.

Without the doors of this assembly there attended a vast number of light, nimble gods, menial servants to Jupiter: these are his ministering instruments in all affairs below. They travel in a caravan, more or less together, and are fastened to each other, like a link of galley-slaves, by a light chain, which passes from them to Jupiter's great toe: and yet, in receiving or delivering a message, they may never approach above the lowest step of his throne, where he and they whisper to each other through a large hollow trunk. These deities are called by mortal men accidents or events; but the gods call them second causes. Jupiter having delivered his message to a certain number of these divinities, they flew immediately down to the pinnacle of the regal library, and consulting a few minutes, entered unseen, and disposed the parties according to their orders.

Meanwhile Momus, fearing the worst, and calling to mind an ancient prophecy which bore no very good face to his children the moderns, bent his flight to the region of a malignant deity called Criticism. She dwelt on the top of a snowy mountain in Nova Zembla; there Momus found her extended in her den, upon the spoils of numberless volumes, half devoured. At her right hand sat Ignorance, her father and husband, blind with age; at her left, Pride, her mother, dressing her up in the scraps of paper herself had torn. There was Opinion, her sister, light of foot, hood-winked, and

[1] On account of the superiority claimed for them in works of humour

headstrong, yet giddy and perpetually turning. About her played her children, Noise and Impudence, Dulness and Vanity, Positiveness, Pedantry, and Ill-manners. The goddess herself had claws like a cat; her head, and ears, and voice, resembled those of an ass; her teeth fallen out before, her eyes turned inward, as if she looked only upon herself; her diet was the overflowing of her own gall; her spleen was so large as to stand prominent, like a dug of the first rate; nor wanted excrescencies in form of teats, at which a crew of ugly monsters were greedily sucking; and, what is wonderful to conceive, the bulk of spleen increased faster than the sucking could diminish it. Goddess, said Momus, can you sit idly here while our devout worshippers, the moderns, are this minute entering into a cruel battle, and perhaps now lying under the swords of their enemies? who then hereafter will ever sacrifice or build altars to our divinities? Haste, therefore, to the British isle, and, if possible, prevent their destruction; while I make factions among the gods, and gain them over to our party.

Momus, having thus delivered himself, staid not for an answer, but left the goddess to her own resentment. Up she rose in a rage, and, as it is the form upon such occasions, began a soliloquy: It is I (said she) who give wisdom to infants and idiots; by me children grow wiser than their parents, by me beaux become politicians, and schoolboys judges of philosophy; by me sophisters debate and conclude upon the depths of knowledge; and coffeehouse wits, instinct by me, can correct an author's style, and display his minutest errors, without understanding a syllable of his matter or his language; by me striplings spend their judgment, as they do their estate, before it comes into their hands. It is I who have deposed wit and knowledge from their empire over poetry, and advanced myself in their stead. And shall a few upstart ancients dare to oppose me?—But come, my aged parent, and you, my children dear, and thou, my beauteous sister; let us ascend my chariot, and haste to assist our devout moderns, who are now sacrificing to us a hecatomb, as I perceive by that grateful smell which from thence reaches my nostrils.

The goddess and her train, having mounted the chariot, which was drawn by tame geese, flew over infinite regions, shedding her influence in due places, till at length she arrived at her beloved island of Britain; but in hovering over its metropolis, what blessings did she not let fall upon her seminaries of Gresham and Covent Garden! And now she reached the fatal plain of St. James's library, at what time the two armies were upon the point to engage; where, entering with all her caravan unseen, and landing upon a case of shelves, now desert, but once inhabited by a colony of virtuosoes, she staid a while to observe the posture of both armies.

But here the tender cares of a mother began to fill her thoughts and move in her breast: for at the head of a troop or modern bowmen she cast her eyes upon her son Wotton, to whom the fates had assigned a very short thread. Wotton, a young hero, whom an unknown father of mortal race begot by stolen embraces with this goddess. He was the darling of his mother above all her children, and she resolved to go and comfort him. But first, according to the good old custom of deities, she cast about to change her shape, for fear the divinity of her countenance might dazzle his mortal sight and overcharge the rest of his senses. She therefore gathered up her person into an octavo compass: her body grew white and arid, and split in pieces with dryness; the thick turned into pasteboard, and the thin into paper; upon which her parents and children artfully strewed a black juice, or decoction of gall and soot, in form of letters: her head, and voice, and spleen, kept their primitive form; and that which before was a cover of skin did still continue so. In this guise she marched on towards the moderns, undistinguishable in shape and dress from the divine Bentley, Wotton's dearest friend. Brave Wotton, said the goddess, why do our troops stand idle here, to spend their present vigour and opportunity of the day? away, let us haste to the generals, and advise to give the onset immediately. Having spoke thus, she took the ugliest of her monsters, full glutted from her spleen, and flung it invisibly into his mouth, which, flying straight up into his head, squeezed out his eye-balls, gave him a distorted look, and half overturned his brain. Then she privately ordered two of her beloved children, Dulness and Ill-manners, closely to attend his person in all encounters. Having thus accoutred him, she vanished in a mist, and the hero perceived it was the goddess his mother.

The destined hour of fate being now arrived, the fight began; whereof, before I dare adventure to make a particular description, I must, after the example of other authors, petition for a hundred tongues, and mouths, and hands, and pens, which would all be too little to perform so immense a work. Say, goddess, that presidest over history, who it was that first advanced in the field of battle! Paracelsus, at the head of his dragoons, observing Galen in the adverse wing, darted his javelin with a mighty force, which the brave ancient received upon his shield, the point breaking in the second fold. . . (*Hic pauca desunt*). . . They bore the wounded aga [1] on their shields to his chariot. . . (*Desunt nonnulla*). . .

Then Aristotle, observing Bacon advance with a furious mien, drew his bow to the head, and let fly his arrow, which missed the valiant modern and went whizzing over his head; but Des Cartes it hit; the steel point quickly found a defect in his headpiece; it pierced the leather and the pasteboard, and went in at his right eye. The torture of the pain whirled the valiant bow-man round till death, like a star of superior influence, drew him into his own vortex.

. . . (*Ingens hiatus hic in MS.*). . . when Homer appeared at the head of the cavalry, mounted on a furious horse, with difficulty managed by the rider himself, but which no other mortal durst approach; he rode among the enemy's ranks, and bore down all before him. Say, goddess, whom he slew first and whom he slew last! First, Gondibert [2] advanced against him, clad in heavy armour and mounted on a staid sober gelding, not so famed for his speed as his docility in kneeling whenever his rider would mount or alight. He had made a vow to Pallas that he would never leave the field till he had spoiled Homer of his armour: madman, who had never once seen the wearer, nor understood his strength! Him Homer overthrew, horse and man, to the ground, there to be trampled and choked in the dirt. Then with a long spear he slew Denham, a stout modern, who from his father's

---

[1] Doctor Harvey. It was not thought proper to name his antagonist, but only to intimate that he was wounded: other moderns are spared by the hiatus that follows.—H.

[2] An heroic poem by Sir W. Davenant in stanzas of four lines.

side derived his lineage from Apollo, but his mother was of mortal race. He fell, and bit the earth. The celestial part Apollo took, and made it a star; but the terrestrial lay wallowing upon the ground. Then Homer slew Wesley with a kick of his horse's heel; he took Perrault by mighty force out of his saddle, then hurled him at Fontenelle, with the same blow dashing out both their brains.

On the left wing of the horse Virgil appeared, in shining armour, completely fitted to his body: he was mounted on a dapple-grey steed, the slowness of whose pace was an effect of the highest mettle and vigour. He cast his eye on the adverse wing, with a desire to find an object worthy of his valour, when behold upon a sorrel gelding of a monstrous size appeared a foe, issuing from among the thickest of the enemy's squadrons; but his speed was less than his noise; for his horse, old and lean, spent the dregs of his strength in a high trot, which, though it made slow advances, yet caused a loud clashing of his armour terrible to hear. The two cavaliers had now approached within the throw of a lance, when the stranger desired a parley, and, lifting up the vizor of his helmet, a face hardly appeared from within which, after a pause, was known for that of the renowned Dryden. The brave ancient suddenly started, as one possessed with surprise and disappointment together; for the helmet was nine times too large for the head, which appeared situate far in the hinder part, even like the lady in a lobster, or like a mouse under a canopy of state, or like a shrivelled beau from within the penthouse of a modern periwig; and the voice was suited to the visage, sounding weak and remote. Dryden, in a long harangue, soothed up the good ancient; called him father, and, by a large deduction of genealogies, made it plainly appear that they were nearly related.[1] Then he humbly proposed an exchange of armour, as a lasting mark of hospitality between them. Virgil consented (for the goddess Diffidence came unseen, and cast a mist before his eyes), though his was of gold and cost a hundred beeves, the other's but of rusty iron. However, this glittering armour became the modern yet worse than his own. Then they agreed to exchange horses; but, when it came to the trial, Dryden was afraid and utterly unable to mount.

[1] Alluding to the Preliminary Dissertations in Dryden's Virgil.

. . . (*Alter hiatus in MS.*) . . . Lucan appeared upon a fiery horse of admirable shape, but headstrong, bearing the rider where he list over the field; he made a mighty slaughter among the enemy's horse; which destruction to stop, Blackmore, a famous modern (but one of the mercenaries), strenuously opposed himself, and darted his javelin with a strong hand, which, falling short of its mark, struck deep in the earth. Then Lucan threw a lance; but Æsculapius came unseen and turned off the point. Brave modern, said Lucan, I perceive some god protects you,[1] for never did my arm so deceive me before: but what mortal can contend with a god? Therefore, let us fight no longer, but present gifts to each other. Lucan then bestowed the modern a pair of spurs, and Blackmore gave Lucan a bridle. . . . (*Pauca desunt*). . . . Creech: but the goddess Dulness took a cloud, formed into the shape of Horace, armed and mounted, and placed in a flying posture before him. Glad was the cavalier to begin a combat with a flying foe, and pursued the image, threatening aloud; till at last it led him to the peaceful bower of his father, Ogleby, by whom he was disarmed and assigned to his repose.

Then Pindar slew——, and ——, and Oldham, and——, and Afra [2] the Amazon, light of foot; never advancing in a direct line, but wheeling with incredible agility and force, he made a terrible slaughter among the enemy's light horse. Him when Cowley observed, his generous heart burnt within him, and he advanced against the fierce ancient, imitating his address, his pace, and career, as well as the vigour of his horse and his own skill would allow. When the two cavaliers had approached within the length of three javelins, first Cowley threw a lance, which missed Pindar, and, passing into the enemy's ranks, fell ineffectual to the ground. Then Pindar darted a javelin so large and weighty, that scarce a dozen cavaliers, as cavaliers are in our degenerate days, could raise it from the ground; yet he threw it with ease, and it went, by an unerring hand, singing through the air; nor could the modern have avoided present death if he had not luckily opposed the shield that had been given him by Venus.[3] And now both heroes drew their swords; but the modern was so

---

[1] His skill as a physician atoned for his dulness as a poet.—H.
[2] Mrs. Afra Behn.—H.   [3] His poem called "The Mistress."—H.

aghast and disordered that he knew not where he was; his shield dropped from his hands; thrice he fled, and thrice he could not escape; at last he turned, and lifting up his hand in the posture of a suppliant, Godlike Pindar, said he, spare my life, and possess my horse, with these arms, beside the ransom, which my friends will give when they hear I am alive and your prisoner. Dog! said Pindar, let your ransom stay with your frends; but your carcase shall be left for the fowls of the air and the beasts of the field. With that he raised his sword, and, with a mighty stroke, cleft the wretched modern in twain, the sword pursuing the blow; and one half lay panting on the ground, to be trod in pieces by the horses' feet; the other half was borne by the frighted steed through the field. This Venus took, washed it seven times in ambrosia, then struck it thrice with a sprig of amaranth; upon which the leather grew round and soft, and the leaves turned into feathers, and, being gilded before, continued gilded still; so it became a dove, and she harnessed it to her chariot.

. . . . (*Hiatus valde deflendus in MS.*). . . .

THE EPISODE OF BENTLEY AND WOTTON

Day being far spent, and the numerous forces of the moderns half inclining to a retreat, there issued forth from a squadron of their heavy-armed foot a captain whose name was Bentley, the most deformed of all the moderns; tall, but without shape or comeliness; large, but without strength or proportion. His armour was patched up of a thousand incoherent pieces; and the sound of it, as he marched, was loud and dry, like that made by the fall of a sheet of lead, which an Etesian wind blows suddenly down from the roof of some steeple. His helmet was of old rusty iron, but the vizor was brass, which, tainted by his breath, corrupted into copperas, nor wanted gall from the same fountain; so that, whenever provoked by anger or labour, an atramentous quality, of most malignant nature, was seen to distil from his lips. In his right hand he grasped a flail, and (that he might never be unprovided of an offensive weapon) a vessel full of ordure in his left.[1] Thus completely armed, he advanced with a slow and heavy pace where the modern chiefs were holding a consult upon the sum of things; who, as he came onwards, laughed to behold his crooked leg and humped shoulder, which his boot and armour, vainly endeavouring to hide, were forced to comply with and expose. The generals made use of him for his talent of railing; which, kept within government, proved frequently of great service to their cause, but, at other times, did more mischief than good; for, at the least touch of offence, and often without any at all, he would, like a wounded elephant, convert it against his leaders. Such, at this juncture, was the disposition of Bentley; grieved to see the enemy prevail, and dissatisfied with everybody's conduct but his own. He humbly gave the modern generals to understand that he conceived, with great submission, they were all a pack of rogues, and fools, and sons of whores, and d—d cowards, and confounded loggerheads, and illiterate whelps, and nonsensical scoundrels; that, if himself had been constituted general, those presumptuous dogs, the ancients, would long before this have been beaten out of the field. You, said he, sit here idle; but when I, or any other valiant modern, kill an enemy, you are sure to seize the spoil. But I will not march one foot against the foe till you all swear to me that whomever I take or kill, his arms I shall quietly possess. Bentley having spoken thus, Scaliger, bestowing him a sour look, Miscreant prater! said he, eloquent only in thine own eyes, thou railest without wit, or truth, or discretion. The malignity of thy temper perverteth nature; thy learning makes thee more barbarous; thy study of humanity more inhuman; thy converse among poets, more grovelling, miry, and dull. All arts of civilising others render thee rude and untractable; courts have taught thee ill manners, and polite conversation has finished thee a pedant. Besides, a greater coward burdeneth not the army. But never despond; I pass my word, whatever spoil thou takest shall certainly be thy own; though I hope that vile carcase will first become a prey to kites and worms.

Bentley durst not reply; but, half choked with spleen and

[1] The person here spoken of is famous for letting fly at everybody without distinction.—W.

rage, withdrew, in full resolution of performing some great achievement. With him, for his aid and companion, he took his beloved Wotton; resolving by policy or surprise to attempt some neglected quarter of the ancient's army. They began their march over carcases of their slaughtered friends; then to the right of their own forces; then wheeled northward, till they came to Aldrovandus's tomb, which they passed on the side of the declining sun. And now they arrived, with fear, toward the enemy's out-guards; looking about, if haply they might spy the quarters of the wounded, or some straggling sleepers, unarmed and remote from the rest. As when two mongrel curs, whom native greediness and domestic want provoke and join in partnership, though fearful, nightly to invade the folds of some rich grazier, they, with tails depressed and lolling tongues, creep soft and slow; meanwhile the conscious moon, now in her zenith, on their guilty heads darts perpendicular rays; nor dare they bark, though much provoked at her refulgent visage, whether seen in puddle by reflection or in sphere direct; but one surveys the region round, while the other scouts the plain, if haply to discover, at distance from the flock, some carcase half devoured, the refuse of gorged wolves or ominous ravens. So marched this lovely, loving pair of friends, nor with less fear and circumspection, when at a distance they might perceive two shining suits of armour hanging upon an oak, and the owners not far off in a profound sleep. The two friends drew lots, and the pursuing of this adventure fell to Bentley; on he went, and in his van Confusion and Amaze, while Horror and Affright brought up the rear. As he came near, behold two heroes of the ancient's army, Phalaris and Æsop, lay fast asleep; Bentley would fain have despatched them both, and, stealing close, aimed his flail at Phalaris's breast. But then the goddess Affright, interposing, caught the modern in her icy arms, and dragged him from the danger she foresaw; both the dormant heroes happened to turn at the same instant, though soundly sleeping, and busy in a dream. For Phalaris [1] was just that minute dreaming how a most vile poetaster had lampooned him, and how he had got him roaring in his bull. And Æsop dreamed that, as he

[1] According to Homer, who tells the dreams of those who were killed in their sleep.—H.

and the ancient chiefs were lying on the ground, a wild ass broke loose, ran about, trampling and kicking and dunging in their faces. Bentley, leaving the two heroes asleep, seized on both their armours, and withdrew in quest of his darling Wotton.

He, in the meantime, had wandered long in search of some enterprise, till at length he arrived at a small rivulet that issued from a fountain hard by, called, in the language of mortal men, Helicon. Here he stopped, and, parched with thirst, resolved to allay it in this limpid stream. Thrice with profane hands he essayed to raise the water to his lips, and thrice it slipped all through his fingers. Then he stooped prone on his breast, but, ere his mouth had kissed the liquid crystal, Apollo came, and in the channel held his shield betwixt the modern and the fountain, so that he drew up nothing but mud. For, although no fountain on earth can compare with the clearness of Helicon, yet there lies at bottom a thick sediment of slime and mud; for so Apollo begged of Jupiter, as a punishment to those who durst attempt to taste it with unhallowed lips, and for a lesson to all not to draw too deep or far from the spring.

At the fountain-head Wotton discerned two heroes; the one he could not distinguish, but the other was soon known for Temple, general of the allies to the ancients. His back was turned, and he was employed in drinking large draughts in his helmet from the fountain, where he had withdrawn himself to rest from the toils of the war. Wotton, observing him, with quaking knees and trembling hands, spoke thus to himself: O that I could kill this destroyer of our army, what renown should I purchase among the chiefs! but to issue out against him, man against man, shield against shield, and lance against lance, what modern of us dare? for he fights like a god, and Pallas or Apollo are ever at his elbow. But, O mother! if what Fame reports be true, that I am the son of so great a goddess, grant me to hit Temple with this lance, that the stroke may send him to hell, and that I may return in safety and triumph, laden with his spoils. The first part of this prayer the gods granted at the intercession of his mother and of Momus; but the rest, by a perverse wind sent from Fate, was scattered in the air. Then Wotton grasped his lance, and, brandishing it thrice over his head, darted it with all his might; the goddess, his mother, at the same time adding strength to his arm. Away the lance went hizzing, and reached even to the belt of the averted ancient, upon which lightly grazing, it fell to the ground. Temple neither felt the weapon touch him nor heard it fall: and Wotton might have escaped to his army, with the honour of having remitted his lance against so great a leader unrevenged; but Apollo, enraged that a javelin flung by the assistance of so foul a goddess should pollute his fountain, put on the shape of ————, and softly came to young Boyle, who then accompanied Temple: he pointed first to the lance, then to the distant modern that flung it, and commanded the young hero to take immediate revenge. Boyle, clad in a suit of armour which had been given him by all the gods,[1] immediately advanced against the trembling foe, who now fled before him. As a young lion in the Libyan plains, or Araby desert, sent by his aged sire to hunt for prey, or health, or exercise, he scours along, wishing to meet some tiger from the mountains, or a furious boar; if chance a wild ass, with brayings importune, affronts his ear, the generous beast, though loathing to distain his claws with blood so vile, yet, much provoked at the offensive noise, which Echo, foolish nymph, like her ill-judging sex, repeats much louder, and with more delight than Philomela's song, he vindicates the honour of the forest, and hunts the noisy long-eared animal. So Wotton fled, so Boyle pursued. But Wotton, heavy-armed and slow of foot, began to slack his course, when his lover Bentley appeared, returning laden with the spoils of the two sleeping ancients. Boyle observed him well, and soon discovering the helmet and shield of Phalaris his friend, both which he had lately with his own hands new polished and gilt, rage sparkled in his eyes, and, leaving his pursuit after Wotton, he furiously rushed on against this new approacher. Fain would he be revenged on both; but both now fled different ways: and, as a woman in a little house that gets a painful livelihood by spinning, if chance her geese be scattered o'er the common, she courses round the plain from side to side, compelling here and there the stragglers to the flock; they cackle loud, and flutter o'er the champaign;

[1] Boyle was assisted in this dispute by Dean Aldrich, Dr. Atterbury, afterwards Bishop of Rochester, and other persons at Oxford.—H.

so Boyle pursued, so fled this pair of friends: finding at length their flight was vain, they bravely joined, and drew themselves in phalanx. First Bentley threw a spear with all his force, hoping to pierce the enemy's breast; but Pallas came unseen, and in the air took off the point, and clapped on one of lead, which, after a dead bang against the enemy's shield, fell blunted to the ground. Then Boyle, observing well his time, took up a lance of wondrous length and sharpness; and, as this pair of friends compacted, stood close side to side, he wheeled him to the right, and, with unusual force, darted the weapon. Bentley saw his fate approach, and flanking down his arms close to his ribs, hoping to save his body, in went the point, passing through arm and side, nor stopped or spent its force till it had also pierced the valiant Wotton, who, going to sustain his dying friend, shared his fate. As when a skilful cook has trussed a brace of woodcocks, he with iron skewer pierces the tender sides of both, their legs and wings close pinioned to the ribs; so was this pair of friends transfixed, till down they fell, joined in their lives, joined in their deaths; so closely joined that Charon would mistake them both for one, and waft them over Styx, for half his fare. Farewell, beloved, loving pair; few equals have you left behind: and happy and immortal shall you be, if all my wit and eloquence can make you.

And now . . . *(Desunt cætera)*. . . .

A DISCOURSE CONCERNING THE
MECHANICAL OPERATION OF THE SPIRIT
IN A LETTER TO A FRIEND. A FRAGMENT

THE BOOKSELLER'S ADVERTISEMENT

THE following Discourse came into my hands perfect and entire; but there being several things in it which the present age would not very well bear, I kept it by me some years, resolving it should never see the light. At length, by the advice and assistance of a judicious friend, I retrenched those parts that might give most offence, and have now ventured to publish the remainder. Concerning the author I am wholly ignorant; neither can I conjecture whether it be the same with that of the two foregoing pieces, the original having been sent me at a different time, and in a different hand. The learned reader will better determine, to whose judgment I entirely submit it.

A DISCOURSE, ETC.

For T. H. Esquire,[1] at his chambers in the Academy of the Beaux Esprits, in New England.

SIR,—It is now a good while since I have had in my head something, not only very material, but absolutely necessary to my health, that the world should be informed in; for, to tell you a secret, I am able to contain it no longer. However,

---

[1] Supposed to be Col. Hunter, believed to be the author of the *Letter of Enthusiasm*. See *Tale of a Tub*, p. 13. (W.S.) This Discourse is not altogether equal to the former, the best parts of it being omitted; whether the bookseller's account be true, that he durst not print the rest, I know not; nor indeed is it easy to determine, whether he may be relied on in anything he says of this or the former treatises. (J.S.)

I have been perplexed for some time to resolve what would be the most proper form to send it abroad in. To which end I have been three days coursing through Westminster Hall, and St. Paul's churchyard, and Fleet Street, to peruse titles; and I do not find any which holds so general a vogue as that of a Letter to a Friend: nothing is more common than to meet with long epistles addressed to persons and places where, at first thinking, one would be apt to imagine it not altogether so necessary or convenient; such as, a neighbour at next door, a mortal enemy, a perfect stranger, or a person of quality in the clouds; and these upon subjects, in appearance, the least proper for conveyance by the post; as long schemes in philosophy, dark and wonderful mysteries of state, laborious dissertations in criticism and philosophy, advice to parliaments, and the like.

Now, sir, to proceed after the method in present wear; for, let me say what I will to the contrary, I am afraid you will publish this letter as soon as ever it comes to your hand. I desire you will be my witness to the world how careless and sudden a scribble it has been; that it was but yesterday when you and I began accidentally to fall into discourse on this matter; that I was not very well when we parted; that the post is in such haste I have had not manner of time to digest it into order or correct the style; and if any other modern excuses for haste and negligence shall occur to you in reading, I beg you to insert them, faithfully promising they shall be thankfully acknowledged.

Pray, sir, in your next letter to the Iroquois virtuosi, do me the favour to present my humble service to that illustrious body, and assume them I shall send an account of those phenomena as soon as we can determine them at Gresham.

I have not had a line from the literati of Topinambou these three last ordinaries.

And now, sir, having despatched what I had to say of form or of business, let me entreat you will suffer me to proceed upon my subject, and to pardon me if I make no farther use of the epistolary style till I come to conclude.

SECTION I

It is recorded of Mahomet that, upon a visit he was going to pay in Paradise, he had an offer of several vehicles to conduct him upwards; as fiery chariots, winged horses, and celestial sedans; but he refused them all, and would be borne to heaven upon nothing but his ass. Now this inclination of Mahomet, as singular as it seems, has been since taken up by a great number of devout Christians, and doubtless with very good reason. For, since that Arabian is known to have borrowed a moiety of his religious system from the Christian faith, it is but just he should pay reprisals to such as would challenge them; wherein the good people of England, to do them all right, have not been backward; for, though there is not any other nation in the world so plentifully provided with carriages for that journey, either as to safety or ease, yet there are abundance of us who will not be satisfied with any other machine beside this of Mahomet.

For my own part, I must confess to bear a very singular respect to this animal, by whom I take human nature to be most admirably held forth in all its qualities, as well as operations; and therefore, whatever in my small reading occurs concerning this our fellow-creature, I do never fail to set it down by way of commonplace; and when I have occasion to write upon human reason, politics, eloquence, or knowledge, I lay my memorandums before me, and insert them with a wonderful facility of application. However, among all the qualifications ascribed to this distinguished brute, by ancient or modern authors, I cannot remember this talent of bearing his rider to heaven has been recorded for a part of his character, except in the two examples mentioned already; therefore I conceive the methods of this art to be a point of useful knowledge in very few hands, and which the learned world would gladly be better informed in: this is what I have undertaken to perform in the following discourse. For towards the operation already mentioned many peculiar properties are required both in the rider and the ass, which I shall endeavour to set in as clear a light as I can.

But, because I am resolved, by all means, to avoid giving offence to any party whatever, I will leave off discoursing so closely to the letter as I have hitherto done, and go on for the future by way of allegory; though in such a manner that the judicious reader may, without much straining, make his applications as often as he shall think fit. Therefore, if you please, from henceforward, instead of the term ass, we shall make use of gifted or enlightened teacher; and the word rider we will exchange for that of fanatic auditory, or any other denomination of the like import. Having settled this weighty point, the great subject of inquiry before us is to examine by what methods this teacher arrives at his gifts, or spirit, or light; and by what intercourse between him and his assembly it is cultivated and supported.

In all my writings I have had constant regard to this great end, not to suit and apply them to particular occasions and circumstances of time, of place, or of person, but to calculate them for universal nature and mankind in general. And of such catholic use I esteem this present disquisition; for I do not remember any other temper of body, or quality of mind, wherein all nations and ages of the world have so unanimously agreed as that of a fanatic strain or tincture of enthusiasm; which, improved by certain persons or societies of men, and by them practised upon the rest, has been able to produce revolutions of the greatest figure in history, as will soon appear to those who know anything of Arabia, Persia, India, or China, of Morocco and Peru. Farther, it has possessed as great a power in the kingdom of knowledge, where it is hard to assign one art or science which has not annexed to it some fanatic branch; such are, the philosopher's stone, the grand elixir,[1] the planetary worlds, the squaring of the circle, the *summum bonum*, Utopian commonwealths, with some others of less or subordinate note, which all serve for nothing else but to employ or amuse this grain of enthusiasm dealt into every composition.

But if this plant has found a root in the fields of empire and of knowledge, it has fixed deeper and spread yet farther upon holy ground; wherein, though it has passed under the general name of enthusiasm, and perhaps arisen from the same original, yet has it produced certain branches of a very

[1] Some writers hold them for the same, others not.

different nature, however often mistaken for each other. The word, in its universal acceptation, may be defined, a lifting up of the soul, or its faculties, above matter. This description will hold good in general, but I am only to understand it as applied to religion; wherein there are three general ways of ejaculating the soul, or transporting it beyond the sphere of matter. The first is the immediate act of God, and is called prophecy or inspiration. The second is the immediate act of the devil, and is termed possession. The third is the product of natural causes, the effect of strong imagination, spleen, violent anger, fear, grief, pain, and the like. These three have been abundantly treated on by authors, and therefore shall not employ my inquiry. But the fourth method of religious enthusiasm, or launching out of the soul, as it is purely an effect of artifice and mechanic operation, has been sparingly handled, or not at all, by any writer; because, though it is an art of great antiquity, yet, having been confined to few persons, it long wanted those advancements and refinements which it afterwards met with, since it has grown so epidemic, and fallen into so many cultivating hands.

It is therefore upon this mechanical operation of the spirit that I mean to treat, as it is at present performed by our British workmen. I shall deliver to the reader the result of many judicious observations upon the matter; tracing, as near as I can, the whole course and method of this trade, producing parallel instances and relating certain discoveries that have luckily fallen in my way.

I have said that there is one branch of religious enthusiasm which is purely an effect of nature; whereas the part I mean to handle is wholly an effect of art, which however is inclined to work upon certain natures and constitutions more than others. Besides, there is many an operation which in its original was purely an artifice, but through a long succession of ages has grown to be natural. Hippocrates tells us that among our ancestors the Scythians there was a nation called Long-heads, which at first began by a custom among midwives and nurses of moulding, and squeezing, and bracing up the heads of infants; by which means nature, shut out at one passage, was forced to seek another, and, finding room above, shot upwards in the form of a sugar-loaf; and, being diverted that way for some generations, at last found it out of herself, needing no assistance from the nurse's hand. This was the original of the Scythian Long-heads, and thus did custom, from being a second nature, proceed to be a first. To all which there is something very analogous among us of this nation, who are the undoubted posterity of that refined people. For in the age of our fathers there arose a generation of men in this island called Round-heads, whose race is now spread over three kingdoms; yet in its beginning was merely an operation of art produced by a pair of scissors, a squeeze of the face, and a black cap. These heads, thus formed into a perfect sphere in all assemblies, were most exposed to the view of the female sort, which did influence their conceptions so effectually, that nature at last took the hint and did it of herself; so that a round-head has been ever since as familiar a sight among us as a long-head among the Scythians.

Upon these examples, and others easy to produce, I desire the curious reader to distinguish, first, between an effect grown from art into nature, and one that is natural from its beginning: secondly, between an effect wholly natural, and one which has only a natural foundation, but where the superstructure is entirely artificial. For the first and the last of these I understand to come within the districts of my subject. And having obtained these allowances, they will serve to remove any objections that may be raised hereafter against what I shall advance.

The practitioners of this famous art proceed, in general, upon the following fundamental: that the corruption of the senses is the generation of the spirit; because the senses in men are so many avenues to the fort of reason, which in this operation is wholly blocked up. All endeavours must be therefore used, either to divert, bind up, stupify, fluster, and amuse the senses, or else to justle them out of their stations; and, while they are either absent or otherwise employed, or engaged in a civil war against each other, the spirit enters and performs its part.

Now, the usual methods of managing the senses upon such conjunctures are, what I shall be very particular in delivering, as far as it is lawful for me to do; but, having had the honour to be initiated into the mysteries of every society, I desire to be excused from divulging any rites wherein the profane must have no part.

But here, before I can proceed farther, a very dangerous objection must if possible be removed. For it is positively denied by certain critics that the spirit can, by any means, be introduced into an assembly of modern saints; the disparity being so great in many material circumstances between the primitive way of inspiration and that which is practised in the present age. This they pretend to prove from the second chapter of the Acts, where, comparing both, it appears, first, That the apostles were gathered together with one accord, in one place; by which is meant a universal agreement in opinion and form of worship; a harmony, say they, so far from being found between any two conventicles among us, that it is in vain to expect it between any two heads in the same. Secondly, The spirit instructed the apostles in the gift of speaking several languages; a knowledge so remote from our dealers in this art, that they neither understand propriety of words or phrases in their own. Lastly, say these objectors, the modern artists do utterly exclude all approaches of the spirit, and bar up its ancient way of entering, by covering themselves so close and so industriously a-top: for they will needs have it as a point clearly gained, that the cloven tongues never sat upon the apostles' heads while their hats were on.

Now, the force of these objections seems to consist in the different acceptation of the word spirit; which, if it be understood for a supernatural assistance approaching from without, the objectors have reason, and their assertions may be allowed; but the spirit we treat of here proceeding entirely from within, the argument of these adversaries is wholly eluded. And upon the same account, our modern artificers find it an expedient of absolute necessity to cover their heads as close as they can in order to prevent perspiration, than which nothing is observed to be a greater spender of mechanic light, as we may perhaps further show in a convenient place.

To proceed therefore upon the phenomenon of spiritual mechanism, it is here to be noted that in forming and working up the spirit the assembly has a considerable share as well as the preacher. The method of this arcanum is as follows they violently strain their eyeballs inward, half closing the lids; then, as they sit, they are in a perpetual motion of see-saw, making long hums at proper periods, and continuing the sound at equal height, choosing their time in those intermissions while the preacher is at ebb. Neither is this practice in any part of it so singular and improbable as not to be traced in distant regions from reading and observation. For, first, the Jauguis [Bernier, Mem. de Mogol.], or enlightened saints of India, see all their visions by help of an acquired straining and pressure of the eyes. Secondly, the art of see-saw on a beam, and swinging by session upon a cord, in order to raise artificial ecstasies, has been derived to us from our Scythian [Guagnini Hist. Sarmat.] ancestors, where it is practised at this day among the women. Lastly, the whole proceeding, as I have here related it, as performed by the natives of Ireland with a considerable improvement; and it is granted that this noble nation has, of all others, admitted fewer corruptions and degenerated least from the purity of the old Tartars. Now, it is usual for a knot of Irish men and women to abstract themselves from matter, bind up all their senses, grow visionary and spiritual, by influence of a short pipe of tobacco handed round the company, each preserving the smoke in his mouth till it comes again to his turn to take in fresh; at the same time there is a concert of a continued gentle hum, repeated and renewed by instinct as occasion requires; and they move their bodies up and down to a degree that sometimes their heads and points lie parallel to the horizon. Meanwhile you may observe their eyes turned up, in the posture of one who endeavours to keep himself awake; by which, and many other symptoms among them, it manifestly appears that the reasoning faculties are all suspended and superseded, that imagination has usurped the seat, scattering a thousand deliriums over the brain. Returning from this digression, I shall describe the methods by which the spirit approaches. The eyes being disposed according to art, at first you can see nothing; but after a short pause a small glimmering light begins to appear and dance before you: then, by frequently moving your body up and down, you perceive the vapours to ascend very fast, till you are perfectly dosed and flustered like one who drinks too much in a morning. Meanwhile the preacher is also at work; he begins a loud hum which pierces you quite through; this is immediately returned by the audience, and you find yourself prompted to imitate them by a mere spontaneous impulse, without knowing what you do. The *interstitia* are duly filled up by the preacher to prevent too long a pause, under which the spirit would soon faint and grow languid.

This is all I am allowed to discover about the progress of the spirit with relation to that part which is borne by the assembly; but in the methods of the preacher to which I now proceed I shall be more large and particular.

SECTION II

You will read it very gravely remarked in the books of those illustrious and right eloquent penmen, the modern travellers, that the fundamental difference in point of religion between the wild Indians and us, lies in this—that we worship God, and they worship the devil. But there are certain critics who will by no means admit of this distinction, rather believing that all nations whatsoever adore the true God, because they seem to intend their devotions to some invisible power of greatest goodness and ability to help them; which perhaps will take in the brightest attributes ascribed to the Divinity. Others again inform us that those idolators adore two principles—the principle of good, and that of evil; which indeed I am apt to look upon as the most universal notion that mankind, by the mere light of nature, ever entertained of things invisible. How this idea has been managed by the Indians and us, and with what advantage to the understandings of either, may well deserve to be examined. To me the difference appears little more than this, that they are put oftener upon their knees by their fears, and we by our desires; that the former set them a praying, and us a cursing. What I applaud them for is, their discretion in limiting their devotions and their deities to their several districts, nor ever suffering the liturgy of the white God to cross or to interfere with that of the black. Not so with us, who, pretending by the lines and measures of our reason to extend the dominion of one invisible power, and contract that of the other, have discovered a gross ignorance in the natures of good and evil, and most horribly confounded the frontiers of both. After men have lifted up the throne of their divinity to the *cœlum empyræum*, adorned with all such qualities and accomplishments as themselves seem most to value and possess—after they have sunk their principle of evil to the lowest centre, bound him with chains, loaded him with curses, furnished him with viler dispositions than any rake-hell of the town, accoutred him with tail, and horns, and huge claws, and saucer eyes—I laugh aloud to see these reasoners at the same time engaged in wise dispute, about certain walks and purlieus, whether they are in the verge of God or the devil; seriously debating whether such and such influences come into men's minds from above or below; whether certain passions and affections are guided by the evil spirit or the good:

> Dum fas atque nefas exiguo fine libidinum
> Discernunt avidi.

Thus do men establish a fellowship of Christ with Belial, and such is the analogy they make between cloven tongues and cloven feet. Of the like nature is the disquisition before us: it has continued these hundred years an even debate whether the deportment and the cant of our English enthusiastic preachers were possession or inspiration; and a world of argument has been drained on either side, perhaps to little purpose. For I think it is in life as in tragedy, where it is held a conviction of great defect, both in order and invention, to interpose the assistance of preternatural power without an absolute and last necessity. However, it is a sketch of human vanity for every individual to imagine the whole universe is interested in his meanest concern. If he has got cleanly over a kennel, some angel unseen descended on purpose to help him by the hand; if he has knocked his head against a post, it was the devil for his sins let loose from hell on purpose to buffet him. Who that sees a little paltry mortal, droning, and dreaming, and drivelling to a multitude, can think it agreeable to common good sense that either heaven or hell should be put to the trouble of influence or inspection upon what he is about? therefore I am resolved immediately to weed this error out of mankind, by making it clear that this mystery of vending spiritual gifts is nothing but a trade, acquired by as much instruction, and mastered by equal practice and application, as others are. This will best appear by describing and deducting the whole process of the operation, as variously as it hath fallen under my knowledge or experience.

.   .   .   .

[*Here the whole scheme of spiritual mechanism was deduced and explained, with an appearance of great reading and observation; but it was thought neither safe nor convenient to print it.*]

.   .   .   .

Here it may not be amiss to add a few words upon the laudable practice of wearing quilted caps; which is not a matter of mere custom, humour, or fashion, as some would pretend, but an institution of great sagacity and use: these, when moistened with sweat, stop all perspiration; and, by reverberating the heat, prevent the spirit from evaporating any way but at the mouth; even as a skilful housewife that covers her still with a wet clout for the same reason, and finds the same effect. For it is the opinion of choice *virtuosi* that the brain is only a crowd of little animals, but with teeth and claws extremely sharp, and therefore cling together in the contexture we behold, like the picture of Hobbes' *Leviathan,* or like bees in perpendicular swarm upon a tree, or like a carrion corrupted into vermin, still preserving the shape and figure of the mother animal: that all invention is formed by the morsure of two or more of these animals upon certain capillary nerves which proceed from thence, whereof three branches spread into the tongue, and two into the right hand. They hold also that these animals are of a constitution extremely cold; that their food is the air we attract, their excrement phlegm; and that what we vulgarly call rheums, and colds, and distillations, is nothing else but an epidemical looseness, to which that little commonwealth is very subject from the climate it lies under. Further, that nothing less than a violent heat can disentangle these creatures from their hamated station of life, or give them vigour and humour to imprint the marks of their little teeth. That if the morsure be hexagonal it produces poetry; the circular gives eloquence: if the bite hath been conical, the person whose nerve is so affected shall be disposed to write upon politics; and so of the rest.

I shall now discourse briefly by what kind of practices the voice is best governed toward the composition and improve-

ment of the spirit; for, without a competent skill in tuning
and toning each word, and syllable, and letter, to their due
cadence, the whole operation is incomplete, misses entirely
of its effect on the hearers, and puts the workman himself to
continual pains for new supplies, without success. For it is
to be understood that, in the language of the spirit, cant and
droning supply the place of sense and reason in the language
of men: because, in spiritual harangues, the disposition of
the words according to the art of grammar has not the least
use, but the skill and influence wholly lie in the choice and
cadence of the syllables; even as a discreet composer, who,
in setting a song, changes the words and order so often, that
he is forced to make it nonsense before he can make it music.
For this reason it has been held by some that the art of
canting is ever in greatest perfection when managed by
ignorance; which is thought to be enigmatically meant by
Plutarch, when he tells us that the best musical instruments
were made from the bones of an ass. And the profounder
critics upon that passage are of opinion, the word, in its
genuine signification, means no other than a jaw-bone;
though some rather think it to have been the *os sacrum;* but
in so nice a case I shall not take upon me to decide; the
curious are at liberty to pick from it whatever they please.

The first ingredient toward the art of canting is, a competent share of inward light; that is to say, a large memory,
plentifully fraught with theological polysyllables and
mysterious texts from holy writ, applied and digested by
those methods and mechanical operations already related:
the bearers of this light resembling lanterns compact of
leaves from old Geneva bibles; which invention, Sir
Humphrey Edwin,[1] during his mayoralty, of happy memory,
highly approved and advanced; affirming the Scripture to
be now fulfilled, where it says, Thy word is a lantern to my
feet, and a light to my paths.

Now, the art of canting consists in skilfully adapting the
voice to whatever words the spirit delivers, that each may
strike the ears of the audience with its most significant
cadence. The force or energy of this eloquence is not to be
found, as among ancient orators, in the disposition of words

---

[1] A presbyterian, who, ascending to the dignity of Lord Mayor of
London, went in his official character to a meeting-house.—W.S.

to a sentence, or the turning of long periods; but, agreeably to the modern refinements in music, is taken up wholly in dwelling and dilating upon syllables and letters. Thus, it is frequent for a single vowel to draw sighs from a multitude, and for a whole assembly of saints to sob to the music of one solitary liquid. But these are trifles, when even sounds inarticulate are observed to produce as forcible effects. A master workman shall blow his nose so powerfully as to pierce the hearts of his people, who were disposed to receive the excrements of his brain with the same reverence as the issue of it. Hawking, spitting, and belching, the defects of other men's rhetoric, are the flowers, and figures, and ornaments of his. For the spirit being the same in all, it is of no import through what vehicle it is conveyed.

It is a point of too much difficulty to draw the principles of this famous art within the compass of certain adequate rules. However, perhaps I may one day oblige the world with my critical essay upon the art of canting; philosophically, physically, and musically considered.

But, among all improvements of the spirit, wherein the voice has borne a part, there is none to be compared with that of conveying the sound through the nose, which, under the denomination of snuffling,[1] has passed with so great applause in the world. The originals of this institution are very dark: but, having been initiated into the mystery of it, and leave being given me to publish it to the world, I shall deliver as direct a relation as I can.

This art, like many other famous inventions, owed its birth, or at least improvement and perfection, to an effect of chance; but was established upon solid reasons, and has flourished in this island ever since with great lustre. All agree that it first appeared upon the decay and discouragement of bagpipes, which, having long suffered under the mortal hatred of the brethren, tottered for a time, and at last fell with monarchy. The story is thus related.

As yet snuffling was not, when the following adventure happened to a Banbury saint. Upon a certain day, while he was far engaged among the tabernacles of the wicked, he felt

---

[1] The snuffling of men who have lost their noses by lewd courses is said to have given rise to that tone which our dissenters did too much affect.—W.

the outward man put into odd commotions, and strangely pricked forward by the inward; an effect very usual among the modern inspired. For some think that the spirit is apt to feed on the flesh, like hungry wines upon raw beef. Others rather believe there is a perpetual game at leap-frog between both; and sometimes the flesh is uppermost, and sometimes the spirit; adding that the former, while it is in the state of a rider, wears huge Rippon spurs; and, when it comes to the turn of being bearer, is wonderfully headstrong and hard-mouthed. However it came about, the saint felt his vessel full extended in every part; (a very natural effect of strong inspiration); and the place and time falling out so unluckily that he could not have the convenience of evacuating upwards, by repetition, prayer, or lecture, he was forced to open an inferior vent. In short, he wrestled with the flesh so long, that he at length subdued it, coming off with honourable wounds all before. The surgeon had now cured the parts primarily affected; but the disease, driven from its post, flew up into his head; and, as a skilful general, valiantly attacked in his trenches, and beaten from the field, by flying marches withdraws to the capital city, breaking down the bridges to prevent pursuit; so the disease, repelled from its first station, fled before the rod of Hermes to the upper region, there fortifying itself; but, finding the foe making attacks at the nose, broke down the bridge and retired to the head-quarters. Now, the naturalists observe that there is in human noses an idiosyncrasy, by virtue of which, the more the passage is obstructed, the more our speech delights to go through, as the music of a flageolet is made by the stops. By this method the twang of the nose becomes perfectly to resemble the snuffle of a bagpipe, and is found to be equally attractive of British ears; whereof the saint had sudden experience, by practising his new faculty with wonderful success, in the operation of the spirit; for, in a short time, no doctrine passed for sound and orthodox unless it were delivered through the nose. Straight every pastor copied after this original; and those who could not otherwise arrive to a perfection, spirited by a noble zeal, made use of the same experiment to acquire it; so that, I think, it may be truly affirmed the saints owe their empire to the snuffling of one animal, as Darius did his to the neighing of another; and both stratagems were performed by the same art; for we read how the Persian beast acquired his faculty by covering a mare the day before. [Herodotus.]

I should now have done, if I were not convinced that whatever I have yet advanced upon this subject is liable to great exception. For, allowing all I have said to be true, it may still be justly objected that there is in the commonwealth of artificial enthusiasm some real foundation for art to work upon, in the temper and complexion of individuals, which other mortals seem to want. Observe but the gesture, the motion, and the countenance of some choice professors, though in their most familiar actions, you will find them of a different race from the rest of human creatures. Remark your commonest pretender to a light within, how dark, and dirty, and gloomy he is without; as lanterns, which, the more light they bear in their bodies, cast out so much the more soot, and smoke, and fuliginous matter to adhere to the sides. Listen but to their ordinary talk, and look on the mouth that delivers it, you will imagine you are hearing some ancient oracle, and your understanding will be equally informed. Upon these, and the like reasons, certain objectors pretend to put it beyond all doubt that there must be a sort of preternatural spirit possessing the heads of the modern saints; and some will have it to be the heat of zeal working upon the dregs of ignorance, as other spirits are produced from lees by the force of fire. Some again think, that when our earthly tabernacles are disordered and desolate, shaken and out of repair, the spirit delights to dwell within them; as houses are said to be haunted when they are forsaken and gone to decay.

To set this matter in as fair a light as possible, I shall here very briefly deduce the history of fanaticism from the most early ages to the present. And if we are able to fix upon any one material or fundamental point, wherein the chief professors have universally agreed, I think we may reasonably lay hold on that, and assign it for the great seed or principle of the spirit.

The most early traces we meet with of fanatics in ancient story are among the Egyptians, who instituted those rites known in Greece by the names of Orgia, Panegyres, and Dionysia; whether introduced there by Orpheus or Melampus we shall not dispute at present, nor in all likelihood at any time for the future [Diod. Sic., l. i. Plut. de Iside et Osiride]. These feasts were celebrated to the honour of Osiris, whom the Grecians called Dionysius, and is the same with Bacchus: which has betrayed some superficial readers to imagine that the whole business was nothing more than a set of roaring, scouring companions, overcharged with wine; but this is a scandalous mistake, foisted on the world by a sort of modern authors, who have too literal an understanding; and, because antiquity is to be traced backwards, do therefore, like Jews, begin their books at the wrong end, as if learning were a sort of conjuring. These are the men who pretend to understand a book by scouring through the index; as if a traveller should go about to describe a palace, when he had seen nothing but the privy; or like certain fortune-tellers in Northern America, who have a way of reading a man's destiny by peeping into his breech. For, at the time of instituting these mysteries, there was not one vine in all Egypt [Herodotus, l. ii.], the natives drinking nothing but ale; which liquor seems to have been far more ancient than wine, and has the honour of owing its invention and progress, not only to the Egyptian Osiris [Diod. Sic., l. i. and iii.], but to the Grecian Bacchus; who, in their famous expedition, carried the receipt of it along with them, and gave it to the nations they visited or subdued. Besides, Bacchus himself was very seldom or never drunk; for it is recorded of him that he was the first inventor of the mitre [Id., l. iv.], which he wore continually on his head (as the whole company of bacchanals did), to prevent vapours and the headache after hard drinking. And for this reason, say some, the scarlet whore, when she makes the kings of the earth drunk with her cup of abomination, is always sober herself, though she never balks the glass in her turn, being, it seems, kept upon her legs by the virtue of her triple mitre. Now these feasts were instituted in imitation of the famous expedition Osiris made through the world, and of the company that attended him, whereof the bacchanalian ceremonies were so many types and symbols. From which account [Diod. Sic., l. i. and iii.] it is manifest that the fanatic rites of these bacchanals cannot be imputed to intoxications by wine, but must needs have had a deeper foundation. What this was, we may gather large hints from certain circumstances in the course of their mysteries. For, in the first place, there was, in their processions, an entire mixture and confusion of sexes; they affected to ramble about hills and deserts; their garlands were of ivy and vine, emblems of cleaving and clinging; or of fir, the parent of turpentine. It is added that they imitated satyrs, were attended by goats, and rode upon asses, all companions of great skill and practice in affairs of gallantry. They bore for their ensigns certain curious figures, perched upon long poles, made into the shape and size of the *virga genitalis*, with its appurtenances; which were so many shadows and emblems of the whole mystery, as well as trophies set up by the female conquerors. Lastly, in a certain town of Attica, the whole solemnity, stripped of all its types [Dionysia Brauronia], was performed *in puris naturalibus*, the votaries not flying in coveys, but sorted into couples. The same may be further conjectured from the death of Orpheus, one of the institutors of these mysteries, who was torn in pieces by women, because he refused to communicate his orgies to them [*Vide* Photium in excerptis è Conone]; which others explained by telling us he had castrated himself upon grief for the loss of his wife.

Omitting many others of less note, the next fanatics we meet with of any eminence were the numerous sects of heretics appearing in the five first centuries of the Christian era, from Simon Magus and his followers to those of Eutyches. I have collected their systems from infinite reading, and, comparing them with those of their successors in the several ages since, I find there are certain bounds set even to the irregularity of human thought, and those a great deal narrower than is commonly apprehended. For, as they all freqently interfere even in their wildest ravings, so there is one fundamental point wherein they are sure to meet, as lines in a centre, and that is, the community of women. Great were their solicitudes in this matter, and they never failed of certain articles, in their schemes of worship, on purpose to establish it.

The last fanatics of note were those which started up in Germany a little after the reformation of Luther, springing as mushrooms do at the end of a harvest; such were John of Leyden, David George, Adam Neuster, and many others, whose visions and revelations always terminated in leading about half a dozen sisters a-piece, and making that practice a fundamental part of their system. For human life is a continual navigation, and if we expect our vessels to pass with safety through the waves and tempests of this fluctuating world, it is necessary to make a good provision of the flesh, as seamen lay in store of beef for a long voyage.

Now, from this brief survey of some principal sects among the fanatics in all ages (having omitted the Mahometans and others, who might also help to confirm the argument I am about), to which I might add several among ourselves, such as the family of love, sweet singers of Israel, and the like; and, from reflecting upon that fundamental point in their doctrines about women wherein they have so unanimously agreed, I am apt to imagine that the seed or principle which has ever put men upon visions in things invisible is of a corporeal nature; for the profounder chemists inform us that the strongest spirits may be extracted from human flesh. Besides, the spinal marrow, being nothing else but a continuation of the brain, must needs create a very free communication between the superior faculties and those below; and thus the thorn in the flesh serves for a spur to the spirit. I think it is agreed among physicians that nothing affects the head so much as a tentiginous humour, repelled and elated to the upper region, found, by daily practice, to run frequently up into madness. A very eminent member of the faculty assured me that when the Quakers first appeared he seldom was without some female patients among them for the *furor—*; persons of a visionary devotion, either men or women, are, in their complexion, of all others, the most amorous; for zeal is frequently kindled from the same spark with other fires, and, from inflaming brotherly love, will proceed to raise that of a gallant. If we inspect into the usual process of modern courtship, we shall find it to consist in a devout turn of the eyes, called ogling; an artificial form of canting and whining by rote, every interval for want of other matter, made up with a shrug or a hum, a sigh or a groan; the style compact of insignificant words, incoherences, and repetition. These I take to be the most accomplished rules of address to a mistress; and where are these performed with more dexterity than by the saints? Nay, to bring this argument yet closer, I have been informed by certain sanguine brethren of the first class, that, in the height and orgasmus of their spiritual exercise, it has been frequent with them . . . ; immediately after which, they found the spirit to relax and flag of a sudden with the nerves, and they were forced to hasten to a conclusion. This may be further strengthened by observing, with wonder, how unaccountably all females are attracted by visionary or enthusiastic preachers, though ever so contemptible in their outward mien; which is usually supposed to be done upon considerations purely spiritual, without any carnal regards at all. But I have reason to think the sex has certain characteristics, by which they form a truer judgment of human abilities and performings than we ourselves can possibly do of each other. Let that be as it will, thus much is certain, that, however spiritual intrigues begin, they generally conclude like all others; they may branch upward toward heaven, but the root is in the earth. Too intense a contemplation is not the business of flesh and blood; it must, by the necessary course of things, in a little time let go its hold, and fall into matter. Lovers for the sake of celestial converse are but another sort of Platonics, who pretend to see stars and heaven in ladies' eyes, and to look or think no lower; but the same pit is provided for both; and they seem a perfect moral to the story of that philosopher, who, while his thoughts and eyes were fixed upon the constellations, found himself seduced by his lower parts into a ditch.

I had somewhat more to say upon this part of the subject; but the post is just going, which forces me in great haste to conclude,

Sir, yours, etc.

Pray burn this letter as soon as it comes to your hands.

A MEDITATION UPON A BROOMSTICK

ACCORDING TO THE STYLE AND MANNER OF THE
HONOURABLE ROBERT BOYLE'S MEDITATIONS

THIS Parody is said by Mr. Thomas Sheridan to have been
composed upon the following occasion:—

"In the yearly visits which Swift made to London, during
his stay there he passed much of his time at Lord Berkeley's,
officiating as chaplain to the family, and attending her ladyship in her private devotions; after which the doctor, by her
desire, used to read to her some moral or religious discourse.
The Countess had at this time taken a great liking to Mr.
Boyle's Meditations, and was determined to go through them
in that manner; but as Swift had by no means the same
relish for that kind of writing which her ladyship had, he
soon grew weary of the task; and a whim coming into his
head, resolved to get rid of it in a way which might occasion
some sport in the family; for which they had as high a relish
as himself. The next time he was employed in reading one
of these Meditations, he took an opportunity of conveying
away the book, and dexterously inserted a leaf, on which he
had written his own Meditation on a Broomstick; after which
he took care to have the book restored to its proper place, and
in his next attendance on my lady, when he was desired to
proceed to the next Meditation, Swift opened upon the place
where the leaf had been inserted, and with great composure
read the title, 'A Meditation on a Broomstick.' Lady
Berkeley, a little surprised at the oddity of the title, stopped
him, repeating the words, 'A Meditation on a Broomstick!
What a strange subject! But there is no knowing what
useful lessons of instruction this wonderful man may draw
from things apparently the most trivial. Pray let us hear
what he says upon it.' Swift then, with an inflexible gravity
of countenance, proceeded to read the Meditation, in the same
solemn tone which he had used in delivering the former.

Lady Berkeley, not at all suspecting a trick, in the fulness of
her prepossession, was every now and then, during the reading
of it, expressing her admiration of this extraordinary man,
who could draw such fine moral reflections from so contemptible a subject; with which, though Swift must have been
inwardly not a little tickled, yet he preserved a most perfect
composure of features, so that she had not the least room to
suspect any deceit.   Soon after, some company coming in,
Swift pretended business, and withdrew, foreseeing what was
to follow.   Lady Berkeley, full of the subject, soon entered
upon the praises of those heavenly Meditations of Mr. Boyle.
'But,' said she, 'the doctor has been just reading one to me,
which has surprised me more than all the rest.'   One of the
company asked which of the Meditations she meant?   She
answered directly, in the simplicity of her heart, 'I mean,
that excellent Meditation upon the Broomstick.'   The company looked at each other with some surprise, and could
scarce refrain from laughing.   But they all agreed that they
had never heard of such a Meditation before.   'Upon my
word,' said my lady, 'there it is, look into that book, and
convince yourselves.'   One of them opened the book, and
found it there indeed, but in Swift's handwriting; upon
which a general burst of laughter ensued; and my lady, when
the first surprise was over, enjoyed the joke as much as any of
them; saying, 'What a vile trick has that rogue played me!
But it is his way, he never baulks his humour in anything.'
The affair ended in a great deal of harmless mirth, and Swift,
you may be sure, was not asked to proceed any further into
the Meditations."

This single stick, which you now behold ingloriously lying
in that neglected corner, I once knew in a flourishing state in
a forest: it was full of sap, full of leaves, and full of boughs:
but now, in vain does the busy art of man pretend to vie
with nature, by tying that withered bundle of twigs to its
sapless trunk: it is now, at best, but the reverse of what it
was, a tree turned upside down, the branches on the earth,
and the root in the air; it is now handled by every dirty
wench, condemned to do her drudgery, and, by a capricious
kind of fate, destined to make other things clean, and be
nasty itself: at length, worn to the stumps in the service of

the maids, it is either thrown out of doors, or condemned to the last use, of kindling a fire. When I beheld this I sighed, and said within myself, *Surely man is a Broomstick !* Nature sent him into the world strong and lusty, in a thriving condition, wearing his own hair on his head, the proper branches of this reasoning vegetable, until the axe of intemperance has lopped off his green boughs, and left him a withered trunk: he then flies to art, and puts on a periwig, valuing himself upon an unnatural bundle of hairs (all covered with powder), that never grew on his head; but now, should this our broomstick pretend to enter the scene, proud of those birchen spoils it never bore, and all covered with dust, though the sweepings of the finest lady's chamber, we should be apt to ridicule and despise its vanity. Partial judges that we are of our own excellences and other men's defaults!

But a broomstick, perhaps, you will say, is an emblem of a tree standing on its head; and pray what is man, but a topsyturvy creature, his animal faculties perpetually mounted on his rational, his head where his heels should be, grovelling on the earth! and yet, with all his faults, he sets up to be a universal reformer and corrector of abuses, a remover of grievances, rakes into every slut's corner of nature, bringing hidden corruption to the light, and raises a mighty dust where there was none before; sharing deeply all the while in the very same pollutions he pretends to sweep away; his last days are spent in slavery to women, and generally the least deserving; till, worn out to the stumps, like his brother besom, he is either kicked out of doors, or made use of to kindle flames for others to warm themselves by.

A TRITICAL ESSAY UPON THE FACULTIES OF THE MIND

TO ——————

SIR,—Being so great a lover of antiquities, it was reasonable to suppose, you would be very much obliged with anything that was new. I have been of late offended with many writers of essays and moral discourses, for running into stale topics and threadbare quotations, and not handling their subject fully and closely; all which errors I have carefully avoided in the following essay, which I have proposed as a pattern for young writers to imitate. The thoughts and observations being entirely new, the quotations untouched by others, the subject of mighty importance, and treated with much order and perspicuity, it has cost me a great deal of time; and I desire you will accept and consider it as the utmost effort of my genius.

A TRITICAL ESSAY, ETC.

PHILOSOPHERS say, that man is a microcosm, or little world, resembling in miniature every part of the great; and, in my opinion, the body natural may be compared to the body politic; and if this be so, how can the Epicurean's opinion be true, that the universe was formed by a fortuitous concourse of atoms: which I will no more believe, than that the accidental jumbling of the letters of the alphabet, could fall by chance into a most ingenious and learned treatise of philosophy. *Risum teneatis amici ?* This false opinion must needs create many more: it is like an error in the first concoction, which cannot be corrected in the second; the foundation is weak, and whatever superstructure you raise upon it, must, of necessity, fall to the ground. Thus men are led from one error to another, until, with Ixion, they embrace a cloud instead of Juno; or, like the dog in the fable, lose the substance in gaping at the shadow. For such opinions cannot cohere; but, like the iron and clay in the toes of Nebuchadnezzar's image, must separate and break in pieces. I have read in a certain author, that Alexander wept because he had no more worlds to conquer: which he needed not have done, if the fortuitous concourse of atoms could create one: but this is an opinion fitter for that many-headed beast, the vulgar, to entertain than for so wise a man as Epicurus; the corrupt part of his sect only borrowed his name, as the monkey did the cat's claw to draw the chestnut out of the fire.

However, the first step to the cure is to know the disease; and though truth may be difficult to find, because, as the philosopher observes, she lives in the bottom of a well, yet we need not, like blind men, grope in open daylight. I hope I may be allowed, among so many far more learned men, to offer my mite, since a stander-by may sometimes, perhaps, see more of the game than he that plays it. But I do not think a philosopher obliged to account for every phenomenon in nature, or drown himself with Aristotle, for not being able to solve the ebbing and flowing of the tide in that fatal sentence he passed upon himself, *Quia te non capio, tu capies me.* Wherein he was at once the judge and the criminal, the accuser and executioner. Socrates, on the other hand, who said he knew nothing, was pronounced by the oracle to be the wisest man in the world.

But to return from this digression: I think it as clear as any demonstration of Euclid, that nature does nothing in vain; if we were able to dive into her secret recesses, we should find that the smallest blade of grass, or most contemptible weed, has its particular use: but she is chiefly admirable in her minutest compositions; the least and most contemptible insect most discovers the art of nature, if I may so call it, though nature, which delights in variety, will always triumph over art: and as the poet observes,

> Naturam expellas furcâ licet, usque recurret.

But the various opinions of philosophers have scattered through the world as many plagues of the mind as Pandora's box did those of the body; only with this difference, that they have not left hope at the bottom. And if truth be not fled with Astrea, she is certainly as hidden as the source of Nile, and can be found only in Utopia. Not that I would reflect on those wise sages, which would be a sort of ingratitude; and he that calls a man ungrateful, sums up all the evil that a man can be guilty of,

Ingratum si dixeris, omnia dicis.

But, what I blame the philosophers for (though some may think it a paradox) is chiefly their pride; nothing less than an *ipse dixit,* and you must pin your faith on their sleeve. And though Diogenes lived in a tub, there might be for aught I know as much pride under his rags as in the fine-spun garments of the divine Plato. It is reported of this Diogenes, that when Alexander came to see him, and promised to give him whatever he would ask, the cynic only answered, " Take not from me what thou canst not give me, but stand from between me and the light; " which was almost as extravagant as the philosopher that flung his money into the sea, with this remarkable saying——

How different was this man from the usurer, who, being told his son would spend all he had got, replied, " He cannot take more pleasure in spending than I did in getting it." These men could see the faults of each other, but not their own; those they flung into the bag behind; *non videmus id manticæ quod in tergo est.* I may perhaps be censured for my free opinions by those carping Momuses whom authors worship, as the Indians do the devil, for fear. They will endeavour to give my reputation as many wounds as the man in the almanack; but I value it not; and perhaps, like flies, they may buzz so often about the candle, till they burn their wings. They must pardon me if I venture to give them this advice, not to rail at what they cannot understand; it does but discover that self-tormenting passion of envy, than which the greatest tyrant never invented a more cruel torment:

Invidiâ Siculi non invenere Tyranni
Tormentum majus.—

I must be so bold to tell my critics and witlings, that they can no more judge of this than a man that is born blind can have any true idea of colours. I have always observed that your empty vessels sound loudest: I value their lashes as little as the sea did those of Xerxes, when he whipped it. The utmost favour a man can expect from them is, that which Polyphemus promised Ulysses, that he would devour him the last: they think to subdue a writer, as Cæsar did his enemy, with a *Veni, vidi, vici.* I confess I value the opinion of the judicious few, a Rymer, a Dennis, or a W——k; but for the rest, to give my judgment at once, I think the long dispute among the philosophers about a *vacuum* may be determined in the affirmative, that it is to be found in a critic's head. They are at best but the drones of the learned world, who devour the honey and will not work themselves: and a writer need no more regard them than the moon does the barking of a little senseless cur. For, in spite of their terrible roaring, you may, with half an eye, discover the ass under the lion's skin.

But to return to our discourse: Demosthenes being asked what was the first part of an orator, replied action: what was the second, action: what was the third, action: and so on, *ad infinitum.* This may be true in oratory; but contemplation in other things exceeds action. And, therefore, a wise man is never less alone than when he is alone: *Nunquam minus solus, quam cum solus.*

And Archimedes, the famous mathematician, was so intent upon his problems that he never minded the soldiers who came to kill him. Therefore, not to detract from the just praise which belongs to orators, they ought to consider that nature, which gave us two eyes to see and two ears to hear, has given us but one tongue to speak; wherein, however, some do so abound, that the virtuosi who have been so long in search for the perpetual motion, may infallibly find it there.

Some men admire republics, because orators flourish there most, and are the greatest enemies of tyranny; but my opinion is, that one tyrant is better than a hundred. Besides, these orators inflame the people, whose anger is really but a short fit of madness.

Ira furor brevis est.

After which, laws are like cobwebs, which may catch small flies, but let wasps and hornets break through. But in oratory the greatest art is to hide art. *Artis est celare artem.*

But this must be the work of time, we must lay hold on all opportunities, and let slip no occasion; else we shall be forced to weave Penelope's web, unravel in the night what we spun in the day. And therefore I have observed, that Time is painted with a lock before, and bald behind, signifying thereby, that we must take time (as we say) by the forelock, for when it is once past, there is no recalling it.

The mind of man is at first (if you will pardon the expression) like a *tabula rasa,* or like wax, which, while it is soft, is capable of any impression, till time has hardened it. And at length Death, that grim tyrant, stops us in the midst of our career. The greatest conquerors have at last been conquered by death, which spares none, from the sceptre to the spade: *Mors omnibus communis.*

All rivers go to the sea, but none return from it. Xerxes wept when he beheld his army, to consider that in less than a hundred years they would be all dead. Anacreon was choked with a grape-stone; and violent joy kills as well as violent grief. There is nothing in this world constant, but inconstancy; yet Plato thought, that if Virtue would appear to the world in her own native dress, all men would be enamoured with her. But now, since interest governs the world, and men neglect the golden mean, Jupiter himself, if he came to the earth, would be despised, unless it were, as he did to Danae, in a golden shower: for men now-a-days worship the rising sun, and not the setting:

Donec eris felix multos numerabis amicos.

Thus have I, in obedience to your commands, ventured to expose myself to censure in this critical age. Whether I have done right to my subject must be left to the judgment of my learned reader: however, I cannot but hope that my attempting of it may be encouragement for some able pen to perform it with more success.

THE BICKERSTAFF PAPERS

I.—PREDICTIONS FOR THE YEAR 1708

WHEREIN THE MONTH, AND THE DAY OF THE MONTH, ARE SET
DOWN, THE PERSONS NAMED, AND THE GREAT ACTIONS
AND EVENTS OF NEXT YEAR PARTICULARLY RELATED, AS
THEY WILL COME TO PASS. WRITTEN TO PREVENT THE
PEOPLE OF ENGLAND FROM BEING FURTHER IMPOSED ON
BY THE VULGAR ALMANACK-MAKERS.

BY ISAAC BICKERSTAFF, ESQ.[1]

SWIFT, when he had written these humorous predictions, being at a
loss what name to prefix to them, observed a sign over a black-
smith's house, and the name of Bickerstaff written under it. It
struck his fancy, and he chose to call himself Isaac Bickerstaff.
This amusing tract was seriously burnt by the inquisition in
Portugal, as the author was assured by Sir Paul Methuen, then
ambassador at that court.

I HAVE considered the gross abuse of astrology in this kingdom, and upon debating the matter with myself, I could not
possibly lay the fault upon the art, but upon those gross
impostors who set up to be the artists. I know several
learned men have contended that the whole is a cheat; that
it is absurd and ridiculous to imagine the stars can have any
influence at all upon human actions, thoughts, or inclinations;
and whoever has not bent his studies that way may be excused for thinking so, when he sees in how wretched a manner
that noble art is treated by a few mean, illiterate traders
between us and the stars; who import a yearly stock of nonsense, lies, folly, and impertinence, which they offer to the
world as genuine from the planets, though they descend
from no greater a height than their own brains.

I intend, in a short time, to publish a large and rational

[1] Not in Scott, who gives a quotation from Brown's *Vulgar Errors*,
and few words of his own.

defence of this art, and therefore shall say no more in its
justification at present, than that it has been in all ages
defended by many learned men, and among the rest by
Socrates himself; whom I look upon as undoubtedly the
wisest of uninspired mortals: to which if we add, that those
who have condemned this art, though otherwise learned,
have been such as either did not apply their studies this way,
or at least did not succeed in their applications, their testimony will not be of much weight to its disadvantage, since
they are liable to the common objection, of condemning what
they did not understand.

Nor am I at all offended, or do I think it an injury to the
art, when I see the common dealers in it, the students in
astrology, the philomaths, and the rest of that tribe, treated
by wise men with the utmost scorn and contempt; but I
rather wonder, when I observe gentlemen in the country, rich
enough to serve the nation in parliament, poring in Partridge's
Almanack to find out the events of the year, at home and
abroad; not daring to propose a hunting march till Gadbury [1]
or he have fixed the weather.

I will allow either of the two I have mentioned, or any
other of the fraternity, to be not only astrologers but con-
jurers too, if I do not produce a hundred instances, in all
their almanacks, to convince any reasonable man that they
do not so much as understand common grammar and syntax;
that they are not able to spell any word out of the usual road,
nor, even in their prefaces, to write common sense, or intelligible English. Then, for their observations and predictions,
they are such as will equally suit any age or country in the
world, " This month a certain great person will be threatened
with death or sickness." This the newspapers will tell them;
for there we find at the end of the year, that no month passes
without the death of some person of note; and it would be
hard if it should be otherwise, when there are at least two
thousand persons of note in this kingdom, many of them old,
and the almanack-maker has the liberty of choosing the sick-
liest season of the year, when he may fix his prediction.
Again, " This month an eminent clergyman will be preferred;"
of which there may be many hundreds, half of them with one

---

[1] John Gadbury, bred a tailor at Oxford, long published an
almanack which vied in reputation with that of Partridge.

foot in the grave. Then, " Such a planet in such a house
shows great machinations, plots, and conspiracies that may
in time be brought to light: " after which, if we hear of any
discovery, the astrologer gets the honour; if not, his predictions still stand good. And at last, " God preserve King
William from all his open and secret enemies. Amen."
When, if the king should happen to have died, the astrologer
plainly foretold it; otherwise it passes but for the pious
ejaculation of a loyal subject: though it unluckily happened
in some of their almanacks that poor King William was
prayed for many months after he was dead, because it fell
out, that he died about the beginning of the year.

To mention no more of their impertinent predictions, what
have we to do with their advertisements about " pills and
drinks for the venereal disease? " or their mutual quarrels in
verse and prose of Whig and Tory, wherewith the stars have
little to do.

Having long observed and lamented these, and a hundred
other abuses of this art too tedious to repeat, I resolved to
proceed in a new way, which I doubt not will be to the general
satisfaction of the kingdom: I can this year produce but a
specimen of what I design for the future; having employed
most part of my time in adjusting and correcting the calculations I made for some years past, because I would offer
nothing to the world of which I am not as fully satisfied as
that I am now alive. For these two last years I have not
failed in above one or two particulars, and those of no very
great moment. I exactly foretold the miscarriage at
Toulon,[1] with all its particulars; and the loss of Admiral
Shovel,[2] though I was mistaken as to the day, placing that
article about thirty-six hours sooner than it happened; but
upon reviewing my schemes, I quickly found the cause of that
error. I likewise foretold the battle of Almanza [April 25,
1707] to the very day and hour, with the loss on both sides,
and the consequences thereof. All which I showed to some
friends many months before they happened; that is, I gave
them papers sealed up, to open at such a time, after which
they were at liberty to read them; and there they found

[1] An attempt was made to besiege Toulon in 1707, but it miscarried.
[2] Sir Cloudesly Shovel's fleet was wrecked Oct. 22, 1707.

my predictions true in every article, except one or two very minute.

As for the few following predictions I now offer the world, I forebore to publish them till I had perused the several almanacks for the year we are now entered upon. I found them all in the usual strain, and I beg the reader will compare their manner with mine: and here I make bold to tell the world that I lay the whole credit of my art upon the truth of these predictions; and I will be content that Partridge, and the rest of his clan, may hoot me for a cheat and impostor if I fail in any single particular of moment. I believe any man who reads this paper will look upon me to be at least a person of as much honesty and understanding as a common maker of almanacks. I do not lurk in the dark; I am not wholly unknown in the world; I have set my name at length to be a mark of infamy to mankind if they shall find I deceive them.

In one thing I must desire to be forgiven, that I talk more sparingly of home affairs; as it would be imprudence to discover secrets of state, so it might be dangerous to my person; but in smaller matters, and such as are not of public consequence, I shall be very free; and the truth of my conjectures will as much appear from these as the other. As for the most signal events abroad in France, Flanders, Italy, and Spain, I shall make no scruple to predict them in plain terms: some of them are of importance, and I hope I shall seldom mistake the day they will happen; therefore I think good to inform the reader, that I shall all along make use of the old style observed in England, which I desire he will compare with that of the newspapers, at the time they relate the actions I mention.

I must add one word more; I know it has been the opinion of several learned persons, who think well enough of the true art of astrology, that the stars do only incline, and not force, the actions or wills of men, and therefore, however I may proceed by right rules, yet I cannot in prudence so confidently assure the events will follow exactly as I predict them.

I hope I have maturely considered this objection, which in some cases is of no little weight. For example; a man may, by the influence of an overruling planet, be disposed or inclined to lust, rage, or avarice, and yet by the force of reason overcome that evil influence; and this was the case of

Socrates; but the great events of the world usually depending upon numbers of men, it cannot be expected they should all unite to cross their inclinations, for pursuing a general design, wherein they unanimously agree. Besides, the influence of the stars reaches to many actions and events which are not any way in the power of reason; as sickness, death, and what we commonly call accidents, with many more needless to repeat.

But now it is time to proceed to my predictions, which I have begun to calculate from the time that the sun enters into Aries. And this I take to be properly the beginning of the natural year. I pursue them to the time that he enters Libra, or somewhat more, which is the busy period of the year. The remainder I have not yet adjusted, upon account of several impediments needless here to mention: besides, I must remind the reader again, that this is but a specimen of what I design in succeeding years to treat more at large, if I may have liberty and encouragement.

My first prediction is but a trifle, yet I will mention it, to show how ignorant those sottish pretenders to astrology are in their own concerns: it relates to Partridge the almanack-maker. I have consulted the star of his nativity by my own rules, and find he will infallibly die upon the 29th of March next, about eleven at night, of a raging fever: therefore I advise him to consider of it, and settle his affairs in time.

The month of April will be observable for the death of many great persons. On the 4th will die the Cardinal de Noailles, Archbishop of Paris; on the 11th, the young Prince of Asturias, son to the Duke of Anjou; on the 14th, a great peer of this realm will die at his country-house; on the 19th, an old layman of great fame for learning; and on the 23rd, an eminent goldsmith in Lombard Street. I could mention others, both at home and abroad, if I did not consider such events of very little use or instruction to the reader, or to the world.

As to public affairs: on the 7th of this month there will be an insurrection in Dauphiné, occasioned by the oppressions of the people, which will not be quieted in some months.

On the 15th will be a violent storm on the south-east coast of France, which will destroy many of their ships, and some in the very harbour.

The 19th will be famous for the revolt of a whole province or kingdom, excepting one city, by which the affairs of a certain prince in the alliance will take a better face.

May, against common conjectures, will be no very busy month in Europe, but very signal for the death of the Dauphin, which will happen on the 7th, after a short fit of sickness, and grievous torments with the strangury. He dies less lamented by the court than the kingdom.

On the 9th, a mareschal of France will break his leg by a fall from his horse. I have not been able to discover whether he will then die or not.

On the 11th will begin a most important siege, which the eyes of all Europe will be upon: I cannot be more particular; for, in relating affairs that so nearly concern the confederates, and consequently this kingdom, I am forced to confine myself, for several reasons very obvious to the reader.

On the 15th, news will arrive of a very surprising event, than which, nothing can be more unexpected.

On the 19th, three noble ladies of this kingdom will, against all expectation, prove with child, to the great joy of their husbands.

On the 23rd, a famous buffoon of the playhouse will die a ridiculous death, suitable to his vocation.

June. This month will be distinguished at home by the utter dispersing of those ridiculous deluded enthusiasts commonly called the prophets; [1] occasioned chiefly by seeing the time come when many of their prophecies should be fulfilled, and then finding themselves deceived by contrary events. It is indeed to be admired, how any deceiver can be so weak to foretell things near at hand, when a very few months must, of necessity, discover the imposture to all the world; in this point less prudent than common almanack-makers, who are so wise to wander in generals, and talk dubiously, and leave to the reader the business of interpreting.

On the 1st of this month a French general will be killed by a random shot of a cannon-ball.

On the 6th, a fire will break out in the suburbs of Paris,

[1] The Protestants in Dauphiné, called Casimars, being driven mad by persecution, became of course enthusiasts, and mingled miracles and prophecies with their religious fervour.

which will destroy above a thousand houses; and seems to be the foreboding of what will happen, to the surprise of all Europe, about the end of the following month.

On the 10th, a great battle will be fought, which will begin at four of the clock in the afternoon, and last till nine at night, with great obstinacy, but no very decisive event. I shall not name the place, for the reasons aforesaid; but the commanders on each left wing will be killed. I see bonfires and hear the noise of guns for a victory.

On the 14th there will be a false report of the French king's death.

On the 20th, Cardinal Portocarero will die of a dysentery, with great suspicion of poison; but the report of his intention to revolt to King Charles will prove false.

July. The 6th of this month a certain general will, by a glorious action, recover the reputation he lost by former misfortunes.

On the 12th, a great commander will die a prisoner in the hands of his enemies.

On the 14th, a shameful discovery will be made of a French jesuit giving poison to a great foreign general; and when he is put to the torture, he will make wonderful discoveries.

In short, this will prove a month of great action, if I might have liberty to relate the particulars.

At home, the death of an old famous senator will happen on the 15th, at his country-house, worn out with age and diseases.

But that which will make this month memorable to all posterity, is the death of the French king, Louis XIV., after a week's sickness, at Marli, which will happen on the 29th, about six o'clock in the evening. It seems to be an effect of the gout in the stomach, followed by a flux. And, in three days after, Monsieur Chamillard will follow his master, dying suddenly of an apoplexy.

In this month likewise an ambassador will die in London; but I cannot assign the day.

August. The affairs of France will seem to suffer no change for a while under the Duke of Burgundy's administration; but the genius that animated the whole machine being gone, will be the cause of mighty turns and revolutions in the following year. The new king makes yet little change either

in the army or the ministry; but the libels against his grandfather, that fly about his very court, give him uneasiness.

I see an express in mighty haste, with joy and wonder in
his looks, arriving by break of day on the 26th of this month,
having travelled in three days a prodigious journey by land
and sea. In the evening I hear bells and guns, and see the
blazing of a thousand bonfires.

A young admiral of noble birth does likewise this month
gain immortal honour by a great achievement.

The affairs of Poland are this month entirely settled:
Augustus resigns his pretensions, which he had again taken
up for some time; Stanislaus is peaceably possessed of the
throne; and the king of Sweden declares for the emperor.

I cannot omit one particular accident here at home; that
near the end of this month much mischief will be done at
Bartholomew Fair, by the fall of a booth.

September. This month begins with a very surprising fit
of frosty weather, which will last near twelve days.

The pope having long languished last month, the swellings
in his legs breaking, and the flesh mortifying, will die on the
11th instant: and in three weeks' time, after a mighty
contest, be succeeded by a cardinal of the imperial faction,
but a native of Tuscany, who is now about sixty-one years
old.

The French army now acts wholly on the defensive,
strongly fortified in their trenches: and the young French
king sends overtures for a treaty of peace by the duke of
Mantua, which, because it is a matter of state that concerns
us here at home, I shall speak no further of.

I shall add but one prediction more, and that in mystical
terms, which shall be included in a verse out of Virgil—

> Alter erit jam Tethys, et altera, quæ vehat, Argo,
> Delectos heroas.

Upon the 25th day of this month, the fulfilling of this
prediction will be manifest to everybody.

This is the farthest I have proceeded in my calculations
for the present year. I do not pretend that these are all the
great events which will happen in this period, but that those
I have set down will infallibly come to pass. It will perhaps
still be objected, why I have not spoke more particularly of
affairs at home, or of the success of our armies abroad, which

I might, and could very largely have done; but those in power have wisely discouraged men from meddling in public concerns, and I was resolved by no means to give the least offence.   This I will venture to say, that it will be a glorious campaign for the allies, wherein the English forces, both by sea and land, will have their full share of honour: that her majesty Queen Anne will continue in health and prosperity: and that no ill accident will arrive to any in the chief ministry.

As to the particular events I have mentioned, the reader may judge, by the fulfilling of them, whether I am on the level with common astrologers; who, with an old paltry cant, and a few pot-hooks for planets to amuse the vulgar, have, in my opinion, too long been suffered to abuse the world: but an honest physician ought not to be despised because there are such things as mountebanks.   I hope I have some share of reputation, which I would not willingly forfeit for a frolic or humour: and I believe no gentleman who reads this paper will look upon it to be of the same cast or mould with the common scribbles that are every day hawked about. My fortune has placed me above the little regard of writing for a few pence, which I neither value nor want: therefore let not wise men too hastily condemn this essay, intended for a good design, to cultivate and improve an ancient art, long in disgrace by having fallen into mean unskilful hands.   A little time will determine whether I have deceived others or myself: and I think it no very unreasonable request, that men would please to suspend their judgments till then.   I was once of the opinion with those who despise all predictions from the stars, till, in the year 1686, a man of quality showed me, written in his *album*, that the most learned astronomer, Captain Halley, assured him he would never believe anything of the stars' influence, if there were not a great revolution in England in the year 1688.   Since that time I began to have other thoughts, and after eighteen years' diligent study and application, I think I have no reason to repent of my pains. I shall detain the reader no longer than to let him know, that the account I design to give of next year's events, shall take in the principal affairs that happen in Europe; and if I be denied the liberty of offering it to my own country, I shall appeal to the learned world, by publishing it in Latin, and giving order to have it printed in Holland.

II.—AN ANSWER TO BICKERSTAFF

SOME REFLECTIONS UPON MR. BICKERSTAFF'S PREDICTIONS
FOR THE YEAR MDCCVIII

BY A PERSON OF QUALITY

I HAVE not observed, for some years past, any insignificant paper to have made more noise, or be more greedily bought, than that of these predictions. They are the wonder of the common people, an amusement for the better sort, and a jest only to the wise; yet among these last, I have heard some very much in doubt whether the author meant to deceive others or is deceived himself. Whoever he was, he seems to have with great art adjusted his paper both to please the rabble and to entertain persons of condition. The writer is, without question, a gentleman of wit and learning, although the piece seems hastily written in a sudden frolic, with the scornful thought of the pleasure he will have in putting this great town into a wonderment about nothing: nor do I doubt but he and his friends in the secret laugh often and plentifully in a corner, to reflect how many hundred thousand fools they have already made. And he has them fast for some time: for so they are likely to continue until his prophecies begin to fail in the events. Nay, it is a great question whether the miscarriage of the two or three first will so entirely undeceive people as to hinder them from expecting the accomplishment of the rest. I doubt not but some thousands of these papers are carefully preserved by as many persons, to confront with the events, and try whether the astrologer exactly keeps the day and hour. And these I take to be Mr. Bickerstaff's choicest cullies, for whose sake chiefly he writ his amusement. Meanwhile he has seven weeks good, during which time the world is to be kept in suspense: for it is so long before the almanack-maker is to die, which is the first prediction; and, if that fellow happens to be a splenetic visionary fop, or has any faith in his own art, the prophecy may punctually come to pass by very natural means. As a gentleman of my acquaintance, who was ill used by a mercer in town, wrote him a letter in an unknown hand, to give him notice that care had been taken to convey a slow poison into his drink, which would infallibly kill him in a month; after which, the man began in earnest to languish and decay, by the mere strength of imagination, and would certainly have died, if care had not been taken to undeceive him, before the jest went too far. The like effect upon Partridge would wonderfully rise Mr. Bickerstaff's reputation for a fortnight longer, until we could hear from France whether the Cardinal de Noailles were dead or alive upon the 4th of April, which is the second of his predictions.

For a piece so carelessly written, the observations upon astrology are reasonable and pertinent, the remarks just; and as the paper is partly designed, in my opinion, for a satire upon the credulity of the vulgar, and that idle itch of peeping into futurities; so it is no more than what we all of us deserve. And, since we must be teased with perpetual hawkers of strange and wonderful things, I am glad to see a man of sense find leisure and humour to take up the trade, for his own and our diversion. To speak in the town phrase, it is a bite; he has fully had his jest, and may be satisfied.

I very much approve the serious air he gives himself in his introduction and conclusion, which has gone far to give some people, of no mean rank, an opinion that the author believes himself. He tell us, " He places the whole credit of his art on the truth of these predictions, and will be content to be hooted by Partridge and the rest for a cheat, if he fails in any one particular," with several other strains of the same kind, wherein I perfectly believe him; and that he is very indifferent whether Isaac Bickerstaff be a mark of infamy or not. But it seems, although he has joined an odd surname to no very common Christian one, that in this large town there is a man found to own both the names, although, I believe, not the paper.

I believe it is no small mortification to this gentleman astrologer, as well as his bookseller, to find their piece, which they sent out in a tolerable print and paper, immediately seized on by three or four interloping printers of Grub-street, the title stuffed with an abstract of the whole matter, together with the standard epithets of *strange* and *wonderful*, the price brought down a full half, which was but a penny in its prime, and bawled about by hawkers of the inferior class, with the concluding cadence of "A halfpenny a piece!" But *sic cecidit Phaeton ;* and, to comfort him a little, this production of mine will have the same fate; to-morrow will my ears be grated by the little boys and wenches in straw hats; and I must a hundred times undergo the mortification to have my own work offered me to sale at an under value. Then, which is a great deal worse, my acquaintance in the coffeehouse will ask me whether I have seen the *Answer to 'Squire Bickerstaff's Predictions*, and whether I knew the puppy that writ it; and how to keep a man's countenance in such a juncture is no easy point of conduct. When, in this case, you see a man shy either in praising or condemning, ready to turn off the discourse to another subject, standing as little in the light as he can to hide his blushing, pretending to sneeze, or take snuff, or go off as if sudden business called him; then ply him close, observe his look narrowly, see whether his speech be constrained or affected, then charge him suddenly, or whisper and smile, and you will soon discover whether he be guilty. Although this seem not the purpose I am discoursing on, yet I think it to be so; for I am much deceived if I do not know the true author of *Bickerstaff's Predictions*, and did not meet with him some days ago in a coffeehouse at Covent Garden.

As to the matter of the predictions themselves, I shall not enter upon the examination of them; but think it very incumbent upon the learned Mr. Partridge to take them into his consideration, and lay as many errors in astrology as possible to Mr. Bickerstaff's account. He may justly, I think, challenge the 'squire to publish the calculation he has made of Partridge's nativity, by the credit of which he so determinately pronounces the time and the manner of his death; and Mr. Bickerstaff can do no less, in honour, than give Mr. Partridge the same advantage of calculating his, by sending him an account of the time and place of his birth, with other particulars necessary for such a work. By which, no doubt, the learned world will be engaged in the dispute, and take part on each side according as they are inclined.

I should likewise advise Mr. Partridge to inquire, why Mr. Bickerstaff does not so much as offer at one prediction to be fulfilled until two months after the time of publishing his paper. This looks a little suspicious, as if he were desirous to keep the world in play as long as he decently could; else it were hard he could not afford us one prediction between this and the 29th of March; which is not so fair dealings as we have even from Mr. Partridge and his brethren, who give us their predictions (such as they are indeed) for every month in the year.

There is one passage in Mr. Bickerstaff's paper that seems to be as high a strain of assurance as I have anywhere met with: it is that prediction for the month of June which relates to the French prophets here in town; where he tells us, " They will utterly disperse, by seeing the time come, wherein their prophecies should be fulfilled, and then finding themselves deceived by contrary events." Upon which he adds, with great reason, " his wonder how any deceiver can be so weak to foretell things near at hand, when a very few months must discover the imposture to all the world." This is spoken with a great deal of affected unconcernedness, as if he would have us think himself to be not under the least apprehension, that the same in two months will be his own case. With respect to the gentleman, I do not remember to have heard of so refined and pleasant a piece of impudence; which I hope the author will not resent as an uncivil word, because I am sure I enter into his taste, and take it as he meant it. However, he half deserves a reprimand for writing with so much scorn and contempt for the understandings of the majority.

For the month of July, he tells us " of a general who, by a glorious action, will recover the reputation he lost by former misfortunes." This is commonly understood to be Lord Galway; who, if he be already dead, as some newspapers have it, Mr. Bickerstaff has made a trip. But this I do not much insist on; for it is hard if another general cannot be found under the same circumstances to whom this prediction may be as well applied.

The French king's death is very punctually related; but it was unfortunate to make him die at Marli, where he never goes at that season of the year, as I observed myself during three years I passed in that kingdom: and discoursing some months ago with Monsieur Tallard about the French court, I find that king never goes to Marli for any time, but about the season of hunting there, which is not till August. So that there was an unlucky slip of Mr. Bickerstaff for want of foreign education.

He concludes with resuming his promise of publishing entire predictions for next year; of which the other astrologers need not be in very much pain. I suppose we shall have them much about the same time with *The General History of Ears*. I believe we have done with him for ever in this kind; and though I am no astrologer, may venture to prophecy that Isaac Bickerstaff, esq., is now dead, and died just at the time his *Predictions* were ready for the press: that he dropped out of the clouds about nine days ago, and, in about four hours after, mounted up thither again like a vapour; and will, one day or other, perhaps, descend a second time when he has some new, agreeable, or amusing whimsy to pass upon the town; wherein it is very probable he will succeed as often as he is disposed to try the experiment; that is as long as he can preserve a thorough contempt for his own time and other people's understandings, and is resolved not to laugh cheaper than at the expense of a million of people.

III.—THE ACCOMPLISHMENT OF THE FIRST OF MR. BICKERSTAFF'S PREDICTIONS,

BEING AN ACCOUNT OF THE DEATH OF MR. PARTRIDGE, THE ALMANACK-MAKER, UPON THE 29TH INSTANT, IN A LETTER TO A PERSON OF HONOUR.

WRITTEN IN THE YEAR 1708

MY LORD, in obedience to your Lordship's commands, as well as to satisfy my own curiosity, I have some days past inquired constantly after Partridge the almanack-maker, of whom it was foretold in *Mr. Bickerstaff's Predictions*, published about a month ago, that he should die the 29th instant, about eleven at night, of a raging fever. I had some sort of knowledge of him when I was employed in the revenue, because he used every year to present me with his almanack, as he did other gentlemen, upon the score of some little gratuity we gave him. I saw him accidentally once or twice about ten days before he died, and observed he began very much to droop and languish, though I hear his friends did not seem to apprehend him in any danger. About two or three days ago he grew ill, was confined first to his chamber, and in a few hours after to his bed, where Dr. Case [1] and Mrs. Kirleus [2] were sent for to visit and to prescribe to him. Upon this intelligence I sent thrice every day one servant or other to inquire after his health; and yesterday, about four in the afternoon, word was brought me, " that he was past hopes: " upon which I prevailed with myself to go and see him, partly out of commiseration, and, I confess, partly out of curiosity. He knew me very well, seemed surprised at my condescension, and made me compliments upon it, as well as he could in the condition he was. The people about him said, " he had been for some time delirious; " but when I saw him he had his understanding as well as ever I knew, and spoke strong and hearty, without any seeming uneasiness or constraint. After I had told him " how sorry I was to see him in those melancholy circumstances," and said some other civilities suitable to the occasion, I desired him " to tell me freely and ingenuously whether the predictions Mr. Bickerstaff had published relating to his death had not too much affected and worked on his imagination." He confessed, " he had often had it in his head, but never with much apprehension till about a fortnight before; since which time it had the perpetual possession of his mind and thoughts, and he did verily believe was the true natural cause of his present distemper: for," said he, " I am thoroughly persuaded, and I think I have very good reasons, that Mr. Bickerstaff spoke altogether by guess, and knew no more what will happen this year than I did myself."

I told him " his discourse surprised me; and I would be glad he were in a state of health to be able to tell me what reason he had to be convinced of Mr. Bickerstaff's ignorance." He replied, " I am a poor ignorant fellow, bred to a mean trade, yet I have sense enough to know that all pretences of foretelling by astrology are deceits, for this manifest reason;

[1] John Case was many years a noted practitioner in physic and astrology.   He was looked upon as the successor of Lilly and of Saffold.
[2] Widow of John Kirleus, son of Dr. Thomas Kirleus.

because the wise and the learned, who can only judge whether
there be any truth in this science, do all unanimously agree
to laugh at and despise it; and none but the poor ignorant
vulgar give it any credit, and that only upon the word of
such silly wretches as I and my fellows who can hardly write
or read." I then asked him, " why he had not calculated his
own nativity, to see whether it agreed with Bickerstaff's prediction? " At which he shook his head, and said, " Oh! sir,
this is no time for jesting, but for repenting those fooleries,
as I do now from the very bottom of my heart."—" By what
I can gather from you," said I, " the observations and predictions you printed with your almanacks were mere imposi-
tions on the people." He replied, " If it were otherwise, I
should have the less to answer for. We have a common form
for all those things: as to foretelling the weather, we never
meddle with that, but leave it to the printer, who takes it
out of any old almanack as he thinks fit; the rest was my own
invention, to make my almanack sell, having a wife to maintain and no other way to get my bread; for mending old
shoes is a poor livelihood; and," added he, sighing, " I wish
I may not have done more mischief by my physic than my
astrology; though I had some good receipts from my grandmother, and my own compositions were such as I thought
could at least do no hurt."

I had some other discourse with him, which I now cannot
call to mind; and I fear have already tired your lordship.
I shall only add one circumstance, that on his death-bed he
declared himself a nonconformist, and had a fanatic preacher
to be his spiritual guide. After half an hour's conversation
I took my leave, being almost stifled with the closeness of
the room. I imagined he could not hold out long, and therefore withdrew to a little coffeehouse hard by, leaving a servant
at the house with orders to come immediately and tell me, as
near as he could, the minute when Partridge should expire,
which was not above two hours after; when, looking upon
my watch, I found it to be about five minutes after seven;
by which it is clear that Mr. Bickerstaff was mistaken almost
four hours in his calculation. In the other circumstances he
was exact enough. But whether he has been the cause of
this poor man's death, as well as the predictor, may be very
reasonably disputed. However, it must be confessed the

matter is odd enough, whether we should endeavour to account for it by chance or the effect of imagination: for my own part, though I believe no man has less faith in these matters, yet I shall wait with some impatience, and not without some expectation, the fulfilling of Mr. Bickerstaff's second prediction, that the Cardinal de Noailles is to die upon the 4th of April; and if that should be verified as exactly as this of poor Partridge, I must own I should be wholly surprised and at a loss, and should infallibly expect the accomplishment of all the rest.

IV.—'SQUIRE BICKERSTAFF DETECTED;

OR,

THE ASTROLOGICAL IMPOSTOR CONVICTED

By JOHN PARTRIDGE,

STUDENT IN PHYSIC AND ASTROLOGY

It is hard, my dear countrymen of these united nations, it is very hard that a Briton born, a Protestant astrologer, a man of revolution principles, an assertor of the liberty and property of the people, should cry out in vain for justice against a Frenchman, a papist, and an illiterate pretender to science, that would blast my reputation, most inhumanly bury me alive, and defraud my native country of those services which, in my double capacity, I daily offer the public.

What great provocations I have received let the impartial reader judge, and how unwillingly, even in my own defence, I now enter the lists against falsehood, ignorance, and envy; but I am exasperated, at length, to drag out this Cacus from the den of obscurity where he lurks, detect him by the light of those stars he has so impudently traduced, and show there is not a monster in the skies so pernicious and malevolent to mankind as an ignorant pretender to physic and astrology. I shall not directly fall on the many gross errors, nor expose the notorious absurdities of this prostitute libeller, till I have let the learned world fairly into the controversy depending, and then leave the unprejudiced to judge of the merits and justice of my cause.

It was toward the conclusion of the year 1707, when an impudent pamphlet crept into the world, entitled, *Predictions, etc., by Isaac Bickerstaff, Esq.* Among the many arrogant assertions laid down by that lying spirit of divination, he was pleased to pitch on the Cardinal de Noailles and myself, among many other eminent and illustrious persons, that were to die within the compass of the ensuing year; and peremptorily fixes the month, day, and hour, of our deaths: this, I think, is sporting with great men, and public spirits, to the scandal of religion, and reproach of power; and if sovereign princes and astrologers must make diversion for the vulgar—why then farewell, say I, to all governments, ecclesiastical and civil. But, I thank my better stars, I am alive to confront this false and audacious predictor, and to make him rue the hour he ever affronted a man of science and resentment. The cardinal may take what measures he pleases with him; as his excellency is a foreigner, and a Papist, he has no reason to rely on me for his justification; I shall only assure the world he is alive: but as he was bred to letters and is master of a pen, let him use it in his own defence. In the meantime I shall present the public with a faithful narrative of the ungenerous treatment and hard usage I have received from the virulent papers and malicious practices of this pretended astrologer.

V.—A TRUE AND IMPARTIAL ACCOUNT OF THE PROCEEDINGS OF ISAAC BICKERSTAFF, Esq., AGAINST ME

THE 28th of March, *anna Dom.* 1708, being the night this sham prophet had so impudently fixed for my last, which made little impression on myself; but I cannot answer for my whole family; for my wife, with concern more than usual, prevailed on me to take somewhat to sweat for a cold; and between the hours of eight and nine, to go to bed: the maid, as she was warming my bed, with a curiosity natural to young wenches, runs to the window, and asks of one passing the street, who the bell tolled for? Dr. Partridge, says

he, the famous almanack-maker, who died suddenly this
evening: the poor girl, provoked, told him he lied like a
rascal; the other very sedately replied, the sexton had so
informed him, and if false, he was to blame for imposing upon
a stranger. She asked a second, and a third, as they passed,
and every one was in the same tone. Now, I do not say these
are accomplices to a certain astrological 'squire, and that one
Bickerstaff might be sauntering thereabout, because I will
assert nothing here but what I dare attest for plain matter
of fact. My wife at this fell into a violent disorder, and I
must own I was a little discomposed at the oddness of the
accident. In the meantime one knocks at my door; Betty
runs down, and opening, finds a sober, grave person, who
modestly inquires if this was Dr. Partridge's? She, taking
him for some cautious city patient, that came at that time
for privacy, shows him into the dining-room. As soon as I
could compose myself, I went to him, and was surprised to
find my gentleman mounted on a table with a two-foot rule
in his hand, measuring my walls, and taking the dimensions
of the room. Pray, sir, says I, not to interrupt you, have you
any business with me?—Only, sir, replies he, order the girl
to bring me a better light, for this is but a very dim one.—
Sir, says I, my name is Partridge.—Oh! the doctor's brother,
belike, cries he; the staircase, I believe, and these two apartments hung in close mourning, will be sufficient, and only a
strip of bays round the other rooms. The doctor must needs
die rich, he had great dealings in his way for many years; if
he had no family coat, you had as good use the escutcheons
of the company, they are as showish, and will look as magni-
ficent as if he was descended from the blood royal.—With
that I assumed a greater air of authority, and demanded who
employed him, or how he came there?—Why, I was sent, sir,
by the company of undertakers, says he, and they were employed by the honest gentleman who is executor to the good
doctor departed; and our rascally porter, I believe, is fallen
fast asleep with the black cloth and sconces, or he had been
here, and we might have been tacking up by this time.—Sir,
says I, pray be advised by a friend, and make the best of your
speed out of my doors, for I hear my wife's voice, (which by
the by is pretty distinguishable,) and in that corner of the
room stands a good cudgel, which somebody has felt before

now; if that light in her hands, and she know the business you come about, without consulting the stars, I can assure you it will be employed very much to the detriment of your person.—Sir, cries he, bowing with great civility, I perceive extreme grief for the loss of the doctor disorders you a little at present, but early in the morning I will wait on you with all the necessary materials.—Now, I mention no Bickerstaff; nor do I say that a certain star-gazing 'squire has been playing my executor before his time; but I leave the world to judge, and he that puts things and things fairly together, will not be much wide of the mark.

Well, once more I got my doors closed, and prepared for bed, in hopes of a little repose after so many ruffling adventures; just as I was putting out my light in order to do it, another bounces as hard as he can knock; I open the window, and ask who is there, and what he wants? I am Ned the sexton, replies he, and come to know whether the doctor left any orders for a funeral sermon, and where he is to be laid, and whether his grave is to be plain or bricked?—Why, sirrah, says I, you know me well enough; you know I am not dead, and how dare you affront me after this manner?—Alack-a-day, sir, replies the fellow, why it is in print, and the whole town knows you are dead: why there is Mr. White the joiner is but fitting screws to your coffin, he will be here with it in an instant; he was afraid you would have wanted it before this time. Sirrah, sirrah, says I, you shall know to-morrow, to your cost, that I am alive, and alive like to be!—Why, it is strange, sir, says he, you should make such a secret of your death to us that are your neighbours; it looks as if you had a design to defraud the church of its dues; and, let me tell you, for one that has lived so long by the heavens, that is unhandsomely done.—Hist, hist, says another rogue that stood by him; away, doctor, into your flannel gear as fast as you can, for here is a whole pack of dismals coming to you with their black equipage, and how indecent will it look for you to stand frightening folks at your window when you should have been in your coffin these three hours?—In short, what with undertakers, embalmers, joiners, sextons, and your damned elegy hawkers upon a late practitioner in physic and astrology, I got not one wink of sleep that night, nor scarce a moment's rest ever since. Now, I doubt not but this villainous 'squire has the impudence to assert that these are entirely strangers to him; he, good man, knows nothing of the matter, and honest Isaac Bickerstaff, I warrant you, is more a man of honour than to be an accomplice with a pack of rascals that walk the streets on nights, and disturb good people in their beds; but he is out if he thinks the whole world is blind; for there is one John Partridge can smell a knave as far as Grub Street, although he lies in the most exalted garret, and writes himself 'squire:—but I will keep my temper, and proceed in the narration.

I could not stir out of doors for the space of three months after this, but presently one comes up to me in the street, Mr. Partridge, that coffin you was last buried in I have not yet been paid for: Doctor, cries another dog, how do you think people can live by making of graves for nothing? next time you die, you may even toll out the bell yourself for Ned. A third rogue tips me by the elbow, and wonders how I have the conscience to sneak abroad without paying my funeral expenses.—Lord, says one, I durst have swore that was honest Dr. Partridge, my old friend; but, poor man, he is gone.—I beg your pardon, says another, you look so like my old acquaintance, that I used to consult on some private occasions: but, alack, he is gone the way of all flesh.—Look, look, look, cries a third, after a competent space of staring at me, would not one think our neighbour the almanack-maker was crept out of his grave to take the other peep at the stars in this world, and show how much he is improved in fortune-telling, by having taken a journey to the other?

Nay, the very reader of our parish, a good, sober, discreet person, has sent two or three times for me to come and be buried decently, or send him sufficient reasons to the contrary; or, if I have been interred in any other parish, to produce my certificate, as the act [1] requires. My poor wife is run almost distracted with being called widow Partridge, when she knows it is false; and once a term she is cited into the court to take out letters of administration. But the greatest grievance is, a paltry quack, that takes up my calling just under my nose, and in his printed directions, with N.B.—

---

[1] The statute of 30 Car. II. for burying in woollen, requires that oath shall be made of the compliance with this act, and a certificate thereof lodged with the minister of the parish within eight days after interment.

says, he lives in the house of the late ingenious Mr. John Partridge, an eminent practitioner in leather, physic, and astrology.

But to show how far the wicked spirit of envy, malice, and resentment can hurry some men, my nameless old persecutor had provided me a monument at the stone-cutter's, and would have erected it in the parish church; and this piece of notorious and expensive villainy had actually succeeded if I had not used my utmost interest with the vestry, where it was carried at last but by two voices, that I am alive. That stratagem failing, out comes a long sable elegy, bedecked with hour-glasses, mattocks, skulls, spades, and skeletons, with an epitaph as confidently written to abuse me and my profession as if I had been under ground these twenty years.

And after such barbarous treatment as this, can the world blame me, when I ask, what is become of the freedom of an Englishman? and where is the liberty and property that my old glorious friend came over to assert? we have drove popery out of the nation, and sent slavery to foreign climes. The arts only remain in bondage, when a man of science and character shall be openly insulted, in the midst of the many useful services he is daily paying the public. Was it ever heard, even in Turkey or Algiers, that a state astrologer was bantered out of his life by an ignorant impostor, or bawled out of the world by a pack of villainous deep-mouthed hawkers? though I print almanacks, and publish advertisements; though I produce certificates under the minister's and churchwardens' hands that I am alive, and attest the same on oath at quarter-sessions, out comes a full and true relation of the death and interment of John Partridge; truth is bore down, attestations neglected, the testimony of sober persons despised, and a man is looked upon by his neighbours as if he had been seven years dead, and is buried alive in the midst of his friends and acquaintance.

Now, can any man of common sense think it consistent with the honour of my profession, and not much beneath the dignity of a philosopher, to stand bawling before his own door—Alive! alive! ho! the famous Dr. Partridge! no counterfeit, but all alive!——as if I had the twelve celestial monsters of the zodiac to show within, or was forced for a livelihood to turn retailer to May and Bartholomew fairs?

Therefore, if her majesty would but graciously be pleased to think a hardship of this nature worthy her royal consideration, and the next parliament, in their great wisdom, cast but an eye toward the deplorable case of their old philomath, that annually bestows his good wishes on them, I am sure there is one Isaac Bickerstaff, esq. would soon be trussed up for his bloody predictions, and putting good subjects in terror of their lives: and that henceforward to murder a man by way of prophecy, and bury him in a printed letter, either to a lord or commoner, shall as legally entitle him to the present possession of Tyburn as if he robbed on the highway or cut your throat in bed.

I shall demonstrate to the judicious that France and Rome are at the bottom of this horrid conspiracy against me; and that culprit aforesaid is a popish emissary, has paid his visits to St. Germain's, and is now in the measures of Louis XIV. That, in attempting my reputation, there is a general massacre of learning designed in these realms: and through my sides there is a wound given to all the Protestant almanack-makers in the universe. VIVAT REGINA.

VI.—A VINDICATION OF ISAAC BICKERSTAFF, ESQ.

AGAINST WHAT IS OBJECTED TO HIM BY MR. PARTRIDGE, IN HIS ALMANACK FOR THE YEAR 1709

BY THE SAID ISAAC BICKERSTAFF, ESQ.

MR. PARTRIDGE has been lately pleased to treat me after a very rough manner, in that which is called his almanack for the present year: such usage is very indecent from one gentleman to another, and does not at all contribute to the discovery of truth, which ought to be the great end in all disputes of the learned. To call a man a fool and villain, an impudent fellow, only for differing from him in a point merely speculative, is, in my humble opinion, a very improper style for a person of his education. I appeal to the learned world, whether, in my last year's predictions, I gave him the least provocation for such unworthy treatment. Philosophers have differed in all ages; but the discreetest among them have always differed as became philosophers. Scurrility and passion, in a controversy among scholars, is just so much of nothing to the purpose, and at best a tacit confession of a weak cause: my concern is not so much for my own reputation as that of the republic of letters, which Mr. Partridge has endeavoured to wound through my sides. If men of public spirit must be superciliously treated for their ingenious attempts, how will true useful knowledge be ever advanced? I wish Mr. Partridge knew the thoughts which foreign universities have conceived of his ungenerous proceedings with me; but I am too tender of his reputation to publish them to the world. That spirit of envy and pride, which blasts so many rising geniuses in our nation, is yet unknown among professors abroad: the necessity of justifying myself will excuse my vanity, when I tell the reader that I have near a hundred honorary letters from several parts of Europe (some as far as Muscovy) in praise of my performance; besides several others, which, as I have been credibly informed, were opened in the post office, and never sent me. It is true, the inquisition in Portugal was pleased to burn my predictions, [this is fact,] and condemn the author and the readers of them; but I hope at the same time it will be considered, in how deplorable a state learning lies at present in that kingdom; and, with the profoundest veneration for crowned heads, I will presume to add, that it a little concerned his majesty of Portugal to interpose his authority in behalf of a scholar and a gentleman, the subject of a nation with which he is now in so strict an alliance. But the other kingdoms and states of Europe have treated me with more candour and generosity. If I had leave to print the Latin letters transmitted to me from foreign parts, they would fill a volume, and be a full defence against all that Mr. Partridge or his accomplices of the Portugal inquisition will be ever able to object, who, by the way, are the only enemies my predictions have ever met with at home or abroad. But I hope I know better what is due to the honour of a learned correspondence in so tender a point. Yet some of those illustrious persons will perhaps excuse me for transcribing a passage or two in my vindication.[1] The

----

[1] The quotations here inserted are in imitation of Dr. Bentley in some part of the famous controversy between him and Mr. Boyle.

most learned Monsieur Leibnitz thus addresses to me his third letter:—" *Illustrissimo Bickerstaffio astrologiæ instauratori,*" etc. Monsieur Le Clerc, quoting my predictions in a treatise he published last year, is pleased to say, " *Ita nu perrime Bickerstaffius, magnum illud Angliæ sidus.*" Another great professor, writing of me, has these words: " *Bickerstaffius, nobilis Anglus, astrologorum hujusce sæculi facile princeps.*" Signior Magliabecchi, the great duke's famous library-keeper, spends almost his whole letter in compliments and praises. It is true, the renowned professor of astronomy at Utrecht seems to differ from me in one article; but it is after the modest manner that becomes a philosopher; as, " *pace tanti viri dixerim :* " and, page 55, he seems to lay the error upon the printer (as indeed it ought), and says, " *vel forsan error typographi cum alioquin Bickerstaffius vir doctissimus,*"etc.

If Mr. Partridge had followed these examples in the controversy between us, he might have spared me the trouble of justifying myself in so public a manner. I believe no man is readier to own his errors than I, or more thankful to those who will please to inform him of them. But, it seems, this gentleman, instead of encouraging the progress of his own art, is pleased to look upon all attempts of that kind as an invasion of his province. He has been indeed so wise as to make no objection against the truth of my predictions, except in one single point relating to himself: and to demonstrate how much men are blinded by their own partiality, I do solemnly assure the reader, that he is the only person from whom I ever heard that objection offered, which consideration alone, I think, will take off all its weight.

With my utmost endeavours I have not been able to trace above two objections ever made against the truth of my last year's prophecies: the first was, of a Frenchman, who was pleased to publish to the world " that the Cardinal de Noailles was still alive, notwithstanding the pretended prophecy of Monsieur Biquerstaffe: " but how far a Frenchman, a Papist, and an enemy, is to be believed in his own cause, against an English Protestant, who is true to the government, I shall leave to the candid and impartial reader.

The other objection is the unhappy occasion of this discourse, and relates to an article in my predictions, which foretold the death of Mr. Partridge to happen on March 29, 1708.

This he is pleased to contradict absolutely in the almanack he has published for the present year, and in that ungentlemanly manner (pardon the expression) as I have above related. In that work he very roundly asserts, that he " is not only now alive, but was likewise alive upon that very 29th of March, when I had foretold he should die." This is the subject of the present controversy between us; which I design to handle with all brevity, perspicuity, and calmness. In this dispute I am sensible the eyes, not only of England, but of all Europe, will be upon us; and the learned in every country will, I doubt not, take part on that side where they find most appearance of reason and truth.

Without entering into criticisms of chronology about the hour of his death, I shall only prove that Mr. Partridge is not alive. And my first agrument is this: about a thousand gentlemen having bought his almanacks for this year, merely to find what he said against me, at every line they read they would lift up their eyes and cry out, betwixt rage and laughter, " they were sure no man alive ever writ such damned stuff as this." Neither did I ever hear that opinion disputed; so that Mr. Partridge lies under a dilemma, either of disowning his almanack, or allowing himself to be no man alive. Secondly, death is defined by all philosophers a separation of the soul and body. Now it is certain that the poor woman, who has best reason to know, has gone about for some time to every alley in the neighbourhood, and sworn to the gossips that her husband had neither life nor soul in him. Therefore, if an uninformed carcase walks still about, and is pleased to call itself Partridge, Mr. Bickerstaff does not think himself anyway answerable for that. Neither had the said carcase any right to beat the poor boy, who happened to pass by it in the street, crying, " A full and true account of Dr. Partridge's death ! " etc.

Thirdly, Mr. Partridge pretends to tell fortunes and recover stolen goods, which all the parish says he must do by conversing with the devil and other evil spirits, and no wise man will ever allow he could converse personally with either till after he was dead.

Fourthly, I will plainly prove him to be dead, out of his own almanack for this year, and from the very passage which he produces to make us think him alive. He there says, " he is not only now alive, but was also alive upon that very 29th of March which I foretold he should die on: " by this he declares his opinion that a man may be alive now who was not alive a twelvemonth ago. And, indeed, there lies the sophistry of his argument. He dares not assert he was alive ever since that 29th of March, but that he " is now alive, and was so on that day: " I grant the latter; for he did not die till night, as appears by the printed account of his death, in a letter to a lord; and whether he be since revived I leave the world to judge. This indeed is perfect cavilling, and I am ashamed to dwell any longer upon it.

Fifthly, I will appeal to Mr. Partridge himself whether it be probable I could have been so indiscreet to begin my predictions with the only falsehood that ever was pretended to be in them; and this in an affair at home, where I had so many opportunities to be exact; and must have given such advantages against me to a person of Mr. Partridge's wit and learning, who, if he could possibly have raised one single objection more against the truth of my prophecies, would hardly have spared me.

And here I must take occasion to reprove the above-mentioned writer of the relation of Mr. Partridge's death, in a letter to a lord, who was pleased to tax me with a mistake of four whole hours in my calculation of that event. I must confess, this censure, pronounced with an air of certainty, in a matter that so nearly concerned me, and by a grave, judicious author, moved me not a little. But though I was at that time out of town, yet several of my friends, whose curiosity had led them to be exactly informed, (for as to my own part, having no doubt at all in the matter, I never once thought of it,) assured me I computed to something under half an hour, which (I speak my private opinion) is an error of no very great magnitude that men should raise a clamour about it. I shall only say, it would not be amiss if that author would henceforth be more tender of other men's reputation as well as his own. It is well there were no more mistakes of that kind; if there had, I presume he would have told me of them with as little ceremony.

There is one objection against Mr. Partridge's death which I have sometimes met with, though indeed very slightly offered, that he still continues to write almanacks. But this is no more than what is common to all of that profession. Gadbury, Poor Robin, Dove, Wing, and several others do yearly publish their almanacks, though several of them have been dead since before the Revolution. Now, the natural reason of this I take to be, that, whereas it is the privilege of authors to live after their death, almanack-makers are alone excluded; because their dissertations, treating only upon the minutes as they pass, become useless as those go off. In consideration of which, Time, whose registers they are, gives them a lease in reversion, to continue their works after death.

I should not have given the public or myself the trouble of this vindication if my name had not been made use of by several persons to whom I never lent it; one of which, a few days ago, was pleased to father on me a new set of predictions. But I think these are things too serious to be trifled with. It grieved me to the heart, when I saw my labours, which had cost me so much thought and watching, bawled about by the common hawkers of Grub Street, which I only intended for the weighty consideration of the gravest persons. This prejudiced the world so much at first, that several of my friends had the assurance to ask me whether I were in jest? to which I only answered coldly, " that the event would show." But it is the talent of our age and nation to turn things of the greatest importance into ridicule. When the end of the year had verified all my predictions, out comes Mr. Partridge's almanack, disputing the point of his death; so that I am employed, like the general who was forced to kill his enemies twice over whom a necromancer had raised to life. If Mr. Partridge have practised the same experiment upon himself, and be again alive, long may he continue so; that does not the least contradict my veracity; but I think I have clearly proved, by invincible demonstration, that he died, at farthest, within half an hour of the time I foretold, and not four hours sooner, as the above-mentioned author, in his letter to a lord, has maliciously suggested, with a design to blast my credit, by charging me with so gross a mistake.

VII.—A FAMOUS PREDICTION OF MERLIN, THE BRITISH WIZARD

WRITTEN ABOVE A THOUSAND YEARS AGO, AND RELATING TO THE YEAR 1709, WITH EXPLANATORY NOTES, BY T. N. PHILOMATH

LAST year was published a paper of Predictions, pretended to be written by one Isaac Bickerstaff, Esq., but the true design of it was to ridicule the art of astrology, and expose its professors as ignorant or impostors. Against this imputation Dr. Partridge has learnedly vindicated himself in his almanack for that year.

For a further vindication of this famous art, I have thought fit to present the world with the following prophecy. The original is said to be of the famous Merlin, who lived about a thousand years ago; and the following translation is two hundred years old, for it seems to be written near the end of Henry VII.'s reign. I found it in an old edition of Merlin's prophecies, imprinted at London by Johan Haukyns, in the year 1530, page 39. I set it down word for word in the old orthography, and shall take leave to subjoin a few explanatory notes:—

Seven and Ten addyd to nine,
Of Fraunce her Woe this is the Sygne,
Tamys Rivere twys y-frozen,
Walke sans wetyng Shoes ne Hozen.
Then comyth foorthe, Ich understonde,
From Towne of Stoffe to fattyn Londe,
An Herdie Chyftan, Woe the Morne
To Fraunce, that ever he was born.
Then shall the Fyshe beweyle his Bosse;
Nor shall grin Berrys make up the Losse.
Yonge Symnele shall again miscarrye:
And Norways Pryd again shall marry.
And from the Tree where Blossums feele,
Ripe Fruit shall come, and all is wele,
Reaums shall daunce honde in honde,

And it shall be merrye in old Jnglonde,
Then old Jnglonde shall be no more,
And no man shall be sorie therefore.
Geryon shall have three hedes agayne,
Till Hapsburge makyth them but twayne

EXPLANATORY NOTES

Seven and Ten, etc. This line describes the year when these events shall happen. Seven and ten make seventeen, which I explain seventeen hundred, and this number added to nine, makes the year we are now in; for it must be understood of the natural year, which begins the first of January.

Tamys Rivere twys, etc. The River Thames frozen twice in one year, so as men to walk on it, is a very signal accident, which perhaps hath not fallen out for several hundred years before, and is the reason why some astrologers have thought that this prophecy could never be fulfilled, because they imagined such a thing would never happen in our climate.

From Towne of Stoffe, etc. This is a plain designation of the Duke of Marlborough; one kind of stuff used to fatten and is called marle, and everybody knows that borough is a name for a town; and this way of expression is after the usual dark manner of old astrological predictions.

Then shall the Fyshe, etc. By the fish is understood the Dauphin of France, as their kings' eldest sons are called; it is here said he shall lament the loss of the Duke of Burgundy, called the Bosse, which is an old English word for hump-shoulder, or crook-back, as that duke is known to be; and the prophecy seems to mean that he should be overcome or slain. By the green berrys, in the next line, is meant the young Duke of Berry, the Dauphin's third son, who shall not have valour or fortune enough to supply the loss of his eldest brother.

Yonge Symnele, etc. By Symnele, is meant the pretended Prince of Wales, who, if he offers to attempt anything against England, shall miscarry, as he did before. Lambert Symnele is the name of a young man, noted in our histories for personating the son (as I remember) of Edward IV.

And Norways Pryd, etc. I cannot guess who is meant

by Norway's pride [Queen Anne]; perhaps the reader may, as well as the sense of the two following lines.

𝕽𝖊𝖆𝖚𝖒𝖘 𝖘𝖍𝖆𝖑𝖑, etc. Reaums, or, as the word is now, realms, is the old name for kingdoms: and this is a very plain prediction of our happy union, with the felicities that shall attend it. It is added that Old England shall be no more, and yet no man shall be sorry for it. And indeed, properly speaking, England is now no more, for the whole island is one kingdom, under the name of Britain.

𝕲𝖊𝖗𝖞𝖔𝖓 𝖘𝖍𝖆𝖑𝖑, etc. This prediction, though somewhat obscure, is wonderfully adapt. Geryon is said to have been a king of Spain, whom Hercules slew. It was a fiction of the poets, that he had three heads, which the author says he shall have again: that is, Spain shall have three kings, which is now wonderfully verified; for, beside the King of Portugal, which properly is part of Spain, there are now two rivals for Spain, Charles and Philip; but Charles being descended from the Count of Hapsburg, founder of the Austrian family, shall soon make those heads but two, by overturning Philip, and driving him out of Spain.

Some of these predictions are already fulfilled, and it is highly probable the rest may be in due time; and I think I have not forced the words, by my explication, into any other sense than what they will naturally bear. If this be granted, I am sure it must be also allowed, that the author (whoever he were) was a person of extraordinary sagacity; and that astrology, brought to such perfection as this, is by no means an art to be despised, whatever Mr. Bickerstaff, or other merry gentlemen, are pleased to think. As to the tradition of these lines having been writ in the original by Merlin, I confess I lay not much weight upon it; but it is enough to justify their authority, that the book whence I have transcribed them, was printed 170 years ago, as appears by the title-page. For the satisfaction of any gentleman, who may be either doubtful of the truth, or curious to be informed, I shall give order to have the very book sent to the printer of this paper, with directions to let anybody see it that pleases, because I believe it is pretty scarce.

HINTS TOWARD AN ESSAY ON CONVERSATION

I HAVE observed few obvious subjects to have been so seldom, or at least so slightly, handled as this; and indeed I know few so difficult to be treated as it ought, nor yet upon which there seems so much to be said.

Most things pursued by men for the happiness of public or private life, our wit or folly have so refined, that they seldom subsist but in idea; a true friend, a good marriage, a perfect form of government, with some others, require so many ingredients, so good in their several kinds, and so much niceness in mixing them, that for some thousands of years men have despaired of reducing their schemes to perfection: but in conversation it is, or might be, otherwise; for here we are only to avoid a multitude of errors, which, although a matter of some difficulty, may be in every man's power, for want of which it remains as mere an idea as the other. Therefore it seems to me, that the truest way to understand conversation, is to know the faults and errors to which it is subject, and from thence every man to form maxims to himself whereby it may be regulated, because it requires few talents to which most men are not born, or at least may not acquire, without any great genius or study. For nature has left every man a capacity of being agreeable, though not of shining in company; and there are a hundred men sufficiently qualified for both, who, by a very few faults that they might correct in half an hour, are not so much as tolerable.

I was prompted to write my thoughts upon this subject by mere indignation, to reflect that so useful and innocent a pleasure, so fitted for every period and condition of life, and so much in all men's power, should be so much neglected and abused.

And in this discourse it will be necessary to note those

errors that are obvious, as well as others which are seldomer observed, since there are few so obvious, or acknowledged, into which most men, some time or other, are not apt to run.

For instance: nothing is more generally exploded than the folly of talking too much; yet I rarely remember to have seen five people together, where some one among them has not been predominant in that kind, to the great constraint and disgust of all the rest. But among such as deal in multitudes of words, none are comparable to the sober deliberate talker, who proceeds with much thought and caution, makes his preface, branches out into several digressions, finds a hint that puts him in mind of another story, which he promises to tell you when this is done; comes back regularly to his subject, cannot readily call to mind some person's name, holding his head, complains of his memory; the whole company all this while in suspense; at length says, it is no matter, and so goes on. And, to crown the business, it perhaps proves at last a story the company has heard fifty times before; or, at best, some insipid adventure of the relater.

Another general fault in conversation is that of those who affect to talk of themselves: some, without any ceremony, will run over the history of their lives; will relate the annals of their diseases, with the several symptoms and circumstances of them; will enumerate the hardships and injustice they have suffered in court, in parliament, in love, or in law. Others are more dexterous, and with great art will lie on the watch to hook in their own praise: they will call a witness to remember they always foretold what would happen in such a case, but none would believe them; they advised such a man from the beginning, and told him the consequences, just as they happened; but he would have his own way. Others make a vanity of telling their faults; they are the strangest men in the world; they cannot dissemble; they own it is a folly; they have lost abundance of advantages by it; but if you would give them the world, they cannot help it; there is something in their nature that abhors insincerity and constraint; with many other insufferable topics of the same altitude.

Of such mighty importance every man is to himself, and ready to think he is so to others; without once making this easy and obvious reflection, that his affairs can have no more weight with other men, than theirs have with him; and how little that is he is sensible enough.

Where a company has met, I often have observed two persons discover, by some accident, that they were bred together at the same school or university; after which the rest are condemned to silence, and to listen while these two are refreshing each other's memory, with the arch tricks and passages of themselves and their comrades.

I know a great officer of the army who will sit for some time with a supercilious and impatient silence, full of anger and contempt for those who are talking; at length, of a sudden, demanding audience, decide the matter in a short dogmatical way; then withdraw within himself again, and vouchsafe to talk no more, until his spirits circulate again to the same point.

There are some faults in conversation which none are so subject to as the men of wit, nor ever so much as when they are with each other. If they have opened their mouths without endeavouring to say a witty thing, they think it is so many words lost: it is a torment to the hearers, as much as to themselves, to see them upon the rack for invention, and in perpetual constraint, with so little success. They must do something extraordinary in order to acquit themselves, and answer their character, else the standers-by may be disappointed, and be apt to think them only like the rest of mortals. I have known two men of wit industriously brought together in order to entertain the company, where they have made a very ridiculous figure, and provided all the mirth at their own expense.

I know a man of wit who is never easy but where he can be allowed to dictate and preside: he neither expects to be informed or entertained, but to display his own talents. His business is to be good company, and not good conversation; and therefore he chooses to frequent those who are content to listen, and profess themselves his admirers. And indeed the worst conversation I ever remember to have heard in my life was that at Will's coffee-house, where the wits (as they were called) used formerly to assemble; that is to say, five or six men who had writ plays, or at least prologues, or had share in a miscellany, came thither, and entertained one another with their trifling composures, in so important an air as if they had been the noblest efforts of human nature, or that the fate of kingdoms depended on them; and they were usually attended with an humble audience of young students from the inns of court, or the universities; who, at due distance, listened to these oracles, and returned home with great contempt for their law and philosophy, their heads filled with trash, under the name of politeness, criticism, and belles lettres.

By these means the poets, for many years past, were all overrun with pedantry. For, as I take it, the word is not properly used; because pedantry is the too frequent or unseasonable obtruding our own knowledge in common discourse, and placing too great a value upon it; by which definition, men of the court, or the army, may be as guilty of pedantry as a philosopher or a divine; and it is the same vice in women, when they are over copious upon the subject of their petticoats, or their fans, or their china. For which reason, although it be a piece of prudence, as well as good manners, to put men upon talking on subjects they are best versed in, yet that is a liberty a wise man could hardly take; because, beside the imputation of pedantry, it is what he would never improve by.

The great town is usually provided with some player, mimic, or buffoon, who has a general reception at the good tables; familiar and domestic with persons of the first quality, and usually sent for at every meeting to divert the company; against which I have no objection. You go there as to a farce or a puppetshow; your business is only to laugh in season, either out of inclination or civility, while this merry companion is acting his part. It is a business he has undertaken, and we are to suppose he is paid for his day's work. I only quarrel, when, in select and private meetings, where men of wit and learning are invited to pass an evening, this jester should be admitted to run over his circle of tricks, and make the whole company unfit for any other conversation, beside the indignity of confounding men's talents at so shameful a rate.

Raillery is the finest part of conversation; but, as it is our usual custom to counterfeit and adulterate whatever is too clear for us, so we have done with this, and turned it all into what is generally called repartee, or being smart; just as when an expensive fashion comes up, those who are not able to reach it, content themselves with some paltry imitation. It now passes for raillery to run a man down in discourse, to put him out of countenance, and make him ridiculous; sometimes to expose the defects of his person or understanding; on all which occasions, he is obliged not to be angry, to avoid the imputation of not being able to take a jest. It is admirable to observe one who is dexterous at this art, singling out a weak adversary, getting the laugh on his side, and then carrying all before him. The French, from whence we borrow the word, have a quite different idea of the thing, and so had we in the politer age of our fathers. Raillery was to say something that at first appeared a reproach or reflection, but, by some turn of wit, unexpected and surprising, ended always in a compliment, and to the advantage of the person it was addressed to. And surely one of the best rules in conversation is, never to say a thing which any of the company can reasonably wish we had rather left unsaid: nor can there anything be well more contrary to the ends for which people meet together, than to part unsatisfied with each other or themselves.

There are two faults in conversation, which appear very different, yet arise from the same root, and are equally blameable; I mean an impatience to interrupt others; and the uneasiness of being interrupted ourselves. The two chief ends of conversation are to entertain and improve those we are among, or to receive those benefits ourselves; which whoever will consider, cannot easily run into either of these two errors; because, when any man speaks in company, it is to be supposed he does it for his hearers' sake, and not his own; so that common discretion will teach us not to force their attention, if they are not willing to lend it; nor, on the other side, to interrupt him who is in possession, because that is in the grossest manner to give the preference to our own good sense.

There are some people whose good manners will not suffer them to interrupt you, but, what is almost as bad, will discover abundance of impatience, and lie upon the watch until you have done, because they have started something in their own thoughts, which they long to be delivered of. Meantime, they are so far from regarding what passes, that their imaginations are wholly turned upon what they have in reserve, for fear it should slip out of their memory; and thus they confine their invention, which might otherwise range over a hundred things full as good, and that might be much more naturally introduced.

There is a sort of rude familiarity, which some people, by practising among their intimates, have introduced into their general conversation, and would have it pass for innocent freedom or humour; which is a dangerous experiment in our northern climate, where all the little decorum and politeness we have are purely forced by art, and are so ready to lapse into barbarity. This, among the Romans, was the raillery of slaves, of which we have many instances in Plautus. It seems to have been introduced among us by Cromwell, who, by preferring the scum of the people, made it a court enter-tainment, of which I have heard many particulars; and, considering all things were turned upside down, it was reasonable and judicious: although it was a piece of policy found out to ridicule a point of honour in the other extreme, when the smallest word misplaced among gentlemen ended in a duel.

There are some men excellent at telling a story, and provided with a plentiful stock of them, which they can draw out upon occasion in all companies; and, considering how low conversation runs now among us, it is not altogether a contemptible talent; however, it is subject to two unavoid-able defects, frequent repetition, and being soon exhausted; so that, whoever values this gift in himself, has need of a good memory, and ought frequently to shift his company, that he may not discover the weakness of his fund; for those who are thus endued have seldom any other revenue, but live upon the main stock.

Great speakers in public are seldom agreeable in private conversation, whether their faculty be natural, or acquired by practice, and often venturing. Natural elocution, although it may seem a paradox, usually springs from a barrenness of invention, and of words; by which men who have only one stock of notions upon every subject, and one set of phrases to express them in, they swim upon the super-ficies, and offer themselves on every occasion; therefore men of much learning, and who know the compass of a language, are generally the worst talkers on a sudden, until much practice has inured and emboldened them; because they are confounded with plenty of matter, variety of notions and of words, which they cannot readily choose, but are perplexed and entangled by too great a choice; which is no disadvantage in private conversation; where, on the other side, the talent of haranguing is, of all others, most unsupportable.

Nothing has spoiled men more for conversation than the character of being wits; to support which they never fail of encouraging a number of followers and admirers, who list themselves in their service, wherein they find their accounts on both sides by pleasing their mutual vanity. This has given the former such an air of superiority, and made the latter so pragmatical, that neither of them are well to be endured. I say nothing here of the itch of dispute and contradiction, telling of lies, or of those who are troubled with the diseases called the wandering of the thoughts, so that they are never present in mind at what passes in discourse; for whoever labours under any of these possessions, is as unfit for conversation as a madman in Bedlam.

I think I have gone over most of the errors in conversation that have fallen under my notice or memory, except some that are merely personal, and others too gross to need exploding; such as lewd or profane talk; but I pretend only to treat the errors of conversation in general, and not the several subjects of discourse, which would be infinite. Thus we see how human nature is most debased, by the abuse of that faculty which is held the great distinction between men and brutes: and how little advantage we make of that, which might be the greatest, the most lasting, and the most innocent, as well as useful pleasure of life: in default of which we are forced to take up with those poor amusements of dress and visiting, or the more pernicious ones of play, drink, and vicious amours; whereby the nobility and gentry of both sexes are entirely corrupted, both in body and mind, and have lost all notions of love, honour, friendship, generosity: which, under the name of fopperies, have been for some time laughed out of doors.

This degeneracy of conversation, with the pernicious consequences thereof upon our humours and dispositions, has been owing, among other causes, to the custom arisen, for some time past, of excluding women from any share in our society, further than in parties at play, or dancing, or in the pursuit of an amour. I take the highest period of politeness in England (and it is of the same date in France) to have been the peaceable part of King Charles I.'s reign, and from what we read of those times, as well as from the accounts I have formerly met with from some who lived in that court, the methods then used for raising and cultivating conversation were altogether different from ours: several ladies, whom we find celebrated by the poets of that age, had assemblies at their houses, where persons of the best understanding, and of both sexes, met to pass the evenings in discoursing upon whatever agreeable subjects were occasionally started; and although we are apt to ridicule the sublime Platonic notions they had, or personated, in love and friendship, I conceive their refinements were grounded upon reason, and that a little grain of the romance is no ill ingredient to preserve and exalt the dignity of human nature, without which it is apt to degenerate into everything that is sordid, vicious, and low. If there were no other use in the conversation of ladies, it is sufficient that it would lay a restraint upon those odious topics of immodesty and indecencies, into which the rudeness of our northern genius is so apt to fall. And, therefore, it is observable in those sprightly gentlemen about the town, who are so very dexterous at entertaining a vizard mask in the park or the playhouse, that in the company of ladies of virtue and honour, they are silent and disconcerted, and out of their element.

There are some people who think they sufficiently acquit themselves, and entertain their company, with relating facts of no consequence, nor at all out of the road of such common incidents as happen every day; and this I have observed more frequently among the Scots than any other nation, who are very careful not to omit the minutest circumstance of time or place; which kind of discourse, if it were not a little relieved by the uncouth terms and phrases, as well as accent and gesture peculiar to that country, would be hardly tolerable. It is not a fault in company to talk much; but to continue it long is certainly one; for, if the majority of those who are got together be naturally silent or cautious, the conversation will flag, unless it be often renewed by one among them, who can start new subjects, provided he does not dwell upon them, that leave room for answers and replies.

A COMPLETE COLLECTION OF GENTEEL AND INGENIOUS CONVERSATION [*]

ACCORDING TO THE MOST POLITE MODE AND METHOD, NOW USED AT COURT, AND IN THE BEST COMPANIES OF ENGLAND

IN THREE DIALOGUES

By SIMON WAGSTAFF, Esq.

INTRODUCTION

As my life has been chiefly spent in consulting the honour and welfare of my country for more than forty years past, not without answerable success, if the world and my friends have not flattered me, so there is no point wherein I have so much laboured as that of improving and polishing all parts of conversation between persons of quality, whether they meet by accident or invitation, at meals, tea, or visits, mornings, noon, or evenings.

I have passed perhaps more time than any other man of my age and country in visits and assemblies, where the polite persons of both sexes distinguish themselves; and could not without much grief observe how frequently both gentlemen and ladies are at a loss for questions, answers, replies, and rejoinders. However, my concern was much abated when I found that these defects were not occasioned by any want of materials, but because those materials were not in every hand: for instance, one lady can give an answer better than ask a question; one gentleman is happy at a reply; another excels in a rejoinder: one can revive a languishing conversation by a sudden surprising sentence; another is more dex-

---

[*] Swift, referring to these Dialogues, said they were intended " to reduce the whole politeness, wit, humour, and style of England into a short system for the use of all persons of quality, and particularly the maids of honour."

terous in seconding; a third can fill up the gap with laughing, or commending what has been said: thus fresh hints may be started, and the ball of the discourse kept up.

But, alas! this is too seldom the case, even in the most select companies. How often do we see at court, at public visiting days, at great men's levees, and other places of general meeting, that the conversation falls and drops to nothing, like a fire without supply of fuel! This is what we all ought to lament; and against this dangerous evil I take upon me to affirm, that I have in the following papers provided an infallible remedy:—

It was in the year 1695, and the sixth of his late majesty king William III., of ever-glorious and immortal memory, who rescued three kingdoms from popery and slavery, when, being about the age of six-and-thirty, my judgment mature, of good reputation in the world, and well acquainted with the best families in Town, I determined to spend five mornings, to dine four times, pass three afternoons, and six evenings every week in the houses of the most polite families, of which I would confine myself to fifty; only changing as the masters or ladies died, or left the town, or grew out of vogue, or sunk in their fortunes, or (which to me was of the highest moment) became disaffected to the government; which practice I have followed ever since to this very day; except when I happened to be sick, or in the spleen upon cloudy weather; and except when I entertained four of each sex at my own lodgings once in a month, by way of retaliation.

I always kept a large table-book in my pocket; and as soon as I left the company I immediately entered the choicest expressions that passed during the visit: which, returning home, I transcribed in a fair hand, but somewhat enlarged; and had made the greatest part of my collection in twelve years, but not digested into any method, for this I found was a work of infinite labour, and what required the nicest judgment, and consequently could not be brought to any degree of perfection in less than sixteen years more.

Herein I resolved to exceed the advice of Horace, a Roman poet, which I have read in Mr. Creech's admirable translation, that an author should keep his works nine years in his closet before he ventured to publish them: and, finding that I still received some additional flowers of wit and language, although in a very small number, I determined to defer the publication, to pursue my design, and exhaust (if possible) the whole subject, that I might present a complete system to the world: for I am convinced, by long experience, that the critics will be as severe as their old envy against me can make them: I foresee they will object, that I have inserted many answers and replies, which are neither witty, humorous, polite, nor authentic; and have omitted others that would have been highly useful, as well as entertaining. But let them come to particulars, and I will boldly engage to confute their malice.

For these last six or seven years I have not been able to add above nine valuable sentences to enrich my collection: from whence I conclude that what remains will amount only to a trifle. However, if, after the publication of this work, any lady or gentleman, when they have read it, shall find the least thing of importance omitted, I desire they will please to supply my defects by communicating to me their discoveries; and their letters may be directed to Simon Wagstaff, Esq., at his lodgings next door to the Gloucester Head in St. James's Street, paying the postage. In return of which favour, I shall make honourable mention of their names in a short preface to the second edition.

In the meantime, I cannot but with some pride and much pleasure congratulate with my dear country, which has outdone all the nations of Europe, in advancing the whole art of conversation to the greatest height it is capable of reaching; and, therefore, being entirely convinced that the collection I now offer to the public is full and complete, I may at the same time boldly affirm, that the whole genius, humour, politeness, and eloquence of England are summed up in it; nor is the treasure small, wherein are to be found at least a thousand shining questions, answers, repartees, replies, and rejoinders, fitted to adorn every kind of discourse that an assembly of English ladies and gentlemen, met together for their mutual entertainment, can possibly want: especially when the several flowers shall be set off and improved by the speakers, with every circumstance of preface and circumlocution, in proper terms; and attended with praise, laughter, or admiration.

There is a natural involuntary distortion of the muscles,

which is the anatomical cause of laughter: but there is another cause of laughter, which decency requires, and is the undoubted mark of a good taste, as well as of a polite obliging behaviour; neither is this to be acquired without much observation, long practice, and sound judgment; I did therefore once intend, for the ease of the learner, to set down, in all parts of the following dialogues, certain marks, asterisks, or *nota benes* (in English, mark-wells) after most questions, and every reply or answer; directing exactly the moment when one, two, or all the company are to laugh: but, having duly considered that this expedient would too much enlarge the bulk of the volume, and consequently the price; and likewise that something ought to be left for ingenious readers to find out, I have determined to leave that whole affair, although of great importance, to their own discretion.

The reader must learn by all means to distinguish between proverbs and those polite speeches which beautify conversation; for, as to the former, I utterly reject them out of all ingenious discourse. I acknowledge, indeed, that there may possibly be found in this treatise a few sayings, among so great a number of smart turns of wit and humour as I have produced, which have a proverbial air; however, I hope it will be considered that even these were not originally proverbs, but the genuine productions of superior wits, to embellish and support conversation; whence, with great impropriety as well as plagiarism (if you will forgive a hard word), they have most injuriously been transferred into proverbial maxims; and therefore, in justice, ought to be resumed out of vulgar hands, to adorn the drawing-rooms of princes both male and female, the levees of great ministers, as well as the toilet and tea-table of the ladies.

I can faithfully assure the reader that there is not one single witty phrase in this whole collection which has not received the stamp and approbation of at least one hundred years, and how much longer it is hard to determine; he may therefore be secure to find them all genuine, sterling, and authentic.

But, before this elaborate treatise can become of universal use and ornament to my native country, two points, that will require much time and much application, are absolutely necessary.

For, first, whatever person would aspire to be completely witty, smart, humorous, and polite, must, by hard labour, be able to retain in his memory every single sentence contained in this work, so as never to be once at a loss in applying the right answers, questions, repartees, and the like immediately, and without study or hesitation.

And, secondly, after a lady or gentleman has so well overcome this difficulty as never to be at a loss upon any emergency, the true management of every feature, and almost of every limb, is equally necessary; without which an infinite number of absurdities will inevitably ensue. For instance, there is hardly a polite sentence in the following dialogues which does not absolutely require some peculiar graceful motion in the eyes, or nose, or mouth, or forehead, or chin, or suitable toss of the head, with certain offices assigned to each hand; and in ladies, the whole exercise of the fan, fitted to the energy of every word they deliver; by no means omitting the various turns and cadence of the voice, the twistings, and movements, and different postures of the body, the several kinds and gradations of laughter, which the ladies must daily practise by the looking-glass, and consult upon them with their waiting-maids.

My readers will soon observe what a great compass of real and useful knowledge this science includes; wherein, although nature, assisted by genius, may be very instrumental, yet a strong memory and constant application, together with example and precept, will be highly necessary. For these reasons I have often wished that certain male and female instructors, perfectly versed in this science, would set up schools for the instruction of young ladies and gentlemen therein.

I remember, about thirty years ago, there was a Bohemian woman, of that species commonly known by the name of gypsies, who came over hither from France, and generally attended ISAAC the dancing-master, when he was teaching his art to misses of quality; and while the young ladies were thus employed, the Bohemian, standing at some distance, but full in their sight, acted before them all proper airs, and heavings of the head, and motion of the hand, and twistings of the body; whereof you may still observe the good effects in several of our elder ladies.

After the same manner, it were much to be desired that some expert gentlewomen gone to decay would set up public schools, wherein young girls of quality or great fortunes might first be taught to repeat this following system of conversation, which I have been at so much pains to compile; and then to adapt every feature of their countenances, every turn of their hands, every screwing of their bodies, every exercise of their fans, to the humour of the sentences they hear or deliver in conversation. But, above all, to instruct them in every species and degree of laughing in the proper seasons, at their own wit or that of the company. And if the sons of the nobility and gentry, instead of being sent to common schools, or put into the hands of tutors at home, to learn nothing but words, were consigned to able instructors in the same art, I cannot find what use there could be of books, except in the hands of those who are to make learning their trade, which is below the dignity of persons born to titles or estates.

It would be another infinite advantage, that, by cultivating this science, we should wholly avoid the vexations and impertinence of pedants, who affect to talk in a language not to be understood; and whenever a polite person offers accidentally to use any of their jargon terms, have the presumption to laugh at us for pronouncing those words in a genteeler manner. Whereas I do here affirm that, whenever any fine gentleman or lady condescends to let a hard word pass out of their mouths, every syllable is smoothed and polished in the passage; and it is a true mark of politeness, both in writing and reading, to vary the orthography as well as the sound; because we are infinitely better judges of what will please a distinguishing ear, than those who call themselves scholars can possibly be; who, consequently, ought to correct their books and manner of pronouncing, by the authority of our example, from whose lips they proceed with infinitely more beauty and significancy.

But, in the meantime, until so great, so useful, and so necessary a design can be put in execution (which, considering the good disposition of our country at present, I shall not despair of living to see), let me recommend the following treatise to be carried about as a pocket companion by all gentlemen and ladies, when they are going to visit, or dine, or drink tea; or where they happen to pass the evening without cards, as I have sometimes known it to be the case upon disappointments or accidents unforeseen; desiring they would read their several parts in their chairs or coaches, to prepare themselves for every kind of conversation that can possibly happen.

Although I have, in justice to my country, allowed the genius of our people to excel that of any other nation upon earth, and have confirmed this truth by an argument not to be controlled, I mean, by producing so great a number of witty sentences in the ensuing dialogues, all of undoubted authority, as well as of our own production, yet I must confess at the same time that we are wholly indebted for them to our ancestors; for, as long as my memory reaches, I do not recollect one new phrase of importance to have been added; which defect in us moderns I take to have been occasioned by the introduction of cant words in the reign of King Charles II. And those have so often varied, that hardly one of them, of above a year's standing, is now intelligible; nor anywhere to be found, excepting a small number strewed here and there in the comedies, and other fantastic writings of that age.

The Honourable Colonel James Graham, my old friend and companion, did likewise, toward the end of the same reign, invent a set of words and phrases, which continued almost to the time of his death. But, as these terms of art were adapted only to courts and politicians, and extended little further than among his particular acquaintance (of whom I had the honour to be one), they are now almost forgotten.

Nor did the late D. of R—— and E. of E—— succeed much better, although they proceeded no further than single words· whereof, except bite, bamboozle, and one or two more, the whole vocabulary is antiquated.

The same fate has already attended those other town wits, who furnish us with a great variety of new terms, which are annually changed, and those of the late season sunk in oblivion. Of these I was once favoured with a complete list by the Right Honourable the Lord and Lady H——, with which I made a considerable figure one summer in the country; but returning up to Town in winter, and venturing to produce them again, I was partly hooted, and partly not understood.

The only invention of late years, which has any way contributed towards politeness in discourse, is that of abbreviating or reducing words of many syllables into one, by lopping off the rest. This refinement having begun about the time of the Revolution, I had some share in the honour of promoting it; and I observe, to my great satisfaction, that it makes daily advancements, and I hope in time will raise our language to the utmost perfection; although I must confess, to avoid obscurity, I have been very sparing of this ornament in the following dialogues.

But as for phrases invented to cultivate conversation, I defy all the clubs or coffee-houses in this town to invent a new one equal in wit, humour, smartness, or politeness to the very worst of my set, which clearly shows, either that we are much degenerated or that the whole stock of materials has been already employed. I would willingly hope, as I do confidently believe, the latter; because, having myself for several months racked my invention to enrich this treasure (if possible) with some additions of my own (which, however, should have been printed in a different character, that I might not be charged with imposing upon the public), and having shown them to some injudicious friends, they dealt very sincerely with me, all unanimously agreeing that mine were infinitely below the true old helps to discourse drawn up in my present collection, and confirmed their opinion with reasons, by which I was perfectly convinced, as will as ashamed of my great presumption.

But I lately met a much stronger argument to confirm me in the same sentiments; for, as the great Bishop Burnet of Salisbury informs us, in the preface to his admirable *History of his Own Times*, that he intended to employ himself in polishing it every day of his life (and indeed in its kind it is almost equally polished with this work of mine), so it has been my constant business, for some years past, to examine, with the utmost strictness, whether I could possibly find the smallest lapse in style or propriety through my whole collection, that, in emulation with the bishop, I might send it abroad as the most finished piece of the age.

It happened one day, as I was dining in good company of

both sexes, and watching, according to my custom, for new materials wherewith to fill my pocket-book, I succeeded well enough till after dinner, when the ladies retired to their tea, and left us over a bottle of wine. But I found we were not able to furnish any more materials that were worth the pains of transcribing: for the discourse of the company was all degenerated into smart sayings of their own invention, and not of the true old standard; so that, in absolute despair, I withdrew, and went to attend the ladies at their tea; whence I did then conclude, and still continue to believe, either that wine does not inspire politeness, or that our sex is not able to support it without the company of women, who never fail to lead us into the right way, and there to keep us.

It much increases the value of these apophthegms, that unto them we owe the continuance of our language for at least a hundred years; neither is this to be wondered at, because indeed, beside the smartness of the wit, and fineness of the raillery, such is the propriety and energy of expression in them all, that they never can be changed, but to disadvantage, except in the circumstance of using abbreviations; which, however, I do not despair in due time to see introduced, having already met them at some of the choice companies in Town.

Although this work be calculated for all persons of quality and fortune of both sexes, yet the reader may perceive, that my particular view was to the officers of the army, the gentlemen of the inns of court, and of both the universities; to all courtiers, male and female, but principally to the maids of honour; of whom I have been personally acquainted with two-and-twenty sets, all excelling in this noble endowment, till, for some years past, I know not how, they came to degenerate into selling of bargains and free-thinking; not that I am against either of these entertainments, at proper seasons, in compliance with company who may want a taste for more exalted discourse, whose memories may be short, who are too young to be perfect in their lessons, or (although it be hard to conceive) who have no inclination to read and learn my instructions. And, besides, there is a strong temptation for court ladies to fall into the two amusements above mentioned, that they may avoid the censure of affecting singularity against the general current and fashion of all about them: but, however, no man will pretend to affirm that either bargains or blasphemy, which are the principal ornaments of free-thinking, are so good a fund of polite discourse as what is to be met with in my collection. For, as to bargains, few of them seem to be excellent in their kind, and have not much variety, because they all terminate in one single point; and to multiply them would require more invention than people have to spare. And as to blasphemy or free-thinking, I have known some scrupulous persons of both sexes, who, by prejudiced education, are afraid of sprites. I must, however, except the maids of honour, who have been fully convinced by a famous court chaplain that there is no such place as hell.

I cannot, indeed, controvert the lawfulness of free-thinking, because it has been universally allowed that thought is free. But, however, although it may afford a large field of matter, yet in my poor opinion, it seems to contain very little of wit or humour, because it has not been ancient enough among us to furnish established authentic expressions: I mean such as must receive a sanction from the polite world before their authority can be allowed; neither was the art of blasphemy or free-thinking invented by the court, or by persons of great quality, who, properly speaking, were patrons rather than inventors of it; but first brought in by the fanatic faction toward the end of their power, and after the Restoration carried to Whitehall by the converted Rumpers, with very good reason, because they knew that King Charles II., from a wrong education, occasioned by the troubles of his father, had time enough to observe, that fanatic enthusiasm directly led to atheism, which agreed with the dissolute inclinations of his youth; and perhaps these principles were further cultivated in him by the French Huguenots, who have been often charged with spreading them among us; however, I cannot see where the necessity lies of introducing new and foreign topics for conversation, while we have so plentiful a stock of our own growth.

I have likewise, for some reasons of equal weight, been very sparing in double *entendres;* because they often put ladies upon affected constraints, and affected ignorance. In short they break, or very much entangle, the thread of discourse; neither am I master of any rules to settle the disconcerted countenances of the females in such a juncture; I can therefore only allow innuendoes of this kind to be delivered in whispers, and only to young ladies under twenty, who being in honour obliged to blush, it may produce a new subject for discourse.

Perhaps the critics may accuse me of a defect in my following system of polite conversation; that there is one great ornament of discourse, whereof I have not produced a single example; which indeed I purposely omitted, for some reasons that I shall immediately offer; and, if those reasons will not satisfy the male part of my gentle readers, the defect may be applied in some manner by an appendix to the second edition; which appendix shall be printed by itself, and sold for sixpence, stitched, and with a marble cover, that my readers may have no occasion to complain of being defrauded.

The defect I mean is, my not having inserted into the body of my book all the oaths now most in fashion for embellishing discourse, especially since it could give no offence to the clergy, who are seldom or never admitted to these polite assemblies. And it must be allowed, that oaths well chosen are not only very useful expletives to matter, but great ornaments of style.

What I shall here offer in my own defence upon this important article, will, I hope, be some extenuation of my fault.

First, I reasoned with myself, that a just collection of oaths, repeated as often as the fashion requires, must have enlarged this volume at least to double the bulk, whereby it would not only double the charge, but likewise make the volume less commodious for pocket carriage.

Secondly, I have been assured by some judicious friends, that themselves have known certain ladies to take offence (whether seriously or not) at too great a profusion of cursing and swearing, even when that kind of ornament was not improperly introduced, which, I confess, did startle me not a little, having never observed the like in the compass of my own several acquaintance, at least for twenty years past. However, I was forced to submit to wiser judgments than my own.

Thirdly, as this most useful treatise is calculated for all future times, I considered, in this maturity of my age, how great a variety of oaths I have heard since I began to study the world, and to know men and manners. And here I found it to be true, what I have read in an ancient poet:

> For, now-a-days, men change their oaths
> As often as they change their clothes.

In short, oaths are the children of fashion; they are in some sense almost annuals, like what I observed before of cant words; and I myself can remember about forty different sets. The old stock oaths, I am confident, do not amount to above forty-five, or fifty at most; but the way of mingling and compounding them is almost as various as that of the alphabet.

Sir JOHN PERROT was the first man of quality whom I find upon the record to have sworn by *God's wounds*. He lived in the reign of Queen Elizabeth, and was supposed to be a natural son of Henry VIII. who might also probably have been his instructor. This oath indeed still continues, and is a stock oath to this day; so do several others that have kept their natural simplicity; but infinitely the greater number has been so frequently changed and dislocated, that if the inventors were now alive, they could hardly understand them.

Upon these considerations, I began to apprehend that if I should insert all the oaths that are now current, my book would be out of vogue with the first change of fashion, and grow as useless as an old dictionary; whereas the case is quite otherwise with my collection of polite discourse; which, as I before observed, has descended by tradition for at least a hundred years, without any change in the phraseology. I therefore determined with myself to leave out the whole system of swearing, because both the male and female oaths are all perfectly well known and distinguished; new ones are easily learned, and with a moderate share of discretion, may be properly applied on every fit occasion. However, I must here, upon this article of swearing, most earnestly recommend to my male readers that they would please a little to study variety. For it is the opinion of our most refined swearers, that the same oath or curse cannot, consistently with true politeness, be repeated above nine times in the same company, by the same person, and at one sitting.

I am far from desiring or expecting that all the polite and

ingenious speeches contained in this work should, in the general conversation between ladies and gentlemen, come in so quick and so close as I have here delivered them. By no means: on the contrary, they ought to be husbanded better, and spread much thinner. Nor do I make the least question but that, by a discreet and thrifty management, they may serve for the entertainment of a whole year to any person who does not make too long, or too frequent visits in the same family. The flowers of wit, fancy, wisdom, humour, and politeness, scattered in this volume, amount to one thousand seventy and four. Allowing then to every gentleman and lady thirty visiting families (not insisting upon fractions), there will want but a little of a hundred polite questions, answers, replies, rejoinders, repartees and remarks, to be daily delivered fresh in every company for twelve solar months; and even this is a higher pitch of delicacy than the world insists on, or has reason to expect. But I am altogether for exalting this science to its utmost perfection.

It may be objected that the publication of my book may, in a long course of time, prostitute this noble art to mean and vulgar people; but I answer, that it is not so easy an acquirement as a few ignorant pretenders may imagine. A footman may swear, but he cannot swear like a lord. He can swear as often, but can he swear with equal delicacy, propriety, and judgment? No, certainly, unless he be a lad of superior parts, of good memory, a diligent observer, one who has a skilful ear, some knowledge in music, and an exact taste, which hardly fall to the share of one in a thousand among that fraternity, in as high favour as they now stand with their ladies. Neither has one footman in six so fine a genius as to relish and apply those exalted sentences comprised in this volume which I offer to the world. It is true, I cannot see that the same ill consequences would follow from the waiting-woman, who, if she had been bred to read romances, may have some small subaltern or second-hand politeness; and if she constantly attends the tea, and be a good listener, may, in some years, make a tolerable figure, which will serve, perhaps, to draw in the young chaplain or the old steward. But, alas! after all, how can she acquire those hundred graces, and motions, and airs, the whole military management of the fan, the contortions of every muscular motion in the face, the risings and fallings, the quickness and slowness of the voice, with the several turns and cadences; the proper juncture of smiling and frowning, how often and how loud to laugh, when to gibe and when to flout, with all the other branches of doctrine and discipline above recited?

I am, therefore, not under the least apprehension that this art will ever be in danger of falling into common hands, which requires so much time, study, practice, and genius before it arrives at perfection; and, therefore, I must repeat my proposal for erecting public schools, provided with the best and ablest masters and mistresses, at the charge of the nation.

I have drawn this work into the form of a dialogue, after the pattern of other famous writers in history, law, politics, and most other arts and sciences; and I hope it will have the same success: for who can contest it to be of greater consequence to the happiness of these kingdoms than all human knowledge put together? Dialogue is held the best method of inculcating any part of knowledge; and I am confident that public schools will soon be founded for teaching wit and politeness, after my scheme, to young people of quality and fortune. I have determined next session to deliver a petition to the House of Lords, for an act of parliament to establish my book as the standard grammar in all the principal cities of the kingdom, where this art is to be taught by able masters, who are to be approved and recommended by me; which is no more than Lilly obtained only for teaching words in a language wholly useless. Neither shall I be so far wanting to myself as not to desire a patent, granted, of course, to all useful projectors; I mean, that I may have the sole profit of giving a licence to every school to read my grammar for fourteen years.

The reader cannot but observe what pains I have been at in polishing the style of my book to the greatest exactness; nor have I been less diligent in refining the orthography, by spelling the words in the very same manner as they are pronounced by the chief patterns of politeness at court, at levees, at assemblies, at playhouses, at the prime visiting-places, by young templars, and by gentlemen-commoners of both universities, who have lived at least a twelvemonth in Town, and kept the best company. Of these spellings the public will meet with many examples in the following book.

For instance, *can't, han't, shan't, didn't, cou'dn't, wou'dn't, isn't, en't*, with many more; besides several words which scholars pretend are derived from Greek and Latin, but now pared into a polite sound by ladies, officers of the army, courtiers and templars, such as *jommetry* for *geometry, vardi* for *verdict, lard* for *lord, learnen* for *learning;* together with some abbreviations exquisitely refined; as *pozz* for *positive; mob* for *mobile; phizz* for *physiognomy; rep* for *reputation; plenipo* for *plenipotentiary; incog* for *incognito; hypps,* or *hippo,* for *hypochondriacs; bam* for *bamboozle;* and *bamboozle* for *God knows what;* whereby much time is saved, and the high road to conversation cut short by many a mile.

I have, as it will be apparent, laboured very much, and, I hope, with felicity enough, to make every character in the dialogue agreeable with itself to a degree, that whenever any judicious person shall read my book aloud, for the entertainment and instruction of a select company, he need not so much as name the particular speakers, because all the persons, throughout the several subjects of conversation, strictly observe a different manner peculiar to their characters, which are of different kinds; but this I leave entirely to the prudent and impartial reader's discernment.

Perhaps the very manner of introducing the several points of wit and humour may not be less entertaining and instructing than the matter itself. In the latter I can pretend to little merit; because it entirely depends upon memory, and the happiness of having kept polite company; but the art of contriving that those speeches should be introduced naturally, as the most proper sentiments to be delivered upon so great a variety of subjects, I take to be a talent somewhat uncommon, and a labour that few people could hope to succeed in, unless they had a genius particularly turned that way, added to a sincere, disinterested love of the public.

Although every curious question, smart answer, and witty reply be little known to many people, yet there is not one single sentence in the whole collection, for which I cannot bring most authentic vouchers, whenever I shall be called: and even for some expressions, which, to a few nice ears, may, perhaps, appear somewhat gross, I can produce the stamp of authority from courts, chocolate-houses, theatres, assemblies, drawing-rooms, levees, card-meetings, balls, and masquerades, from persons of both sexes, and of the highest titles next to royal. However, to say the truth, I have been very sparing in my quotations of such sentiments as seem to be over free; because, when I began my collection, such kind of converse was almost in its infancy, till it was taken into the protection of my honoured patronesses at court, by whose countenance and sanction it has become a choice flower in the nosegay of wit and politeness.

Some will perhaps object, that, when I bring my company to dinner, I mention too great a variety of dishes, not always consistent with the art of cookery, or proper for the season of the year; and part of the first course mingled with the second; besides a failure in politeness, by introducing a black pudding to a lord's table, and at a great entertainment; but, if I had omitted the black pudding, I desire to know what would have become of that exquisite reason given by Miss Notable for not eating it? the world, perhaps might have lost it for ever, and I should have been justly answerable for having left it out of my collection. I therefore cannot but hope, that such hypercritical readers will please to consider, my business was to make so full and complete a body of refined sayings as compact as I could, only taking care to produce them in the most natural and probable manner, in order to allure my readers into the very substance and marrow of this most admirable and necessary art.

I am heartily sorry, and was much disappointed to find, that so universal and polite an entertainment as cards, has hitherto contributed very little to the enlargement of my work. I have sat by many hundred times with the utmost vigilance, and my table-book ready, without being able, in eight hours, to gather matter for one single phrase in my book. But this, I think, may be easily accounted for, by the turbulence and justling of passions, upon the various and surprising turns, incidents, revolutions, and events of good and evil fortune, that arrive in the course of a long evening at play; the mind being wholly taken up, and the consequences of non-attention so fatal.

Play is supported upon the two great pillars of deliberation and action. The terms of art are few, prescribed by law and custom; no time allowed for digressions or trials of wit. Quadrille, in particular, bears some resemblance to a state of nature, which, we are told, is a state of war, wherein every woman is against every woman; the unions short, inconstant, and soon broke; the league made this minute without knowing the ally, and dissolved in the next. Thus, at the game of quadrille, female brains are always employed in stratagem, or their hands in action. Neither can I find that our art has gained much by the happy revival of masquerading among us; the whole dialogue in those meetings being summed up in one (sprightly, I confess, but) single question, and as sprightly an answer. "Do you know me?" "Yes, I do." And, "Do you know me?" "Yes, I do." For this reason I did not think it proper to give my readers the trouble of introducing a masquerade, merely for the sake of a single question, and a single answer; especially when, to perform this in a proper manner, I must have brought in a hundred persons together of both sexes, dressed in fantastic habits for one minute, and dismiss them the next.

Neither is it reasonable to conceive that our science can be much improved by masquerades, where the wit of both sexes is altogether taken up in contriving singular and humorous disguises; and their thoughts entirely employed in bringing intrigues and assignations of gallantry to a happy conclusion.

The judicious reader will readily discover that I make Miss Notable my heroine, and Mr. Thomas Neverout my hero. I have laboured both their characters with my utmost ability. It is into their mouths that I have put the liveliest questions, answers, repartees, and rejoinders, because my design was, to propose them both as patterns, for all young bachelors and single ladies to copy after. By which I hope very soon to see polite conversation flourish between both sexes, in a more consummate degree of perfection than these kingdoms have yet ever known.

I have drawn some lines of Sir John Linger's character, the Derbyshire knight, on purpose to place it in counterview or contrast with that of the other company, wherein I can assure the reader, that I intended not the least reflection upon Derbyshire, the place of my nativity. But my intention was only to show the misfortune of those persons who have the disadvantage to be bred out of the circle of politeness, whereof I take the present limits to extend no further than London and ten miles round; although others are pleased to confine it within the bills of mortality. If you compare the discourses of my gentlemen and ladies, with those of Sir John, you will hardly conceive him to have been bred in the same climate, or under the same laws, language, religion, or government; and, accordingly, I have introduced him speaking in his own rude dialect, for no other reason than to teach my scholars how to avoid it.

The curious reader will observe, that when conversation appears in danger to flag, which in some places I have artfully contrived, I took care to invent some sudden question, or turn of wit, to revive it; such as these that follow: " What! I think here's a silent meeting! Come, madam, a penny for your thought;" with several others of the like sort. I have rejected all provincial or country turns of wit and fancy, because I am acquainted with very few; but indeed chiefly, because I found them so much inferior to those at court, especially among the gentlemen-ushers, the ladies of the bedchamber, and the maids of honour; I must also add the hither end of our noble metropolis.

When this happy art of polite conversing shall be thoroughly improved, good company will be no longer pestered with dull, dry, tedious story-tellers, no brangling disputers; for a right scholar of either sex in our science, will perpetually interrupt them with some sudden surprising piece of wit, that shall engage all the company in a loud laugh; and if, after a pause, the grave companion resumes his thread in the following manner: " Well, but to go on with my story," new interruptions come from the left and the right, till he is forced to give over.

I have likewise made some few essays toward the selling of bargains, as well for instructing those who delight in that accomplishment as in compliance with my female friends at court. However, I have transgressed a little in this point, by doing it in a manner somewhat more reserved than is now practised at St. James's. At the same time, I can hardly allow this accomplishment to pass properly for a branch of that perfect polite conversation which makes the constituent subject of my treatise; and for this I have already given my reasons. I have likewise, for further caution, left a blank in the critical point of each bargain, which the sagacious reader may fill up in his own mind.

As to myself, I am proud to own that, except some smattering in the French, I am what the pedants and scholars call a man wholly illiterate, that is to say, unlearned. But as to my own language, I shall not readily yield to many persons. I have read most of the plays and all the miscellany poems that have been published for twenty years past. I have read Mr. Thomas Brown's works entire, and had the honour to be his intimate friend, who was universally allowed to be the greatest genius of his age.

Upon what foot I stand with the present chief reigning wits, their verses recommendatory, which they have commanded me to prefix before my book, will be more than a thousand witnesses. I am, and have been, likewise particularly acquainted with Mr. Charles Gildon,[1] Mr. Ward,[2] Mr. Dennis, that admirable critic and poet, and several others. Each of these eminent persons (I mean those who are still alive) have done me the honour to read this production five times over, with the strictest eye of friendly severity, and proposed some, although very few amendments, which I gratefully accepted, and do here publicly return my acknowledgment for so singular a favour.

And I cannot conceal, without ingratitude, the great assistance I have received from those two illustrious writers, Mr. Ozell and Captain Stevens. These, and some others of distinguished eminence, in whose company I have passed so many agreeable hours, as they have been the great refiners of our language, so it has been my chief ambition to imitate them. Let the Popes, the Gays, the Arbuthnots, the Youngs, and the rest of that snarling brood, burst with envy at the praises we receive from the court and kingdom.

But to return from this digression.

The reader will find that the following collection of polite expressions will easily incorporate with all subjects of genteel and fashionable life. Those which are proper for morning tea will be equally useful at the same entertainment in the afternoon, even in the same company, only by shifting the several questions, answers, and replies, into different hands; and such as are adapted to meals will indifferently serve for

---

[1] A well-known hero of the *Dunciad*.
[2] Edward Ward, who wrote doggrel verses upon the political occurrences of the day.

dinners or suppers, only distinguishing between day-light and candle-light. By this method no diligent person of a tolerable memory can ever be at a loss.

It has been my constant opinion, that every man who is intrusted by nature with any useful talent of the mind, is bound by all the ties of honour and that justice which we all owe our country, to propose to himself some one illustrious action to be performed in his life for the public emolument: and I freely confess that so grand, so important an enterprise, as I have undertaken and executed to the best of my power, well deserved a much abler hand, as well as a liberal encouragement from the crown. However, I am bound so far to acquit myself, as to declare, that I have often and most earnestly entreated several of my above-named friends, universally allowed to be of the first rank in wit and politeness, that they would undertake a work so honourable to themselves, and so beneficial to the kingdom; but so great was their modesty, that they all thought fit to excuse themselves, and impose the task on me; yet in so obliging a manner, and attended with such compliments on my poor qualifications, that I dare not repeat. And at last their entreaties, or rather their commands, added to that inviolable love I bear to the land of my nativity, prevailed upon me to engage in so bold an attempt.

I may venture to affirm, without the least violation of modesty, that there is no man now alive who has, by many degrees, so just pretensions as myself to the highest encouragement from the crown, the parliament, and the ministry, toward bringing this work to due perfection. I have been assured, that several great heroes of antiquity were worshipped as gods, upon the merit of having civilised a fierce and barbarous people. It is manifest I could have no other intentions; and I dare appeal to my very enemies, if such a treatise as mine had been published some years ago, and with as much success as I am confident this will meet, I mean, by turning the thoughts of the whole nobility and gentry to the study and practice of polite conversation, whether such mean stupid writers as the Craftsmen, and his abettors, could have been able to corrupt the principles of so many hundred thousand subjects, as, to the shame and grief of every Whiggish, loyal, and true Protestant heart, it is too manifest they have done. For I desire the honest judicious reader to make one remark, that, after having exhausted the whole *in sickly pay-day* [1] (if I may so call it) of politeness and refinement, and faithfully digested it into the following dialogues, there cannot be found one expression relating to politics; that the ministry is never mentioned, nor the word king, above twice or thrice, and then only to the honour of his majesty; so very cautious were our wiser ancestors in forming rules for conversation, as never to give offence to crowned heads nor interfere with party-disputes in the state. And, indeed, although there seems to be a close resemblance between the two words politeness and politics, yet no ideas are more inconsistent in their natures. However, to avoid all appearance of disaffection, I have taken care to enforce loyalty by an invincible argument, drawn from the very fountain of this noble science, in the following short terms, that ought to be writ in gold,—" MUST is for the king: " which uncontrollable maxim I took particular care of introducing in the first page of my book, thereby to instil early the best Protestant loyal notions into the minds of my readers. Neither is it merely my own private opinion, that politeness is the firmest foundation upon which loyalty can be supported; for thus happily sings the divine Mr. Tibbalds, or Theobalds, in one of his birth-day poems:

> I am no schollard, but I am polite;
> Therefore be sure I am no Jacobite.

Hear, likewise, to the same purpose, that great master of the whole poetic choir, our most illustrious laureat, Mr. Colley Cibber:

> Who in his talk can't speak a polite thing
> Will never loyal be to George our king.

I could produce many more shining passages out of our principal poets of both sexes to confirm this momentous truth: whence I think it may be fairly concluded, that whoever can most contribute towards propagating the science contained in the following sheets through the kingdoms of Great Britain and Ireland, may justly demand all the favour that the wisest court and most judicious senate are able to confer

----

[1] This word is spelt by Latinists *Encyclopædia ;* but the judicious author wisely prefers the polite reading before the pedantic.

on the most deserving subject. I leave the application to my readers.

This is the work which I have been so hardy as to attempt, and without the least mercenary view. Neither do I doubt of succeeding to my full wish, except among the Tories and their abettors, who, being all Jacobites, and consequently Papists in their hearts, from a want of true taste, or by strong affectation, may perhaps resolve not to read my book, choosing rather to deny themselves the pleasure and honour of shining in polite company, among the principal geniuses of both sexes throughout the kingdom than adorn their minds with this noble art; and probably apprehending (as I confess nothing is more likely to happen), that a true spirit of loyalty to the Protestant succession should steal in along with it.

If my favourable and gentle readers could possibly conceive the perpetual watchings, the numberless toils, the frequent risings in the night, to set down several ingenious sentences that I suddenly or accidentally recollected, and which, without my utmost vigilance, had been irrecoverably lost for ever; if they would consider with what incredible diligence I daily and nightly attended at those houses where persons of both sexes, and of the most distinguished merit, used to meet and display their talents; with what attention I listened to all their discourses, the better to retain them in my memory, and then, at proper seasons, withdrew, unobserved, to enter them in my table-book, while the company little suspected what a noble work I had then in embryo: I say, if all these were known to the world, I think it would be no great presumption in me to expect, at a proper juncture, the public thanks of both houses of parliament for the service and honour I have done to the whole nation by my single pen.

Although I have never been once charged with the least tincture of vanity, the reader will, I hope, give me leave to put an easy question: What is become of all the King of Sweden's victories? where are the fruits of them at this day? or of what benefit will they be to posterity? Were not many of his greatest actions owing, at least in part, to fortune? were not all of them owing to the valour of his troops, as much as to his own conduct? Could he have conquered the Polish king, or the Czar of Muscovy, with his single arm? Far be it from me to envy or lessen the fame he has acquired;

but, at the same time, I will venture to say, without breach of modesty, that I, who have alone, with this right hand, subdued barbarism, rudeness, and rusticity, who have established and fixed for ever the whole system of all true politeness and refinement in conversation, should think myself most inhumanly treated by my countrymen, and would accordingly resent it as the highest indignity, to be put on a level, in point of fame, in after ages, with Charles XII. late King of Sweden.

And yet so incurable is the love of detraction, perhaps beyond what the charitable reader will easily believe, that I have been assured, by more than one credible person, how some of my enemies have industriously whispered about, that one Isaac Newton, an instrument-maker, formerly living near Leicester Fields, and afterwards a workman in the mint at the Tower, might possibly pretend to vie with me for fame in future times. The man, it seems, was knighted for making sun-dials better than others of his trade, and was thought to be a conjurer, because he knew how to draw lines and circles upon a slate, which nobody could understand. But adieu to all noble attempts for endless renown, if the ghost of an obscure mechanic shall be raised up to enter into competition with me, only for his skill in making pot-hooks and hangers with a pencil, which many thousand accomplished gentlemen and ladies can perform as well with pen and ink upon a piece of paper, and in a manner as little intelligible as those of Sir Isaac.

My most ingenious friend already mentioned, Mr. Colley Cibber, who does so much honour to the laurel crown he deservedly wears (as he has often done to many imperial diadems placed on his head), was pleased to tell me, that, if my treatise was shaped into a comedy,[1] the representation, performed to advantage on our theatre, might very much contribute to the spreading of polite conversation among all persons of distinction through the whole kingdom.

I own the thought was ingenious, and my friend's intention good: but I cannot agree to his proposal; for Mr. Cibber himself allowed that the subjects handled in my work being so numerous and extensive, it would be absolutely impossible for one, two, or even six comedies, to contain them: whence

[1] The proposal here stated in jest actually took place in Dublin.

it will follow, that many admirable and essential rules for polite conversation must be omitted.

And here let me do justice to my friend Mr. Tibbalds, who plainly confessed before Mr. Cibber himself, that such a project, as it would be a great diminution to my honour, so it would intolerably mangle my scheme, and thereby destroy the principal end at which I aimed, to form a complete body or system of this most useful science in all its parts: and therefore Mr. Tibbalds, whose judgment was never disputed, chose rather to fall in with my proposal, mentioned before, of erecting public schools and seminaries all over the kingdom, to instruct the young people of both sexes in this art, according to my rules, and in the method that I have laid down.

I shall conclude this long, but necessary introduction, with a request, or, indeed, rather a just and reasonable demand, from all lords, ladies and gentlemen, that while they are entertaining and improving each other with those polite questions, answers, repartees, replies, and rejoinders, which I have, with infinite labour and close application, during the space of thirty-six years, been collecting for their service and improvement, they shall, as an instance of gratitude, on every proper occasion, quote my name after this or the like manner: "Madam, as our Master Wagstaff says."—"My lord, as our friend Wagstaff has it." I do likewise expect that all my pupils shall drink my health every day at dinner and supper during my life, and that they, or their posterity, shall continue the same ceremony to my not inglorious memory, after my decease, for ever.

THE FIRST DIALOGUE

The Men.	*The Ladies.*
Lord SPARKISH.	Lady SMART.
Lord SMART.	Miss NOTABLE.
Sir JOHN LINGER.	Lady ANSWERALL.
Mr. NEVEROUT.	
Colonel ATWIT.	

ARGUMENT

LORD Sparkish and Colonel Atwit meet in the morning upon the Mall: Mr. Neverout joins them: they all go to breakfast at Lady Smart's. Their conversation over their tea: after which they part; but my lord and the two gentlemen are invited to dinner;—Sir John Linger invited likewise, and comes a little too late. The whole conversation at dinner: after which, the ladies retire to their tea. The conversation of the ladies without the men, who are supposed to stay and drink a bottle, but, in some time, go to the ladies, and drink tea with them. The conversation there. After which, a party at quadrille until three in the morning; but no conversation set down. They all take leave and go home.

ST. JAMES'S PARK

LORD SPARKISH *meeting* COL. ATWIT.

Col. WELL met, my lord.

Spark. Thank ye, colonel. A parson would have said, I hope we shall meet in heaven. When did you see Tom Neverout?

Col. He's just coming toward us. Talk of the devil—

NEVEROUT *comes up.*

Col. How do you do, Tom?

Never. Never the better for you.

Col. I hope you are never the worse: but pray where's your manners? Don't you see my Lord Sparkish?

Never. My lord, I beg your lordship's pardon.

Spark. Tom, how is it that you can't see the wood for trees? What wind blew you hither?

Never. Why, my lord, it is an ill wind blows nobody good; for it gives me the honour of seeing your lordship.

Col. Tom, you must go with us to Lady Smart's to breakfast.

Never. Must! why, colonel, must's for the king.

        [Col. offering, in jest, to draw his sword.

Col. Have you spoke with all your friends?

Never. Colonel, as you are stout be merciful.

Spark. Come, agree, agree; the law's costly.

        [Col. taking his hand from his hilt.

Col. Well, Tom, you are never the worse man to be afraid of me. Come along.

Never. What! do you think I was born in a wood, to be afraid of an owl? I'll wait on you. I hope Miss Notable will be there; 'egad, she's very handsome, and has wit at will.

Col. Why, every one as they like, as the good woman said when she kiss'd her cow.

        LORD SMART'S *House: they knock at the door;*
             the Porter comes out.

Spark. Pray are you the porter?

Porter. Yes, for want of a better.

Spark. Is your lady at home?

Porter. She was at home just now, but she's not gone out yet.

Never. I warrant this rogue's tongue is well hung.

          LADY SMART'S *Ante-chamber.*

    LADY SMART *and* LADY ANSWERALL *at the Tea-table.*

Lady S. My lord, your lordship's most humble servant.

Spark. Madam, you spoke too late; I was your ladyship's before.

Lady S. Oh! colonel, are you here?

Col. As sure as you're there, madam.

Lady S. O, Mr. Neverout! What, such a man alive!

Never. Ay, madam, alive, and alive like to be, at your ladyship's service.

Lady S. Well, I'll get a knife, and nick it down, that Mr. Neverout came to our house. And pray, what news, Mr. Neverout?

Never. Why, madam, Queen Elizabeth's dead.

Lady S. Well, Mr. Neverout, I see you are no changeling.

MISS NOTABLE *comes in.*

Never. Miss, your slave: I hope your early rising will do you no harm. I find you are but just come out of the cloth market.

Miss. I always rise at eleven, whether it be day or not.

Col. Miss, I hope you are up for all day.

Miss. Yes, if I don't get a fall before night.

Col. Miss, I heard you were out of order; pray how are you now?

Miss. Pretty well, colonel, I thank you.

Col. Pretty and well, miss! that's two very good things.

Miss. I mean I am better than I was.

Never. Why then 'tis well you were sick.

Miss. What! Mr. Neverout, you take me up before I'm down.

Lady S. Come, let us leave off children's play, and go to push-pin.

Miss. [*To Lady S.*] Pray, madam, give me some more sugar to my tea.

Col. O! miss, you must needs be very good humour'd, you love sweet things so well.

Never. Stir it up with the spoon, miss; for the deeper the sweeter.

Lady S. I assure you, miss, the colonel has made you a great compliment.

Miss. I am sorry for it; for I have heard say, complimenting is lying.

Lady S. [*To Sparkish.*] My lord, methinks the sight of you is good for sore eyes; if we had known of your coming, we should have strewn rushes for you: How has your lordship done this long time?

Col. Faith, madam, he's better in health than in good conditions.

Spark. Well, I see there's no worse friend than one brings from home with one; and I am not the first man has carried a rod to whip himself.

Never. Here's poor miss has not a word to throw at a dog. Come, a penny for your thought.

Miss. It is not worth a farthing; for I was thinking of you.

COLONEL *rising up.*

Lady S. Colonel, where are you going so soon? I hope you did not come to fetch fire.

Col. Madam, I must needs go home for half an hour.

Miss. Why, colonel, they say the devil's at home.

Lady A. Well, but sit while you stay, 'tis as cheap sitting as standing.

Col. No, madam, while I'm standing, I'm going.

Miss. Nay, let him go; I promise him we won't tear his clothes to hold him.

Lady S. I suppose, colonel, we keep you from better company, I mean only as to myself.

Col. Madam, I am all obedience.   [*Colonel sits down.*

Lady S. Lord, miss, how can you drink your tea so hot? sure your mouth's pav'd. How do you like this tea, colonel?

Col. Well enough, madam; but methinks it is a little more-ish.

Lady S. O! colonel, I understand you.—Betty, bring the cannister. I have but very little of this tea left; but I don't love to make two wants of one; want when I have it, and want when I have it not. He, he, he, he!   [*Laughs.*

Lady A. [*To the maid.*] Why, sure, Betty, you are bewitched; the cream is burnt too.

Betty. Why, madam, the bishop has set his foot in it.

Lady S. Go, run, girl, and warm some fresh cream.

Betty. Indeed, madam, there's none left; for the cat has eaten it all.

Lady S. I doubt it was a cat with two legs.

Miss. Colonel, don't you love bread and butter with your tea?

Col. Yes, in a morning, miss; for they say, butter is gold in a morning, silver at noon, but it is lead at night.

Never. Miss, the weather is so hot that my butter melts on my bread.

Lady A. Why, butter, I've heard 'em say, is mad twice a year.

Spark. [*To the maid.*] Mrs. Betty, how does your body politic?

Col. Fie, my lord, you'll make Mrs. Betty blush.

Lady S. Blush! ay, blush like a blue dog.

Never. Pray, Mrs. Betty, are you not Tom Johnson's daughter?

Betty. So my mother tells me, sir.

Spark. But, Mrs. Betty, I hear you are in love.

Betty. My lord, I thank God I hate nobody; I am in charity with all the world.

Lady S. Why, wench, I think thy tongue runs upon wheels this morning. How came you by that scratch upon your nose? Have you been fighting with the cats?

Col. [*To Miss.*] Miss, when will you be married?

Miss. One of these odd-come-shortly's, colonel.

Never. Yes; they say the match is half made; the spark is willing but miss is not.

Miss. I suppose the gentleman has got his own consent for it.

Lady A. Pray, my lord, did you walk through the Park in the rain?

Spark. Yes, madam, we were neither sugar nor salt; we were not afraid the rain would melt us. He, he, he! [*Laughs.*

Col. It rained, and the sun shone at the same time.

Never. Why, then the devil was beating his wife behind the door with a shoulder of mutton. [*Laughs.*

Col. A blind man would be glad to see that.

Lady S. Mr. Neverout, methinks you stand in your own light.

Never. Ah! madam, I have done so all my life.

Spark. I'm sure he sits in mine. Pr'ythee, Tom, sit a little further; I believe your father was no glazier.

Lady S. Miss, dear girl, fill me out a dish of tea, for I'm very lazy.

MISS *fills a dish of tea, sweetens it, and then tastes it.*

Lady S. What, miss, will you be my taster?

Miss. No, madam; but they say 'tis an ill cook that can't lick her own fingers.

Never. Pray, miss, fill me another.

Miss. Will you have it now, or stay till you get it?

Lady A. But, colonel, they say you went to court last night very drunk; nay, I'm told for certain, you had been among the Philistines: no wonder the cat wink'd, when both her eyes were out.

Col. Indeed, madam, that's a lie.

Lady A. 'Tis better I should lie than you should lose your good manners: besides, I don't lie; I sit.

Never. O! faith, colonel, you must own you had a drop in your eye; when I left you, you were half seas over.

Spark. Well, I fear Lady Answerall can't live long, she has so much wit.

Never. No; she can't live, that's certain; but she may linger thirty or forty years.

Miss. Live long! ay, longer than a cat or a dog, or a better thing.

Lady A. O! miss, you must give your vardi too!

Spark. Miss, shall I fill you another dish of tea?

Miss. Indeed, my lord, I have drank enough.

Spark. Come, it will do you more good than a month's fasting; here, take it.

Miss. No, I thank your lordship; enough's as good as a feast.

Spark. Well; but if you always say no, you'll never be married.

Lady A. Do, my lord, give her a dish; for they say maids will say no, and take it.

Spark. Well; and I dare say miss is a maid, in thought, word and deed.

Never. I would not take my oath of that.

Miss. Pray, sir, speak for yourself.

Lady S. Fie, miss; they say maids should be seen and not heard.

Lady A. Good miss, stir the fire, that the teakettle may boil.—You have done it very well: now it burns purely. Well, miss, you'll have a cheerful husband.

Miss. Indeed, your ladyship could have stirred it much better.

Lady A. I know that very well, hussy; but I won't keep a dog and bark myself.

Never. What! you are stuck [*sick*], miss.

Miss. Not at all; for her ladyship meant you.

Never. O! faith, miss, you are in Lob's pound; get out as you can.

Miss. I won't quarrel with my bread and butter for all that; I know when I'm well.

Lady A. Well; but, miss—

Never. Ah! dear madam, let the matter fall; take pity on poor miss; don't throw water on a drowned rat.

Miss. Indeed, Mr. Neverout, you should be cut for the simples this morning; say a word more and you had as good eat your nails.

Spark. Pray, miss, will you be so good as to favour us with a song?

Miss. Indeed, my lord, I can't; for I have a great cold.

Col. O! miss, they say all good singers have colds.

Spark. Pray, madam, does not miss sing very well?

Lady A. She sings, as one may say, my lord.

Miss. I hear Mr. Neverout has a very good voice.

Col. Yes, Tom sings well, but his luck's nought.

Never. Faith, colonel, you hit yourself a devilish box on the ear.

Col. Miss, will you take a pinch of snuff?

Miss. No, colonel, you must know that I never take snuff but when I am angry.

Lady A. Yes, yes, she can take snuff, but she has never a box to put it in.

Miss. Pray, colonel, let me see that box.

Col. Madam, there's never a C upon it.

Miss. Maybe there is, colonel.

Col. Ay, but May bees don't fly now, miss.

Never. Colonel, why so hard upon poor miss? Don't set your wit against a child. Miss, give me a blow, and I'll beat him.

Miss. So she prayed me to tell you.

Spark. Pray, my Lady Smart, what kin are you to Lord Pozz?

Lady S. Why, his grandmother and mine had four elbows.

Lady A. Well, methinks here's a silent meeting. Come, miss, hold up your head, girl; there's money bid for you.

[Miss starts.

Miss. Lord, madam, you frighten me out of my seven senses!

Spark. Well, I must be going.

Lady A. I have seen hastier people than you stay all night.

Col. [*To Lady Smart.*] Tom Neverout and I are to leap to-morrow for a guinea.

Miss. I believe colonel, Mr. Neverout can leap at a crust better than you.

Never. Miss, your tongue runs before your wit: nothing can tame you but a husband.

Miss. Peace! I think I hear the church-clock.

Never. Why, you know, as the fool thinks—

Lady S. Mr. Neverout, your handkerchief's fallen.

Miss. Let him set his foot on it, that it mayn't fly in his face.

Never. Well, miss—

Miss. Ay, ay; many a one says well that thinks ill.

Never. Well, miss, I'll think on this.

Miss. That's rhyme, if you take it in time.

Never. What! I see you are a poet.

Miss. Yes, if I had but the wit to show it.

Never. Miss, will you be so kind as to fill me a dish of tea?

Miss. Pray, let your betters be served before you; I'm just going to fill one for myself; and, you know, the parson always christens his own child first.

Never. But I saw you fill one just now for the colonel: well, I find kissing goes by favour.

Miss. But pray, Mr. Neverout, what lady was that you were talking with in the side-box last Tuesday?

Never. Miss, can you keep a secret?

Miss. Yes, I can.

Never. Well, miss, and so can I.

Col. Odd-so! I have cut my thumb with this cursed knife!

Lady A. Ay; that was your mother's fault, because she only warned you not to cut your fingers.

Lady S. No, no; 'tis only fools cut their fingers, but wise folks cut their thumbs.

Miss. I'm sorry for it, but I can't cry.

Col. Don't you think miss is grown?

Lady A. Ay, ill weeds grow apace.

A puff of smoke comes down the chimney.

Lady A. Lord, madam, does your ladyship's chimney smoke?

Col. No, madam; but they say smoke always pursues the fair, and your ladyship sat nearest.

Lady S. Madam, do you love bohea tea?

Lady A. Why, madam, I must confess I do love it, but it does not love me.

Miss. [*To Lady Smart.*] Indeed, madam, your ladyship is very sparing of your tea; I protest, the last I took was no more than water bewitch'd.

Col. Pray, miss, if I may be so bold, what lover gave you that fine etui?

Miss. Don't you know?—then keep counsel.

Lady A. I'll tell you, colonel, who gave it her: it was the best lover she will ever have while she lives—her own dear papa.

Never. Methinks, miss, I don't much like the colour of that ribbon.

Miss. Why, then, Mr. Neverout, do you see, if you don't much like it, you may look off it.

Spark. I don't doubt, madam, but your ladyship has heard that Sir John Brisk has got an employment at court.

Lady S. Yes, yes; and I warrant he thinks himself no small fool now.

Never. Yes, madam; I have heard some people take him for a wise man.

Lady S. Ay, ay; some are wise, and some are otherwise.

Lady A. Do you know him, Mr. Neverout?

Never. Know him! ay, as well as the beggar knows his dish.

Col. Well, I can only say that he has better luck than honester folks. But, pray, how came he to get this employment?

Spark. Why, by chance, as the man killed the devil.

Never. Why, miss, you are in a brown study: what's the matter? Methinks you look like Mumchance, that was hanged for saying nothing.

Miss. I'd have you to know, I scorn your words.

Never. Well, but scornful dogs will eat dirty puddings.

Miss. Well, my comfort is, your tongue is no slander. What! you would not have one be always on the high grin!

Never. Cry mapsticks, madam; no offence, I hope.

LADY SMART *breaks a teacup.*

Lady A. Lord, madam, how came you to break your cup?

Lady S. I can't help it, if I would cry my eyes out.

Miss. Why, sell it, madam, and buy a new one with some of the money.

Col. 'Tis folly to cry for spilt milk.

Lady S. Why, if things did not break, or wear out, how would tradesmen live?

Miss. Well, I am very sick, if anybody cared for it.

Never. Come, then, miss, e'en make a die of it, and then we shall have a burying of our own.

Miss. The devil take you, Neverout! besides all small curses.

Lady A. Marry, come up! What, plain Neverout! methinks you might have an M under your girdle, miss.

Lady S. Well, well, nought's never in danger. I warrant miss will spit in her hand, and hold fast.—Colonel, do you like this biscuit?

Col. I'm like all fools; I love everything that's good.

Lady S. Well, and isn't it pure good?

Col. 'Tis better than a worse.

Footman brings the COLONEL *a letter.*

Lady A. I suppose, colonel, that's a billet-doux from your mistress.

Col. 'Egad, I don't know whence it comes; but who'er writ it, writes a hand like a foot.

Miss. Well, you may make a secret of it, but we can spell, and put together.

Never. Miss, what spells b double uzzard?

Miss. Buzzard in your teeth, Mr. Neverout.

Lady S. Now you are up, Mr. Neverout, will you do me the favour to do me the kindness to take off the teakettle.

Spark. I wonder what makes these bells ring.

Lahy A. Why, my lord, I suppose, because they pull the ropes. [*Here all laugh.*

NEVEROUT *plays with a teacup.*

Miss. Now, a child would have cried half an hour before it would have found out such a pretty plaything.

Lady S. Well said, miss! I vow, Mr. Neverout, the girl is too hard for you.

Never. Ay; miss will say anything but her prayers, and those she whistles.

Miss. Pray, colonel, make me a present of that pretty penknife.

Spark. Ay, miss, catch him at that, and hang him.

Col. Not for the world, dear miss; it will cut love.

Spark. Colonel, you shall be married first; I was going to say that.

Lady S. Well, but, for all that, I can tell who is a great admirer of miss. Pray, miss, how do you like Mr. Spruce? I swear I have often seen him cast a sheep's eye out of a calf's head at you: deny it if you can.

Miss. O, madam, all the world knows that Mr. Spruce is a general lover.

Col. Come, miss, 'tis too true to make a jest on.

[*Miss blushes.*

Lady A. Well, however, blushing is some sign of grace.

Never. Miss says nothing; but I warrant she pays it off with thinking.

Miss. Well, ladies and gentlemen, you are pleased to divert yourselves; but, as I hope to be saved, there's nothing in it.

Lady S. Touch a gall'd horse, and he'll wince. Love will creep where it dare not go. I'd hold a hundred pound, Mr. Neverout was the inventor of that story; and, colonel, I doubt you had a finger in the pie.

Lady A. But, colonel, you forgot to salute miss when you came in; she said you had not been here a long time.

Miss. Fie, madam!—I vow, colonel, I said no such thing.— I wonder at your ladyship!

Col. Miss, I beg your pardon—

Goes to salute her; she struggles a little.

Miss. Well, I'd rather give a knave a kiss for once than be troubled with him; but, upon my word, you are more bold than welcome.

Lady S. Fie, fie, miss! for shame of the world, and speech of good people.

NEVEROUT *to* MISS, *who is cooking her tea and bread and butter.*

Never. Come, come, miss, make much of nought; good folks are scarce.

Miss. What! and you must come in with your two eggs a-penny, and three of them rotten.

Col. [*To Sparkish.*] But, my lord, I forgot to ask you how you like my new clothes?

Spark. Why, very well, colonel; only, to deal plainly with you, methinks the worst piece is in the middle.

[*Here a loud laugh, often repeated.*

Col. My lord, you are too severe on your friends.

Miss. Mr. Neverout, I'm hot, are you a sot?

Never. Miss, I'm cold, are you a scold? Take you that.

Lady S. I confess that was home. I find, Mr. Neverout, you won't give your head for the washing, as they say.

Miss. O! he's a sore man where the skin's off. I see Mr. Neverout has a mind to sharpen the edge of his wit on the whetstone of my ignorance.

Spark. Faith, Tom, you are struck! I never heard a better thing.

Never. Pray, miss, give me leave to scratch you for that fine speech.

Miss. Pox on your picture! it cost me a groat the drawing.

Never. [*To Lady S.*] 'Sbuds, madam, I have burnt my hand with your plaguy teakettle.

Lady S. Why, then, Mr. Neverout, you must say, God save the king.

Never. Did you ever see the like?

Miss. Never, but once at a wedding.

Col. Pray, miss, how old are you?

Miss. Why, I am as old as my tongue, and a little older than my teeth.

Spark. [*To Lady A.*] Pray, madam, is Miss Buxom married? I hear 'tis all over the town.

Lady A. My lord, she's either married or worse.

Col. If she ben't married, at least she's lustily promised. But is it certain that Sir John Blunderbuss is dead at last?

Spark. Yes, or else he's sadly wronged, for they have buried him.

Miss. Why, if he be dead, he'll eat no more bread.

Col. But, is he really dead?

Lady A. Yes, colonel, as sure as you're alive.

Col. They say he was an honest man.
Lady A. Yes, with good looking too.

Miss *feels a pimple on her face.*

Miss. Lord! I think my goodness is coming out. Madam, will your ladyship please to lend me a patch?
Never. Miss, if you are a maid, put your hand upon your spot.
Miss. There— [*Covering her face with both her hands.*
Lady S. Well, thou art a mad girl. [*Gives her a tap.*
Miss. Lord, madam, is that a blow to give a child?

Lady Smart *lets fall her handkerchief, and the* Colonel *stoops for it.*

Lady S. Colonel, you shall have a better office.
Col. O, madam, I can't have a better than to serve your ladyship. Madam, has your ladyship read the new play, written by a lord? It is called "Love in a Hollow Tree."
Lady S. No, colonel.
Col. Why, then your ladyship has one pleasure to come.

Miss *sighs.*

Never. Pray, miss, why do you sigh?
Miss. To make a fool ask, and you are the first.
Never. Why, miss, I find there is nothing but a bit and a blow with you.
Lady A. Why, you must know, miss is in love.
Miss. I wish my head may never ache till that day.
Spark. Come, miss, never sigh, but send for him.

Lady Smart *and* Lady Answerall *speaking together.*

If he be hanged, he'll come hopping; and if he be drown'd he'll come dropping.
Miss. Well, I swear you will make one die with laughing.

Miss *plays with a teacup, and* Neverout *plays with another.*

Never. Well, I see one fool makes many.
Miss. And you are the greatest fool of any.
Never. Pray, miss, will you be so kind to tie this string for me, with your fair hands? it will go all in your day's work.

Miss. Marry, come up, indeed! tie it yourself, you have as many hands as I; your man's man will have a fine office truly: come, pray stand out of my spitting-place.

Never. Well, but miss, don't be angry.

Miss. No; I was never angry in my life but once, and then nobody cared for it; so I resolved never to be angry again.

Never. Well; but if you'll tie it, you shall never know what I'll do for you.

Miss. So I suppose, truly.

Never. Well; but I'll make you a fine present one of these days.

Miss. Ay; when the devil's blind, and his eyes are not sore yet.

Never. No, miss, I'll send it you to-morrow.

Miss. Well, well; to-morrow's a new day; but, I suppose, you mean to-morrow come never.

Never. O! 'tis the prettiest thing: I assure you there came but two of them over in three ships.

Miss. Would I could see it, quoth blind Hugh. But why did you not bring me a present of snuff this morning?

Never. Because, miss, you never asked me: and 'tis an ill dog that's not worth whistling for.

Spark. [*To Lady A*.] Pray, madam, how came your ladyship, last Thursday, to go to that odious puppet-show?

Col. Why, to be sure, her ladyship went to see and to be seen.

Lady A. You have made a fine speech, colonel: pray, what will you take for your mouth-piece?

Spark. Take that, colonel: but, pray, madam, was my Lady Snuff there? They say she's extremely handsome.

Lady S. They must not see with my eyes that think so.

Never. She may pass muster well enough.

Lady A. Pray, how old do you take her to be?

Col. Why, about five or six-and-twenty.

Miss. I swear she's no chicken; she's on the wrong side of thirty, if she be a day.

Lady A. Depend upon it, she'll never see five-and-thirty, and a bit to spare.

Col. Why, they say she's one of the chief toasts in town.

Lady S. Ay, when all the rest are out of it.

Miss. Well; I wou'dn't be as sick as she's proud for all the world.

Lady A. She looks as if butter wou'dn't melt in her mouth; but, I warrant, cheese won't choke her.

Never. I hear my Lord What-d'ye-call-him is courting her.

Lady A. What lord d'ye mean, Tom?

Miss. Why, my lord, I suppose Mr. Neverout means the lord of the Lord knows what.

Col. They say she dances very fine.

Lady A. She did; but I doubt her dancing days are over.

Col. I can't pardon her for her rudeness to me.

Lady S. Well; but you must forget and forgive.

FOOTMAN comes in.

Lady S. Did you call Betty?

Footman. She's coming, madam.

Lady S. Coming! ay, so is Christmas.

BETTY comes in.

Lady S. Come, get ready my things. Where has the wench been these three hours?

Betty. Madam, I can't go faster than my legs will carry me.

Lady S. Ay, thou hast a head, and so has a pin. But, my lord, all the town has it that Miss Caper is to be married to Sir Peter Gibeall; one thing is certain, that she has promised to have him.

Spark. Why, madam, you know promises are either broken or kept.

Lady A. I beg your pardon, my lord; promises and pie-crust are made to be broken.

Lady S. Nay, I had it from my Lady Carrylie's own mouth. I tell you my tale and my tale's author; if it be a lie, you had it as cheap as I.

Lady A. She and I had some words last Sunday at church; but I think I gave her her own.

Lady S. Her tongue runs like the clapper of a mill; she talks enough for herself and all the company.

Never. And yet she simpers like a firmity kettle.

Miss *looking in a glass.*

Miss. Lord, how my head is dress'd to-day!

Col. O, madam! a good face needs no band.

Miss. No; and a bad one deserves none.

Col. Pray, Miss, where is your old acquaintance, Mrs. Wayward?

Miss. Why, where should she be? you must needs know, she's in her skin.

Col. I can answer that; what if you were as far out as she's in?——

Miss. Well, I promised to go this evening to Hyde Park on the water; but I protest I'm half afraid.

Never. Never fear, miss; you have the old proverb on your side, Naught's ne'er in danger.

Col. Why, miss, let Tom Neverout wait on you, and then, I warrant, you'll be as safe as a thief in a mill, for you know, he that's born to be hang'd will never be drown'd.

Never. Thank you, colonel, for your good word; but faith, if ever I hang, it shall be about a fair lady's neck.

Lady S. Who's there? Bid the children be quiet, and not laugh so loud.

Lady A. O! madam, let'm laugh, they'll ne'er laugh younger.

Never. Miss, I'll tell you a secret, if you'll promise never to tell it again.

Miss. No, to be sure; I'll tell it to nobody but friends and strangers.

Never. Why then, there's some dirt in my teacup.

Miss. Come, come, the more there's in't, the more there's on't.

Lady A. Poh! you must eat a peck of dirt before you die.

Col. Ay, ay; it goes all one way.

Never. Pray, miss, what's a clock?

Miss. Why, you must know, 'tis a thing like a bell, and you a fool that can't tell.

Never. [*To Lady A.*] Pray, madam, do you tell me; for I have let my watch run down.

Lady A. Why, 'tis half an hour past hanging time.

Col. Well; I'm like the butcher that was looking for his knife and had it in his mouth: I have been searching my pockets for my snuff-box, and, egad, here it is in my hand.

Miss. If it had been a bear, it would have bit you, colonel: well, I wish I had such a snuff-box.

Never. You'll be long enough before you wish your skin full of eyelet holes.

Col. Wish in one hand—

Miss. Out upon you: Lord, what can the man mean?

Spark. This tea is very hot.

Lady A. Why, it came from a hot place, my lord.

COLONEL *spills his tea.*

Lady S. That's as well done as if I had done it myself.

Col. Madam, I find you live by ill-neighbours, when you are forced to praise yourself.

Lady S. So they pray'd me to to tell you.

Never. Well, I won't drink a drop more; if I do 'twill go down like chopt hay.

Miss. Pray, don't say no, till you are asked.

Never. Well, what you please, and the rest again.

MISS, *stooping for a pin.*

Miss. I have heard 'em say, that a pin a-day is a groat a-year. Well, as I hope to be married, forgive me for swearing, I vow 'tis a needle.

Col. O! the wonderful works of nature, that a black hen should lay a white egg!

Never. What! you have found a mare's nest, and laugh at the eggs?

Miss. Pray keep your breath to cool your porridge.

Never. Miss, there was a very pleasant accident last night at St. James's Park.

Miss. [*To Lady S.*] What was it your ladyship was going to say just now?

Never. Well, miss; tell a mare a tale—

Miss. I find you love to hear yourself talk.

Never. Why, if you won't hear my tale, kiss my, etc.

Miss. Out upon you, for a filthy creature!

Never. What, miss! must I tell you a story and find you ears?

Spark. [*To Lady S.*] Pray, madam, don't you think Mrs. Spendall very genteel?

Lady S. Why, my lord, I think she was cut out for a gentlewoman, but she was spoil'd in the making: she wears her clothes as if they were thrown on her with a pitchfork; and, for the fashion, I believe they were made in the reign of Queen Bess.

Never. Well, that's neither here nor there; for, you know, the more careless the more modish.

Col. Well, I'd hold a wager there will be a match between her and Dick Dolt: and I believe I can see as far into a millstone as another man.

Miss. Colonel, I must beg your pardon a thousand times; but they say, an old ape has an old eye.

Never. Miss, what do you mean? you'll spoil the colonel's marriage if you call him old.

Col. Not so old, nor yet so cold—You know the rest, miss.

Miss. Manners is a fine thing, truly.

Col. Faith, miss, depend upon't, I'll give you as good as you bring: what! if you give a jest you must take a jest.

Lady S. Well, Mr. Neverout, you'll ne'er have done till you break that knife, and then the man won't take it again.

Miss. Why, madam, fools will be meddling; I wish he may cut his fingers. I hope you can see your own blood without fainting.

Never. Why, miss, you shine this morning like a sh—n barn door: you'll never hold out at this rate; pray save a little wit for to-morrow.

Miss. Well, you have said your say; if people will be rude, I have done; my comfort is, 'twill be all one a thousand years hence.

Never. Miss, you have shot your bolt: I find you must have the last word—Well, I'll go to the opera to-night.—No, I can't, neither, for I have some business—and yet I think I must, for I promised to squire the countess to her box.

Miss. The Countess of Puddledock, I suppose.

Never. Peace or war, miss?

Lady S. Well, Mr. Neverout, you'll never be mad, you are of so many minds.

As MISS *rises, the chair falls behind her.*

Miss. Well; I shan't be lady mayoress this year.

Never. No, miss, 'tis worse than that; you won't be married this year.

Miss. Lord! you make me laugh, though I an't well.

NEVEROUT, *as* MISS *is standing, pulls her suddenly on his lap.*

Never. Now, colonel, come sit down on my lap; more sacks upon the mill.

Miss. Let me go; ar'n't you sorry for my heaviness?

Never. No, miss; you are very light; but I don't say you are a light hussy.   Pray take up the chair for your pains.

Miss. 'Tis but one body's labour, you may do it yourself; I wish you would be quiet, you have more tricks than a dancing bear.

NEVEROUT *rises to take up the chair, and* MISS *sits in his.*

Never. You wouldn't be so soon in my grave, madam.

Miss. Lord! I have torn my petticoat with your odious romping; my rents are coming in; I'm afraid I shall fall into the ragman's hands.

Never. I'll mend it, miss.

Miss. You mend it! go, teach your grannam to suck eggs.

Never. Why, miss, you are so cross, I could find in my heart to hate you.

Miss. With all my heart; there will be no love lost between us.

Never. But pray, my Lady Smart, does not miss look as if she could eat me without salt?

Miss. I'll make you one day sup sorrow for this.

Never. Well, follow your own way, you'll live the longer.

Miss. See, madam, how well I have mended it.

Lady S. 'Tis indifferent, as Doll danced.

Never. 'Twill last as many nights as days.

Miss. Well, I knew it should never have your good word.

Lady S. My lord, my Lady Answerall and I was walking in the park last night till near eleven; 'twas a very fine night.

Never. Egad, so was I; and I'll tell you a comical accident; egad, I lost my understanding.

Miss. I'm glad you had any to lose.

Lady S. Well, but what do you mean?

Never. Egad, I kick'd my foot against a stone, and tore off the heel of my shoe, and was forced to limp to a cobbler in the Pall-Mall to have it put on. He, he, he, he! [*All laugh.*

Col. O! 'twas a delicate night to run away with another man's wife.

NEVEROUT *sneezes.*

Miss. God bless you! if you han't taken snuff.

Never. Why, what if I have, miss?

Miss. Why, then, the deuce take you!

Never. Miss, I want that diamond ring of yours.

Miss. Why, then, want's like to be your master.

NEVEROUT *looking at the ring.*

Never. Ay, marry, this is not only, but also; where did you get it?

Miss. Why, where 'twas to be had; where the devil got the friar.

Never. Well; if I had such a fine diamond ring, I wouldn't stay a day in England: but you know, far-fetch'd and dear bought is fit for ladies. I warrant, this cost your father $2\frac{1}{2}d$.

COLONEL *stretching himself.*

Lady S. Why, colonel, you break the king's laws; you stretch without a halter.

Lady A. Colonel, some ladies of your acquaintance have promised to breakfast with you, and I am to wait on them; what will you give us?

Col. Why, faith, madam, bachelor's fare: bread and cheese and kisses.

Lady A. Poh! what have you bachelors to do with your money, but to treat the ladies? you have nothing to keep but your own four quarters.

Lady S. My lord, has Captain Brag the honour to be related to your lordship?

Spark. Very nearly, madam; he's my cousin-german, quite removed.

Lady A. Pray, is he not rich?

Spark. Ay, a rich rogue, two shirts and a rag.

Col. Well, however, they say he has a great estate, but only the right owner keeps him out of it.

Lady S. What religion is he of?

Spark. Why, he is an Anythingarian.

Lady A. I believe he has his religion to choose, my lord.

NEVEROUT *scratches his head.*

Miss. Fie, Mr. Neverout, ar'n't you ashamed! I beg pardon for the expression, but I'm afraid your bosom friends are become your backbiters.

Never. Well, miss, I saw a flea once in your pinner, and a louse is a man's companion, but a flea is a dog's companion: however, I wish you would scratch my neck with your pretty white hand.

Miss. And who would be fool, then? I wou'dn't touch a man's flesh for the universe. You have the wrong sow by the ear, I assure you; that's meat for your master.

Never. Miss Notable, all quarrels laid aside, pray step hither for a moment.

Miss. I'll wash my hands, and wait on you, sir; but pray come hither, and try to open this lock.

Never. We'll try what we can do.

Miss. We!—what, have you pigs in your belly?

Never. Miss, I assure you I am very handy at all things.

Miss. Marry, hang them that can't give themselves a good word: I believe you may have an even hand to throw a louse in the fire.

Col. Well, I must be plain; here's a very bad smell.

Miss. Perhaps, colonel, the fox is the finder.

Never. No, colonel; 'tis only your teeth against rain: but——

Miss. Colonel, I find you would make a very bad poor man's sow.

COLONEL *coughing.*

Col. I have got a sad cold.

Lady A. Ay; 'tis well if one can get anything these hard times.

Miss. [*To Col.*] Choke, chicken, there's more a-hatching.

Lady S. Pray, colonel, how did you get that cold?

Spark. Why, madam, I suppose the colonel got it by lying a-bed barefoot.

Lady A. Why then, colonel, you must take it for better for worse, as a man takes his wife.

Col. Well, ladies, I apprehend you without a constable.

Miss. Mr. Neverout! Mr. Neverout! come hither this moment.

Lady S. [*Imitating her.*] Mr. Neverout! Mr. Neverout! I wish he were tied to your girdle.

Never. What's the matter? whose mare's dead now?

Miss. Take your labour for your pains; you may go back again, like a fool, as you came.

Never. Well, miss, if you deceive me a second time, 'tis my fault.

Lady S. Colonel, methinks your coat is too short.

Col. It will be long enough before I get another, madam.

Miss. Come, come; the coat's a good coat, and come of good friends.

Never. Ladies, you are mistaken in the stuff: 'tis half silk.

Col. Tom Neverout, you are a fool, and that's your fault.

A great noise below.

Lady S. Hey, what a clattering is here! one would think hell was broke loose.

Miss. Indeed, madam, I must take my leave, for I an't well.

Lady S. What! you are sick of the mulligrubs with eating chopped hay?

Miss. No, indeed, madam; I'm sick and hungry, more need of a cook than a doctor.

Lady A. Poor Miss! she's sick as a cushion; she wants nothing but stuffing.

Col. If you are sick, you shall have a caudle of calf's eggs.

Never. I can't find my gloves.

Miss. I saw the dog running away with some dirty thing a while ago.

Col. Miss, you have got my handkerchief; pray, let me have it.

Lady S. No; keep it, miss: for they say possession is eleven points of the law.

Miss. Madam, he shall never have it again; 'tis in huckster's hands.

Lady A. What! I see 'tis raining again.

Spark. Why, then, madam, we must do as they do in Spain.

Miss. Pray, my lord, how is that?

Spark. Why, madam, we must let it rain.

MISS *whispers Lady* SMART.

Never. There's no whispering, but there's lying.

Miss. Lord! Mr. Neverout, you are as pert as a pear-monger this morning.

Never. Indeed, miss, you are very handsome.

Miss. Poh! I know that already; tell me news.

Somebody knocks at the door.

FOOTMAN *comes in.*

Footman. [*To Col.*] An please your honour, there's a man below wants to speak to you.

Col. Ladies, your pardon for a minute.   [*Goes out.*

Lady S. Miss, I sent yesterday to know how you did, but you were gone abroad early.

Miss. Why, indeed, madam, I was hunch'd up in a hackney-coach with three country acquaintance, who called upon me to take the air as far as Highgate.

Lady S. And had you a pleasant airing?

Miss. No, madam; it rained all the time; I was jolted to death; and the road was so bad that I scream'd every moment, and called to the coachman, Pray, friend, don't spill us.

Never. So, miss, you were afraid that pride would have a fall.

Miss. Mr. Neverout, when I want a fool, I'll send for you.

Spark. Miss, didn't your left ear burn last night?

Miss. Pray why, my lord?

Spark. Because I was then in some company where you were extolled to the skies, I assure you.

Miss. My lord, that was more their goodness than my desert.

Spark. They said that you were a complete beauty.

Miss. My lord, I am as God made me.

Lady S. The girl's well enough, if she had but another nose.

Miss. O! madam, I know I shall always have your good word; you love to help a lame dog over the stile.

One knocks.

Lady S. Who's there? you're on the wrong side of the door; come in, if you be fat.

COLONEL *comes in again.*

Spark. Why, colonel, you are a man of great business.

Col. Ay, ay, my lord, I'm like my lord mayor's fool, full of business and nothing to do.

Lady S. My lord, don't you think the colonel's mightily fall'n away of late?

Spark. Ay, fall'n from a horseload to a cartload.

Col. Why, my lord, egad I am like a rabbit, fat and lean in four-and-twenty hours.

Lady S. I assure you, the colonel walks as straight as a pin.

Miss. Yes; he's a handsome-bodied man in the face.

Never. A handsome foot and leg; god-a-mercy shoe and stocking.

Col. What! three upon one! that's foul play: this would make a parson swear.

Never. Why, miss, what's the matter? you look as if you had neither won nor lost.

Col. Why, you must know, miss lives upon love.

Miss. Yes, upon love and lumps of the cupboard.

Lady A. Ay; they say love and pease-porridge are two dangerous things; one breaks the heart; and the other the belly.

Miss. [*Imitating Lady Answerall's tone.*] Very pretty! one breaks the heart, and the other the belly.

Lady A. Have a care; they say, mocking is catching.

Miss. I never heard that.

Never. Why, then, miss, you have a wrinkle——more than ever you had before.

Miss. Well; live and learn.

Never. Ay; and be hang'd and forget all.

Miss. Well, Mr. Neverout, take it as you please; but, I swear, you are a saucy Jack, to use such expressions.

Never. Why, then, miss, if you go to that, I must tell you there's ne'er a Jack but there's a Gill.

Miss. O! Mr. Neverout, everybody knows that you are the pink of courtesy.

Never. And, miss, all the world allows that you are the flower of civility.

Lady S. Miss, I hear there was a great deal of company where you visited last night: pray, who were they?

Miss. Why, there was old Lady Forward, Miss To-and-again, Sir John Ogle, my Lady Clapper, and I, quoth the dog.

Col. Was your visit long, miss?

Miss. Why, truly, they went all to the opera; and so poor pilgarlic came home alone.

Never. Alackaday, poor miss! methinks it grieves me to pity you.

Miss. What! you think you said a fine thing now; well, if I had a dog with no more wit, I would hang him.

Spark. Miss, if it is manners, may I ask which is oldest, you or Lady Scuttle?

Miss. Why, my lord, when I die for age, she may quake for fear.

Lady S. She's a very great gadder abroad.

Lady A. Lord! she made me follow her last week through all the shops like a Tantiny pig.

Lady S. I remember, you told me you had been with her from Dan to Beersheba.

COLONEL *spits.*

Col. Lord! I shall die; I cannot spit from me.

Miss. O! Mr. Neverout, my little countess has just litter'd; speak me fair, and I'll set you down for a puppy.

Never. Why, miss, if I speak you fair, perhaps I mayn't tell truth.

Spark. Ay, but, Tom, smoke that, she calls you puppy by craft.

Never. Well, miss, you ride the fore-horse to-day.

Miss. Ay, many a one says well, that thinks ill.

Never. Fie, miss; you said that once before; and, you know, too much of one thing is good for nothing.

Miss. Why, sure we can't say a good thing too often.

Spark. Well, so much for that, and butter for fish; let us call another cause. Pray, madam, does your ladyship know Mrs. Nice?

Lady S. Perfectly well, my lord; she's nice by name and nice by nature.

Spark. Is it possible she could take that booby, Tom Blunder, for love?

Miss. She had good skill in horse-flesh that could choose a goose to ride on.

Lady A. Why, my lord, 'twas her fate; they say, marriage and hanging go by destiny.

Col. I believe she'll ne'er be burnt for a witch.

Spark. They say, marriages are made in heaven; but I doubt, when she was married, she had no friend there.

Never. Well, she's got out of God's blessing into the warm sun.

Col. The fellow's well enough, if he had any guts in his brains.

Lady S. They say, thereby hangs a tale.

Spark. Why, he is a mere hobbledehoy, neither a man nor a boy.

Miss. Well, if I were to choose a husband, I would never be married to a little man.

Never. Pray, why so, miss? for they say, of all evils we ought to choose the least.

Miss. Because folks would say, when they saw us together, There goes the woman and her husband.

Col. [*To Lady Smart.*] Will your ladyship be on the Mall to-morrow night?

Lady S. No, that won't be proper; you know to-morrow's Sunday.

Spark. What then, madam! they say, the better day the better deed.

Lady A. Pray, Mr. Neverout, how do you like Lady Fruzz?

Never. Pox on her! She is as old as Poles (*St. Paul's Church*).

Miss. So will you be, if you ben't hanged when you're young.

Never. Come, miss, let us be friends: will you go to the Park this evening?

Miss. With all my heart, and a piece of my liver; but not with you.

Lady S. I'll tell you one thing, and that's not two; I am afraid I shall get a fit of the headache to-day.

Col. O! madam, don't be afraid! it comes with a fright.

Miss. [*To Lady Answerall.*] Madam, one of your ladyship's lappets is longer than t'other.

Lady A. Well, no matter; they that ride on a trotting horse, will ne'er perceive it.

Never. Indeed, miss, your lappets hang worse.

Miss. Well, I love a liar in my heart, and you fit me to a hair.

Miss *rises up.*

Never. Deuce take you, miss; you trod on my foot: I hope you don't intend to come to my bed-side.

Miss. In troth, you are afraid of your friends, and none of them near you.

Spark. Well said, girl! [*Giving her a chuck.*] Take that: they say a chuck under the chin is worth two kisses.

Lady A. But, Mr. Neverout, I wonder why such a handsome, straight young gentleman as you don't get some rich widow.

Spark. Straight! ay, straight as my leg, and that's crooked at knee.

Never. Faith, madam, if it rained such widows, none of them would fall upon me. Egad, I was born under a three-penny planet, never to be worth a groat.

Lady A. No, Mr. Neverout; I believe you were born with a caul on your head, you are such a favourite among the ladies: but what think you of widow Prim? she's immensely rich.

Never. Hang her! they say her father was a baker.

Lady S. Ay; but it is not, What is she? but, What has she? now-a-days.

Col. Tom, faith, put on a bold face for once, and have at the widow. I'll speak a good word for you to her.

Lady A. Ay; I warrant you'll speak one word for him and two for yourself.

Miss. Well, I had that at my tongue's end.

Lady A. Why, miss, they say good wits jump.

Never. Faith, madam, I had rather marry a woman I loved in her smock than widow Prim if she had her weight in gold.

Lady S. Come, come, Mr. Neverout, marriage is honourable, but housekeeping is a shrew.

Lady A. Consider, Mr. Neverout, four bare legs in a bed: and you are a younger brother.

Col. Well, madam, the younger brother is the better gentleman: however, Tom, I would advise you to look before you leap.

Spark. The colonel says true; besides, you can't expect to wive and thrive in the same year.

Miss. [*Shuddering.*] Lord! there's somebody walking over my grave.

Col. Pray, Lady Answerall, where was you last Wednesday; when I did myself the honour to wait on you? I think your ladyship is one of the tribe of Gad.

Lady A. Why, colonel, I was at church.

Col. Nay, then, I will be hang'd, and my horse too.

Never. I believe her ladyship was at a church with a chimney in it.

Miss. Lord, my petticoat! how it hangs by jommetry!

Never. Perhaps the fault may be in your shape.

Miss. [*Looking gravely.*] Come, Mr. Neverout, there's no jest like the true jest; but I suppose you think my back is broad enough to bear everything.

Never. Madam, I humbly beg your pardon.

Miss. Well, sir, your pardon's granted.

Never. Well, all things have an end, and a pudding has two, up-up-on me-my my word.   [*Stutters.*

Miss. What! Mr. Neverout, can't you speak without a spoon?

Spark. [*To Lady Smart.*] Has your ladyship seen the duchess since your falling out?

Lady S. Never, my lord, but once at a visit, and she looked at me as the devil looked over Lincoln.

Never. Pray, miss, take a pinch of my snuff.

Miss. What! you break my head, and give me a plaster; well, with all my heart; once and not use it.

Never. Well, miss, if you wanted me and your victuals, you'd want your two best friends.

Col. [*To Neverout.*] Tom, miss and you must kiss and be friends.

NEVEROUT *salutes* MISS.

Miss. Anything for a quiet life: my nose itch'd, and I knew I should drink wine, or kiss a fool.

Col. Well, Tom, if that ben't fair, hang fair.

Never. I never said a rude thing to a lady in my life.

Miss. Here's a pin for that lie; I'm sure liars had need of good memories. Pray, colonel, was not he very uncivil to me but just now?

Lady A. Mr. Neverout, if miss will be angry for nothing, take my counsel, and bid her turn the buckle of her girdle behind her.

Never. Come, Lady Answerall, I know better things; miss and I are good friends; don't put tricks upon travellers.

Col. Tom, not a word of the pudding, I beg you.

Lady S. Ah, colonel! you'll never be good, nor then neither.

Spark. Which of the goods d'ye mean? good for something, or good for nothing?

Miss. I have a blister on my tongue, yet I don't remember I told a lie.

Lady A. I thought you did just now.

Spark. Pray, madam, what did thought do?

Lady S. Well, for my life, I cannot conceive what your lordship means.

Spark. Indeed, madam, I meant no harm.

Lady S. No, to be sure, my lord! you are as innocent as a devil of two years old.

Never. Madam, they say ill-doers are ill-deemers; but I don't apply it to your ladyship.

Miss, mending a hole in her lace.

Miss. Well, you see I'm mending; I hope I shall be good in time. Look, Lady Answerall, is it not well mended?

Lady A. Ay, this is something like a tansy.

Never. Faith, miss, you have mended as a tinker mends a kettle; stop one hole and make two.

Lady S. Pray, colonel, are you not very much tann'd?

Col. Yes, madam; but a cup of Christmas ale will soon wash it off.

Spark. Lady Smart, does not your ladyship think Mrs. Fade is greatly altered since her marriage?

Lady A. Why, my lord, she was handsome in her time; but she cannot eat her cake and have her cake; I hear she's grown a mere otomy.

Lady S. Poor creature! the black ox has set his foot upon her already.

Miss. Ay; she has quite lost the blue on the plum.

Lady S. And yet, they say, her husband is very fond of her still.

Lady A. O, madam, if she would eat gold he would give it her.

Never. [*To Lady Smart.*] Madam, have you heard that Lady Queasy was lately at the playhouse incog.?

Lady S. What! Lady Queasy of all women in the world! do you say it upon rep.?

Never. Poz, I saw her with my own eyes; she sat among the mob in the gallery; her own ugly phiz: and she saw me look at her.

Col. Her ladyship was plaguily bamb'd; I warrant it put her into the hips.

Never. I smoked her huge nose, and egad, she put me in mind of the woodcock, that strives to hide his long bill, and then thinks nobody sees him.

Col. Tom, I advise you hold your tongue; for you'll never say so good a thing again.

Lady S. Miss, what are you looking for?

Miss. O, madam, I have lost the finest needle—

Lady A. Why, seek till you find it, and then you won't lose your labour.

Never. The loop of my hat is broke, how shall I mend it? [*He fastens it with a pin.*] Well, hang him, say I, that has no shift.

Miss. Ay, and hang him that has one too many.

Never. O, miss, I have heard a sad story of you.

Miss. I defy you, Mr. Neverout; nobody can say black's my eye.

Never. I believe you wish they could.

Miss. Well, but who was your author? Come, tell truth and shame the devil.

Never. Come then, miss; guess who it was that told me? come, put on your considering cap.

Miss. Well, who was it?

Never. Why, one that lives within a mile of an oak.

Miss. Well, go hang yourself in your own garters, for I'm sure the gallows groans for you.

Never. Pretty miss! I was but in jest.

Miss. Well, but don't let that stick in your gizzard.

Col. My lord, does your lordship know Mrs. Talkall?

Spark. Only by sight; but I hear she has a great deal of wit; and, egad, as the saying is, mettle to the back.

Lady S. So I hear.

Col. Why, Dick Lubber said to her t'other day, Madam, you can't cry bo to a goose: yes, but I can, said she: and, egad, cry'd bo full in his face. We all thought we should break our hearts with laughing.

Spark. That was cutting with a vengeance: and, prithee, how did the fool look?

Col. Look! egad, he look'd for all the world like an owl in an ivy-bush.

A Child comes in screaming.

Miss. Well, if that child was mine, I'd whip it till the blood came; peace, you little vixen! if I were near you I would not be far from you.

Lady S. Ay, ay! bachelors' wives and maids' children are finely tutor'd.

Lady A. Come to me, master, and I'll give you a sugar-plum. Why, miss, you forget that ever you was a child yourself. [*She gives the child a lump of sugar.*] I have heard 'em say, boys will long.

Col. My lord, I suppose you know that Mr. Buzzard has married again.

Lady S. This is his fourth wife; then he has been shod round.

Col. Why, you must know she had a month's mind to Dick Frontless, and thought to run away with him; but her parents forced her to take the old fellow for a good settlement.

Spark. So the man got his mare again.

Lady S. I'm told he said a very good thing to Dick; said he, You *think* us old fellows are fools; but we old fellows *know* young fellows are fools.

Col. I know nothing of that; but I know he's devilish old, and she's very young.

Lady A. Why, they call that a match of the world's making.

Miss. What if he had been young and she old?

Never. Why, miss, that would have been a match of the devil's making; but when both are young, that's a match of God's making.

MISS, *searching her pocket for a thimble, brings out a nutmeg.*

Never. O, miss, have a care; for if you carry a nutmeg in your pocket, you'll certainly be married to an old man.

Miss. Well, if I ever be married, it shall be to an old man: they always make the best husbands; and it is better to be an old man's darling than a young man's warling.

Never. Faith, miss, if you speak as you think, I'll give you my mother for a maid.

LADY SMART *rings the bell.*

FOOTMAN *comes in.*

Lady S. Harkee, you fellow; run to my Lady Match, and desire she will remember to be here at six to play at quadrille: d'ye hear, if you fall by the way, don't stay to get up again.

Foot. Madam, I don't know the house.

Lady S. That's not for want of ignorance; follow your nose; go, inquire among the servants.

FOOTMAN *goes out, and leaves the door open.*

Lady S. Here, come back, you fellow; why did you leave the door open? Remember, that a good servant must always come when he's called, do what he's bid, and shut the door after him.

The FOOTMAN *goes out again, and falls down stairs.*

Lady A. Neck or nothing; come down, or I'll fetch you down: well, but I hope the poor fellow has not saved the hangman a labour.

Never. Pray, madam, smoke miss yonder, biting her lips, and playing with her fan.

Miss. Who's that takes my name in vain?

She runs up to them, and falls down.

Lady S. What, more falling! do you intend the frolic should go round?

Lady A. Why, miss, I wish you may not have broke her ladyship's floor.

Never. Miss, come to me, and I'll take you up.

Spark. Well, but, without a jest, I hope, miss, you are not hurt.

Col. Nay, she must be hurt for certain; for you see her head is all of a lump.

Miss. Well, remember this, colonel, when I have money, and you have none.

Lady S. But, colonel, when do you design to get a house, and a wife, and a fire to put her in?

Miss. Lord! who would be married to a soldier, and carry his knapsack?

Never. O, madam: Mars and Venus, you know.

Col. Egad, madam, I'd marry to-morrow, if I thought I could bury my wife just when the honeymoon is over: but, they say, a woman has as many lives as a cat.

Lady A. I find the colonel thinks a dead wife under the table is the best goods in a man's house.

Lady S. O but, colonel, if you had a good wife, it would break your heart to part with her.

Col. Yes, madam; for they say, he that has lost his wife and sixpence, has lost a tester.

Lady S. But, colonel, they say, that every married man should believe there's but one good wife in the world, and that's his own.

Col. For all that, I doubt, a good wife must be bespoke; for there's none ready made.

Miss. I suppose the gentleman's a woman-hater; but, sir, I think you ought to remember that you had a mother: and pray, if it had not been for a woman where would you have been, colonel?

Col. Nay, miss, you cried whore first, when you talked of the knapsack.

Lady A. But I hope you won't blame the whole sex because some are bad.

Never. And they say he that hates woman, sucked a sow.

Col. O madam; there's no general rule without an exception.

Lady S. Then why don't you marry and settle?

Col. Egad, madam, there's nothing will settle me but a bullet.

Spark. Well, colonel, there's one comfort, that you need not fear a cannon-bullet.

Col. Why so, my lord?

Spark. Because they say, he was cursed in his mother's belly that was killed by a cannon-bullet.

Miss. I suppose the colonel was crossed in his first love, which makes him so severe on all the sex.

Lady A. Yes; and I'll hold a hundred to one that the colonel has been over head and ears in love with some lady that has made his heart ache.

Col. O, madam, we soldiers are admirers of all the fair sex.

Miss. I wish I could see the colonel in love till he was ready to die.

Lady S. Ay, but, I doubt few people die for love in these days.

Never. Well, I confess, I differ from the colonel; for I hope to have a rich and a handsome wife yet before I die.

Col. Ay, Tom; live, horse, and thou shalt have grass.

Miss. Well, colonel; but whatever you say against women, they are better creatures than men: for men were made of clay, but woman was made of man.

Col. Miss, you may say what you please; but faith you'll never lead apes in hell.

Never. No, no; I'll be sworn miss has not an inch of nun's flesh about her.

Miss. I understumble you, gentlemen.

Never. Madam, your humblecumdumble.

Spark. Pray, miss, when did you see your old acquaintance, Mrs. Cloudy? you and she are two, I hear.

Miss. See her! marry, I don't care whether I ever see her again! God bless my eyesight!

Lady A. Lord! why she and you were as great as two inkle-weavers. I've seen her hug you as the devil hugged the witch.

Miss. That's true; but I'm told for certain she's no better than she should be.

Lady S. Well, God mend us all; but you must allow the world is very censorious; I never heard that she was a naughty pack.

Col. [*To Neverout.*] Come, Sir Thomas, when the king pleases, when do you intend to march?

Spark. Have patience. Tom, is your friend Ned Rattle married?

Never. Yes, faith, my lord; he has tied a knot with his tongue that he can never untie with his teeth.

Lady S. Ah! marry in haste, and repent at leisure.

Lady A. Has he got a good fortune with his lady? for they say something has some savour, but nothing has no flavour.

Never. Faith, madam, all he gets by her he may put into his eye and see never the worse.

Miss. Then, I believe he heartily wishes her in Abraham's bosom.

Col. Pray, my lord, how does Charles Limber and his fine wife agree?

Spark. Why, they say he's the greatest cuckold in own.

Never. O but, my lord, you should always except my lord mayor.

Miss. Mr. Neverout!

Never. Hay, madam, did you call me?

Miss. Hay! why, hay is for horses.

Never. Why miss, then you may kiss—

Col. Pray, my lord, what's o'clock by your oracle?

Spark. Faith, I can't tell; I think my watch runs upon wheels.

Never. Miss, pray be so kind to call a servant to bring me a glass of small beer: I know you are at home here.

Miss. Every fool can do as they're bid: make a page of your own age, and do it yourself.

Never. Choose, proud fool; I did but ask you.

Miss *puts her hand upon her knee.*

Never. What, miss, are you thinking of your sweetheart? is your garter slipping down?

Miss. Pray, Mr. Neverout, keep your breath to cool your porridge; you measure my corn by your bushel.

Never. Indeed, miss, you lie—

Miss. Did you ever hear anything so rude?

Never. I mean, you lie—under a mistake.

Miss. If a thousand lies could choke you, you would have been choked many a day ago.

Miss *strives to snatch* Mr. Neverout's *snuff-box.*

Never. Madam, you missed that, as you missed your mother's blessing.

She tries again, and misses.

Never. Snap short makes you look so lean, miss.

Miss. Poh! you are so robustious, you had like to put out my eye; I assure you, if you blind me, you must lead me.

Lady S. Dear miss, be quiet; and bring me a pincushion out of that closet.

MISS *opens the closet door and squalls.*

Lady S. Lord bless the girl! what's the matter now?

Miss. I vow, madam, I saw something in black; I thought it was a spirit.

Col. Why, miss, did you ever see a spirit?

Miss. No, sir; I thank God I never saw anything worse than myself.

Never. Well, I did a very foolish thing yesterday, and was a great puppy for my pains.

Miss. Very likely; for they say, many a true word's spoken in jest.

FOOTMAN *returns.*

Lady S. Well, did you deliver your message? you are fit to be sent for sorrow, you stay so long by the way.

Foot. Madam, my lady was not at home, so I did not leave the message.

Lady S. This it is to send a fool of an errand.

Spark. [*Looking at his watch.*] 'Tis past twelve o'clock.

Lady S. Well, what is that among all us?

Spark. Madam, I must take my leave: come, gentlemen, are you for a march?

Lady S. Well, but your lordship and the colonel will dine with us to-day; and, Mr. Neverout, I hope we shall have your good company; there will be no soul else, beside my own lord and these ladies; for everybody knows I hate a crowd; I would rather want victuals than elbow-room; we dine punctually at three.

Spark. Madam, we'll be sure to attend your ladyship.

Col. Madam, my stomach serves me instead of a clock.

Another FOOTMAN *comes back.*

Lady S. Oh! you are the t'other fellow I sent; well, have you been with my Lady Club? you are good to send of a dead man's errand.

Foot. Madam, my Lady Club begs your ladyship's pardon: but she is engaged to-night.

Miss. Well, Mr. Neverout, here's the back of my hand to you.

Never. Miss, I find you will have the last word. Ladies, I am more yours than my own.

THE SECOND DIALOGUE

LORD SMART *and the former company at three o'clock coming to dine. After salutations.*

Smart. I'm sorry I was not at home this morning when you all did us the honour to call here; but I went to the levee to-day.

Spark. Oh! my lord; I am sure the loss was ours.

Lady S. Gentlemen and ladies, you are come to a sad dirty house; I am sorry for it, but we have had our hands in mortar.

Spark. Oh! madam; your ladyship is pleased to say so; but I never saw anything so clean and so fine; I profess it is a perfect paradise.

Lady S. My lord, your lordship is always very obliging.

Spark. Pray, madam, whose picture is that?

Lady S. Why, my lord, it was drawn for me.

Spark. I'll swear the painter did not flatter your ladyship.

Col. My lord, the day is finely cleared up.

Smart. Ay, colonel; 'tis a pity that fair weather should ever do any harm. [*To Neverout.*] Why, Tom, you are high in the mode.

Never. My lord, it is better to be out of the world than out of the fashion.

Smart. But, Tom, I hear you and miss are always quarrelling; I fear it is your fault; for I can assure you she is very good-humoured.

Never. Ay, my lord; so is the devil when he's pleased.

Smart. Miss, what do you think of my friend Tom?

Miss. My lord, I think he's not the wisest man in the world; and truly he's sometimes very rude.

Spark. That may be true; but yet, he that hangs Tom for a fool may find a knave in the halter.

Miss. Well, however, I wish he were hanged, if it were only to try.

Never. Well, miss, if I must be hanged, I won't go far to choose my gallows; it shall be about your fair neck.

Miss. I'll see your nose cheese first and the dogs eating it; but, my lord, Mr. Neverout's wit begins to run low; for, I vow, he said this before; pray, colonel, give him a pinch, and I'll do as much for you.

Spark. My Lady Smart, your ladyship has a very fine scarf.

Lady S. Yes, my lord; it will make a flaming figure in a country church.

FOOTMAN *comes in.*

Foot. Madam, dinner's upon the table.

Col. Faith, I am glad of it; my belly began to cry cupboard.

Never. I wish I may never hear worse news.

Miss. What! Mr. Neverout, you are in great haste; I believe your belly thinks your throat is cut.

Never. No, faith, miss; three meals a-day, and a good supper at night, will serve my turn.

Miss. To say the truth, I'm hungry.

Never. And I'm angry; so let us both go fight.

They go in to dinner, and, after the usual compliments, take their seats.

Lady S. Ladies and gentlemen, will you eat any oysters before dinner?

Col. With all my heart. [*Takes an oyster.*] He was a bold man that first ate an oyster.

Lady S. They say oysters are a cruel meat, because we eat them alive: then they are an uncharitable meat, for we leave nothing to the poor; and they are an ungodly meat, because we never say grace.

Never. Faith, that's as well said as if I had said it myself.

Lady S. Well, we are well set if we be but as well served: come, colonel, handle your arms; shall I help you to some beef?

Col. If your ladyship please; and pray, don't cut like a

mother-in-law, but send me a large slice: for I love to lay a good foundation. I vow, 'tis a noble sirloin.

Never. Ay; here's cut and come again.

Miss. But pray, why is it called a sirloin?

Smart. Why you must know, that our king James I., who loved good eating, being invited to dinner by one of his nobles, and seeing a large loin of beef at his table, he drew out his sword, and in a frolic knighted it. Few people know the secret of this.

Spark. Beef is man's meat, my lord.

Smart. But, my lord, I say beef is the king of meat.

Miss. Pray what have I done, that I must not have a place?

Lady S. [*To Lady A.*] What will your ladyship please to eat?

Lady A. Pray, madam, help yourself.

Col. They say, eating and scratching wants but a beginning: if you'll give me leave, I'll help myself to a slice of this shoulder of veal.

Lady S. Colonel, you can't do a kinder thing; well, you are all heartily welcome, as I may say.

Col. They say there are thirty and two good bits in a shoulder of veal.

Lady S. Ay, colonel, thirty bad bits and two good ones; you see I understand you; but I hope you have got one of the two good ones.

Never. Colonel, I'll be of your mess.

Col. Then, pray, Tom, carve for yourself; they say two hands in a dish, and one in a purse: Hah! said I well, Tom?

Never. Colonel, you spoke like an oracle.

Miss. [*To Lady A.*] Madam, will your ladyship help me to some fish?

Smart. [*To Neverout.*] Tom, they say fish should swim thrice.

Never. How is that, my lord?

Smart. Why, Tom, first it should swim in the sea (do you mind me?); then it should swim in butter; and, at last, sirrah, it should swim in good claret. I think I have made it out.

Foot. [*To Lord Smart.*] My lord, Sir John Linger is coming up.

Smart. God so! I invited him to dine with me to-day, and forgot it: well, desire him to walk in.

SIR JOHN LINGER comes in.

Sir J. What! you are at it! why then I'll be gone.

Lady S. Sir John, I beg you will sit down; come, the more the merrier.

Sir J. Ay; but the fewer the better cheer.

Lady S. Well, I am the worst in the world at making apologies; it was my lord's fault: I doubt you must kiss the hare's foot.

Sir J. I see you are fast by the teeth.

Col. Faith, Sir John, we are killing that that would kill us.

Spark. You see, Sir John, we are upon a business of life and death; come, will you do as we do? you are come in pudding-time.

Sir J. Ay; this would be doing if I were dead. What! you keep court hours, I see: I'll be going, and get a bit of meat at my inn.

Lady S. Why, we won't eat you, Sir John.

Sir J. It is my own fault; but I was kept by a fellow, who bought some Derbyshire oxen of me.

Never. You see, Sir John, we stayed for you as one horse does for another.

Lady S. My lord, will you help Sir John to some beef? Lady Answerall, pray eat, you see your dinner; I am sure, if we had known we should have such good company, we should have been better provided; but you must take the will for the deed. I'm afraid you are invited to your loss.

Col. And pray, Sir John, how do you like the town? you have been absent a long time.

Sir J. Why, I find little London stands just where it did when I left it last.

Never. What do you think of Hanover Square? Why, Sir John, London is gone out of town since you saw it.

Lady S. Sir John, I can only say, you are heartily welcome; and I wish I had something better for you.

Col. Here's no salt; cuckolds will run away with the meat.

Smart. Pray edge a little, to make more room for Sir John: Sir John, fall to: you know half an hour is soon lost at dinner.

Sir J. I protest, I can't eat a bit, for I took share of a beefsteak and two mugs of ale with my chapman, besides a tankard of March beer, as soon as I got out of my bed.

Lady A. Not fresh and fasting, I hope?

Sir J. Yes, faith, madam; I always wash my kettle before I put the meat in it.

Lady S. Poh! Sir John, you have seen nine houses since you ate last: come, you have kept a corner in your stomach for a piece of venison pasty.

Sir J. Well, I'll try what I can do when it comes up.

Lady A. Come, Sir John, you may go further and fare worse.

Miss. [*To Neverout.*] Pray, Mr. Neverout, will you please to send me a piece of tongue?

Never. By no means, madam: one tongue is enough for a woman.

Col. Miss, here's a tongue that never told a lie.

Miss. That was, because it could not speak. Why, colonel, I never told a lie in my life.

Never. I appeal to all the company, whether that be not the greatest lie that ever was told?

Col. [*To Neverout.*] Prithee, Tom, send me the two legs, and rump, and liver of that pigeon; for, you must know, I love what nobody else loves.

Never. But what if any of the ladies should long? Well, here take it, and the d——l do you good with it.

Lady A. Well; this eating and drinking takes away a body's stomach.

Never. I am sure I have lost mine.

Miss. What! the bottom of it, I suppose?

Never. No, really, miss; I have quite lost it.

Miss. I should be very sorry a poor body had found it.

Lady S. But, Sir John, we hear you are married since we saw you last: what! you have stolen a wedding, it seems?

Sir J. Well; one can't do a foolish thing once in one's life, but one must hear of it a hundred times.

Col. And, pray, Sir John, how does your lady unknown?

Sir J. My wife's well, colonel, and at your service in a civil way. Ha, ha!   [*He laughs.*

Miss. Pray, Sir John, is your lady tall or short?

Sir J. Why, miss, I thank God, she is a little evil.

Spark. Come, give me a glass of claret.

FOOTMAN *fills him a bumper.*

Spark. Why do you fill so much?

Never. My lord, he fills as he loves you.

Lady S. Miss, shall I send you some cucumber?

Miss. Madam, I dare not touch it: for they say cucumbers are cold in the third degree.

Lady S. Mr. Neverout, do you love pudding?

Never. Madam, I am like all fools, I love everything that is good; but the proof of the pudding is in the eating.

Col. Sir John, I hear you are a great walker when you are at home.

Sir J. No, faith, colonel; I always love to walk with a horse in my hand: but I have had devilish bad luck in horse-flesh of late.

Smart. Why, then, Sir John, you must kiss a parson's wife.

Lady S. They say, Sir John, that your lady has a great deal of wit.

Sir J. Madam, she can make a pudding, and has just wit enough to know her husband's breeches from another man's.

Smart. My Lord Sparkish, I have some excellent cider; will you please to taste it?

Spark. My lord, I should like it well enough, if it were not treacherous.

Smart. Pray, my lord, how is it treacherous?

Spark. Because it smiles in my face, and cuts my throat.
[*Here a loud laugh.*

Miss. Odd so! madam; your knives are very sharp, for I have cut my finger.

Lady S. I am sorry for it: pray which finger? (God bless the mark!)

Miss. Why, this finger: no, 'tis this: I vow I can't find which it is.

Never. Ay; the fox had a wound, and he could not tell where, etc. Bring some water to throw in her face.

Miss. Pray, Mr. Neverout, did you ever draw a sword in anger? I warrant you would faint at the sight of your own blood.

Lady S. Mr. Neverout, shall I send you some veal?

Never. No, madam, I don't love it.

Miss. Then pray for them that do. I desire your ladyship will send me a bit.

Smart. Tom, my service to you.

Never. My lord, this moment I did myself the honour to drink to your lordship.

Smart. Why, then, that's Hertfordshire kindness.

Never. Faith, my lord, I pledged myself; for I drank twice together without thinking.

Spark. Why, then, colonel, my humble service to you.

Never. Pray, my lord, don't make a bridge of my nose.

Spark. Well, a glass of this wine is as comfortable as matrimony to an old woman.

Col. Sir John, I design, one of these days, to come and beat up your quarters in Derbyshire.

Sir J. Faith, colonel, come, and welcome: and stay away, and heartily welcome: but you were born within the sound of Bow bell, and don't care to stir so far from London.

Miss. Pray, colonel, send me some fritters.

COLONEL *takes them out with his hand.*

Col. Here, miss; they say fingers were made before forks, and hands before knives.

Lady S. Methinks this pudding is too much boil'd.

Lady A. O! madam, they say a pudding is poison when it is too much boiled.

Never. Miss, shall I help you to a pigeon? here's a pigeon so finely roasted, it cries, Come eat me.

Miss. No, sir; I thank you.

Never. Why, then you may choose.

Miss. I have chosen already.

Never. Well, you may be worse offer'd before you are twice married.

The COLONEL *fills a large plate of soup.*

Smart. Why, colonel, you don't mean to eat all that soup?

Col. O! my lord, this is my sick dish; when I'm well I'll have a bigger.

Miss. [*To Col.*] Sup, Simon; very good broth.

Never. This seems to be a good pullet.

Miss. I warrant, Mr. Neverout knows what's good for himself.

Spark. Tom, I shan't take your word for it; help me to a wing.

NEVEROUT *tries to cut off a wing.*

Never. Egad, I can't hit the joint.

Spark. Why then, think of a cuckold.

Never. O! now I have nick'd it. [*Gives it to Lord Sparkish.*]

Spark. Why, a man may eat this, though his wife lay a-dying.

Col. Pray, friend, give me a glass of small beer, if it be good.

Smart. Why, colonel, they say, there is no such thing as good small beer, good brown bread, or a good old woman.

Lady S. [*To Lady A.*] Madam, I beg your ladyship's pardon; I did not see you when I was cutting that bit.

Lady A. O! madam; after you is good manners.

Lady S. Lord! here's a hair in the sauce!

Spark. Then, madam, set the hounds after it.

Never. Pray, colonel, help me, however, to some of that same sauce.

Col. Come, I think you are more sauce than pig.

Smart. Sir John, cheer up: my service to you: well, what do you think of the world to come?

Sir J. Truly, my lord, I think of it as little as I can.

Lady S. [*Putting a skewer on a plate.*] Here, take this skewer, and carry it down to the cook, to dress it for her own dinner.

Never. I beg your ladyship's pardon; but this small beer is dead.

Lady S. Why, then, let it be buried.

Col. This is admirable black-pudding: miss, shall I carve you some? I can just carve pudding and that's all; I am the worst carver in the world; I should never make a good chaplain.

Miss. No, thank ye, colonel; for they say those that eat black-pudding will dream of the devil.

Smart. O, here comes the venison pasty: here, take the soup away. [*He cuts it up, and tastes the venison.*] 'Sbuds! this venison is musty.

NEVEROUT *eats a piece, and it burns his mouth.*

Smart. What's the matter, Tom? you have tears in your eyes, I think: what dost cry for, man?

Never. My lord, I was just thinking of my poor grandmother! she died just this very day seven years.

MISS *takes a bit and burns her mouth.*

Never. And pray, miss, why do you cry, too?

Miss. Because you were not hang'd the day your grandmother died.

Smart. I'd have given £40, miss, to have said that.

Col. Egad, I think the more I eat the hungrier I am.

Spark. Why, colonel, they say, one shoulder of mutton drives down another.

Never. Egad, if I were to fast for my life, I would take a good breakfast in the morning, a good dinner at noon, and a good supper at night.

Spark. My lord, this venison is plaguily pepper'd; your cook has a heavy hand.

Smart. My lord, I hope you are pepper-proof; come, here's a health to the founders.

Lady S. Ay; and to the confounders, too.

Smart. Lady Answerall, does your ladyship love venison?

Lady A. No, my lord, I can't endure it in my sight: therefore please to send me a good piece of meat and crust.

Spark. [*Drinks to Neverout.*] Come, Tom; not always to my friends, but once to you.

Never. [*Drinks to Lady Smart.*] Come, madam; here's a health to our friends, and hang the rest of our kin.

Lady S. [*To Lady A.*] Madam, will your ladyship have any of this hare?

Lady A. No, madam, they say 'tis melancholy meat.

Lady S. Then, madam, shall I send you the brains? I beg your ladyship's pardon; for they say, 'tis not good manners to offer brains.

Lady A. No, madam; for perhaps it will make me hare-brained.

Never. Miss, I must tell you one thing.

Miss. [*With a glass in her hand.*] Hold your tongue, Mr. Neverout; don't speak in my tip.

Col. Well, he was an ingenious man that first found out eating and drinking.

Spark. Of all vittles drink digests the quickest: give me a glass of wine.

Never. My lord, your wine is too strong.

Smart. Ay, Tom, as much as you're too good.

Miss. This almond-pudding was pure good; but it is grown quite cold.

Never. So much the better, miss, cold pudding will settle your love.

Miss. Pray, Mr. Neverout, are you going to take a voyage?

Never. Why do you ask, miss?

Miss. Because you have laid in so much beef.

Sir J. You two have eat up the whole pudding between you.

Miss. Sir John, here's a little bit left; will you please to have it?

Sir J. No, thankee; I don't love to make a fool of my mouth.

Col. [*Calling to the butler.*] John, is your small beer good?

Butler. And please your honour, my lord and lady like it; I think it is good.

Col. Why, then, John, d'ye see, if you are sure your small beer is good, d'ye mark? then, give me a glass of wine.

[*All laugh.*

COLONEL *tasting the wine.*

Smart. Sir John, how does your neighbour Gatherall of the Peak? I hear he has lately made a purchase.

Sir J. O! Dick Gatherall knows how to butter his bread as well as any man in Derbyshire.

Smart. Why he used to go very fine when he was here in town.

Sir J. Ay; and it became him, as a saddle becomes a sow.

Col. I know his lady, and I think she is a very good woman.

Sir J. Faith, she has more goodness in her little finger than he has in his whole body.

Smart. Well, colonel, how do you like that wine?

Col. This wine should be eaten, it is too good to be drunk.

Smart. I'm very glad you like it; and pray don't spare it.

Col. No, my lord; I'll never starve in a cook's shop.

Smart. And pray, Sir John, what do you say to my wine?

Sir J. I'll take another glass first: second thoughts are best.

Spark. Pray, Lady Smart, you sit near that ham; will you please to send me a bit?

Lady S. With all my heart. [*She sends him a piece.*] Pray, my lord, how do you like it?

Spark. I think it is a limb of Lot's wife. [*He eats it with mustard.*] Egad, my lord, your mustard is very uncivil.

Lady S. Why uncivil, my lord?

Spark. Because it takes me by the nose, egad.

Lady S. Mr. Neverout, I find you are a very good carver.

Col. O, madam, that is no wonder; for you must know, Tom Neverout carves o' Sundays.

Neverout *overturns the saltcellar.*

Lady S. Mr. Neverout, you have overturned the salt, and that's a sign of anger: I'm afraid miss and you will fall out.

Lady A. No, no; throw a little of it into the fire, and all will be well.

Never. O, madam, the falling out of lovers, you know.

Miss. Lovers! very fine! fall *out* with him! I wonder when we were *in*.

Sir J. For my part, I believe the young gentlewoman is his sweetheart, there is so much fooling and fiddling betwixt them: I'm sure, they say in our country, that shiddle-come-sh—'s the beginning of love.

Miss. I own I love Mr. Neverout as the devil loves holy water: I love him like pie, I'd rather the devil had him than I.

Never. Miss, I'll tell you one thing.

Miss. Come, here's t'ye, to stop your mouth.

Never. I'd rather you would stop it with a kiss.

Miss. A kiss! marry come up, my dirty cousin; are you no sicker? Lord! I wonder what fool it was that first invented kissing!

Never. Well, I'm very dry.

Miss. Then you're the better to burn and the worse to fry.

Lady A. God bless you, colonel, you have a good stroke with you.

Col. O, madam, formerly I could eat all, but now I leave nothing; I eat but one meal a-day.

Miss. What! I suppose, colonel, that is from morning till night?

Never. Faith, miss; and well was his wont.

Smart. Pray, Lady Answerall, taste this bit of venison.

Lady A. I hope your lordship will set me a good example.

Smart. Here's a glass of cider fill'd: miss, you must drink it.

Miss. Indeed, my lord, I can't.

Never. Come, miss; better belly burst than good liquor be lost.

Miss. Pish! well, in life there was never anything so teazing; I had rather shed it in my shoes: I wish it were in your guts for my share.

Smart. Mr. Neverout, you ha'n't tasted my cider yet.

Never. No, my lord; I have been just eating soup; and they say, if one drinks with one's porridge, one will cough in one's grave.

Smart. Come, take miss's glass, she wish'd it was in your guts; let her have her wish for once: ladies can't abide to have their inclinations cross'd.

Lady S. [*To Sir J.*] I think, Sir John, you have not tasted the venison yet.

Sir J. I seldom eat it, madam; however, please to send me a little of the crust.

Spark. Why, Sir John, you had as good eat the devil as the broth he is boil'd in.

Col. Well, this eating and drinking takes away a body's stomach, as Lady Answerall says.

Never. I have dined as well as my lord mayor.

Miss. I thought I could have eaten this wing of a chicken; but my eye's bigger than my belly.

Smart. Indeed, Lady Answerall, you have eaten nothing.

Lady A. Pray, my lord, see all the bones on my plate: they say a carpenter's known by his chips.

Never. Miss, will you reach me that glass of jelly?

Miss. [*Giving it to him.*] You see, 'tis but ask and have.

Never. Miss, I would have a bigger glass.

Miss. What! you don't know your own mind; you are neither well, full nor fasting; I think that is enough.

Never. Ay, one of the enoughs; I am sure it is little enough.

Miss. Yes; but you know, sweet things are bad for the teeth.

Never. [*To Lady A.*] Madam, I don't like that part of the veal you sent me.

Lady A. Well, Mr. Neverout, I find you are a true Englishman; you never know when you are well.

Col. Well, I have made my whole dinner of beef.

Lady A. Why, colonel, a bellyful's a bellyful, if it be but of wheat-straw.

Col. Well, after all, kitchen physic is the best physic.

Lady S. And the best doctors in the world are Doctor Diet, Doctor Quiet, and Doctor Merryman.

Spark. What do you think of a little house well fill'd?

Sir J. And a little land well till'd?

Col. Ay; and a little wife well will'd?

Never. My Lady Smart, pray help me to some of the breast of that goose.

Smart. Tom, I have heard that goose upon goose is false heraldry.

Miss. What! will you never have done stuffing?

Smart. This goose is quite raw: well, God sends meat, but the devil sends cooks.

Never. Miss, can you tell which is the gander, the white goose or the grey goose?

Miss. They say, a fool will ask more questions than the wisest body can answer.

Col. Indeed, miss, Tom Neverout has posed you.

Miss. Why, colonel, every dog has his day; but I believe I shall never see a goose again without thinking of Mr. Neverout.

Smart. Well said, miss; faith, girl, thou hast brought thyself off cleverly. Tom, what say you to that?

Col. Faith, Tom is nonpluss'd; he looks plaguily down in the mouth.

Miss. Why, my lord, you see he is the provokingest creature in life; I believe there is not such another in the varsal world.

Lady A. O, miss, the world's a wide place.

Never. Well, miss, I'll give you leave to call me anything, if you don't call me spade.

Smart. Well, but after all, Tom, can you tell me what's Latin for a goose?

Never. O, my lord, I know that: why, brandy is Latin for a goose, and *tace* is Latin for a candle.

Miss. Is that manners, to show your learning before ladies? Methinks you are grown very brisk of a sudden; I think the man's glad he's alive.

Sir J. The devil take your wit, if this be wit; for it spoils company: pray, Mr. Butler, bring me a dram after my goose; 'tis very good for the wholesomes.

Smart. Come, bring me the loaf; I sometimes love to cut my own bread.

Miss. I suppose, my lord, you lay longest a-bed to-day?

Smart. Miss, if I had said so, I should have told a fib; I warrant you lay a-bed till the cows came home: but, miss, shall I cut you a little crust, now my hand is in?

Miss. If you please, my lord, a bit of undercrust.

Never. [*Whispering miss.*] I find you love to lie under.

Miss. [*Aloud, pushing him from her.*] What does the man mean! Sir, I don't understand you at all.

Never. Come, all quarrels laid aside: here, miss, may you live a thousand years. [*He drinks to her.*

Miss. Pray, sir, don't stint me.

Smart. Sir John, will you taste my October? I think it is very good; but I believe not equal to yours in Derbyshire.

Sir J. My lord, I beg your pardon; but they say, the devil made askers.

Smart. [*To the butler.*] Here, bring up the great tankard, full of October, for Sir John.

Col. [*Drinking to miss.*] Miss, your health; may you live all the days of your life.

Lady A. Well, miss, you'll certainly be soon married, here's two bachelors drinking to you at once.

Lady S. Indeed, miss, I believe you were wrapt in your mother's smock, you are so well beloved.

Miss. Where's my knife? sure I ha'n't eaten it: O, here it is.

Sir J. No, miss; but your maidenhead hangs in your light.

Miss. Pray, Sir John, is that a Derbyshire compliment? Here, Mr. Neverout, will you take this piece of rabbit that you bid me carve for you?

Never. I don't know.

Miss. Why, take it, or let it alone.

Never. I will.

Miss. What will you?

Never. Why, I'll take it, or let it alone.

Miss. Well, you are a provoking creature.

Sir J. [*Talking with a glass of wine in his hand.*] I remember a farmer in our country—

Smart. [*Interrupting him.*] Pray, Sir John, did you ever hear of Parson Palmer?

Sir J. No, my lord; what of him?

Smart. Why, he used to preach over his liquor.

Sir J. I beg your lordship's pardon; here's your lordship's health; I'd drink it up, if it were a mile to the bottom.

Lady S. Mr. Neverout, have you been at the new play?

Never. Yes, madam, I went the first night.

Lady S. Well, and how did it take?

Never. Why, madam, the poet is damn'd.

Sir J. God forgive you! that's very uncharitable: you ought not to judge so rashly of any Christian.

Never. [*Whispers Lady Smart.*] Was ever such a dunce! How well he knows the town! See how he stares like a stuck pig! Well, but, Sir John, are you acquainted with any one of our fine ladies yet?

Sir J. No; damn your fire-ships, I have a wife of my own.

Lady S. Pray, my Lady Answerall, how do you like these preserved oranges?

Lady A. Indeed, madam, the only fault I find is, that they are too good.

Lady S. O, madam, I have heard 'em say, that too good is stark naught.

Miss *drinking part of a glass of wine.*

Never. Pray, let me drink your snuff.

Miss. No, indeed, you shan't drink after me; for you'll know my thoughts.

Never. I know them already; you are thinking of a good husband. Besides, I can tell your meaning by your mumping.

Lady S. Pray, my lord, did not you order the butler to bring up a tankard of our October to Sir John? I believe they stay to brew it.

The butler brings up the tankard to Sir John.

Sir J. Won't your ladyship please to drink first?

Lady S. No, Sir John; 'tis in a very good hand; I'll pledge you.

Col. [*To Lord Smart.*] My lord, I love October as well as Sir John; and I hope you won't make fish of one and flesh of another.

Smart. Colonel, you're heartily welcome. Come, Sir John, take it by word of mouth, and then give it to the colonel.

SIR JOHN *drinks.*

Smart. Well, Sir John, how do you like it?

Sir J. Not as well as my own in Derbyshire; 'tis plaguy small.

Lady S. I never taste malt liquor; but they say it is well hopp'd.

Sir J. Hopp'd; why, if it had hopp'd a little further, it would have hopp'd into the river. O, my lord, my ale is meat, drink, and cloth; it will make a cat speak and a wise man dumb.

Lady S. I was told ours was very strong.

Sir J. Ay, madam, strong of the water; I believe the brewer forgot the malt, or the river was too near him. Faith, it is mere whip-belly-vengeance; he that drinks most has the worst share.

Col. I believe, Sir John, ale is as plenty as water at your house.

Sir J. Why, faith, at Christmas, we have many comers and goers; and they must not be sent away without a cup of Christmas ale, for fear they should p——s behind the door.

Lady S. I hear Sir John has the nicest garden in England; they say, 'tis kept so clean, that you can't find a place where to spit.

Sir J. O, madam; you are pleased to say so.

Lady S. But, Sir John, your ale is terrible strong and heady in Derbyshire, and will soon make one drunk and sick; what do you then?

Sir J. Why, indeed, it is apt to fox one; but our way is, to take a hair of the same dog next morning. I take a new-laid egg for breakfast; and faith one should drink as much after an egg as after an ox.

Smart. Tom Neverout, will you taste a glass of October?

Never. No, faith, my lord; I like your wine, and won't put a churl upon a gentleman; your honour's claret is good enough for me.

Lady S. What! is this pigeon left for manners? Colonel, shall I send you the legs and rump?

Col. Madam I could not eat a bit more if the house was full.

Smart. [*Carving a partridge.*] Well, one may ride to Rumford upon this knife, it is so blunt.

Lady A. My lord, I beg your pardon; but they say an ill workman never had good tools.

Smart. Will your lordship have a wing of it?

Spark. No, my lord; I love the wing of an ox a great deal better.

Smart. I'm always cold after eating.

Col. My lord, they say, that's a sign of long life.

Smart. Ay; I believe I shall live till my friends are weary of me.

Col. Pray, does anybody here hate cheese? I would be glad of a bit.

Smart. An odd kind of fellow dined with me t'other day; and when the cheese came upon the table, he pretended to faint; so somebody said, Pray take away the cheese: No, said I; pray take away the fool: said I well?

Here a loud and large laugh.

Col. Faith, my lord, you served the coxcomb right enough; and therefore I wish we had a bit of your lordship's Oxfordshire cheese.

Smart. Come, hang saving; bring us up a half-p'orth of cheese.

Lady A. They say, cheese digests everything but itself.

A footman brings a great whole cheese.

Spark. Ay; this would look handsome if anybody should come in.

Sir J. Well: I'm weily brosten, as they say in Lancashire.

Lady S. O! Sir John; I would I had something to brost you withal.

Smart. Come, they say, 'tis merry in the hall when beards wag all.

Lady S. Miss, shall I help you to some cheese, or will you carve for yourself?

Never. I'll hold fifty pounds, miss won't cut the cheese.

Miss. Pray, why so, Mr. Neverout?

Never. O, there is a reason, and you know it well enough.

Miss. I can't for my life understand what the gentleman means.

Smart. Pray, Tom, change the discourse: in troth you are too bad.

Col. [*Whispers Neverout.*] Smoke miss; faith, you have made her fret like gum taffeta.

Lady S. Well, but miss (hold your tongue, Mr. Neverout), shall I cut you a piece of cheese?

Miss. No, really, madam; I have dined this half hour.

Lady S. What! quick at meat, quick at work, they say.

SIR JOHN nods.

Smart. What! are you sleepy, Sir John? do you sleep after dinner?

Sir J. Yes, faith; I sometimes take a nap after my pipe; for when the belly is full, the bones would be at rest.

Lady S. Come, colonel; help yourself, and your friends will love you the better. [*To Lady A.*] Madam, your ladyship eats nothing.

Lady A. Lord, madam, I have fed like a farmer: I shall grow as fat as a porpoise; I swear, my jaws are weary of chewing.

Col. I have a mind to eat a piece of that sturgeon, but fear it will make me sick.

Never. A rare soldier indeed; let it alone, and I warrant it won't hurt you.

Col. Well, it would vex a dog to see a pudding creep.

SIR JOHN rises.

Smart. Sir John, what are you doing?

Sir J. Swolks, I must be going, by'r lady; I have earnest business; I must do as the beggars do, go away when I have got enough.

Smart. Well, but stay till this bottle's out; you know, the man was hang'd that left his liquor behind him: and besides, a cup in the pate is a mile in the gate; and a spur in the head is worth two in the heel.

Sir J. Come then; one brimmer to all your healths. [*The*

footman gives him a glass half full.] Pray, friend, what was the rest of this glass made for? an inch at the top, friend, is worth two at the bottom. [*He gets a brimmer and drinks it off.*] Well, there's no deceit in a brimmer, and there's no false Latin in this; your wine is excellent good, so I thank you for the next, for I am sure of this: madam, has your ladyship any commands in Derbyshire? I must go fifteen miles to-night.

Lady S. None, Sir John, but to take care of yourself; and my most humble service to your lady unknown.

Sir J. Well, madam, I can but love and thank you.

Lady S. Here, bring water to wash; though really, you have all eaten so little, that you have not need to wash your mouths.

Smart. But, prithee, Sir John, stay a while longer.

Sir J. No, my lord; I am to smoke a pipe with a friend before I leave the town.

Col. Why, Sir John, had not you better set out to-morrow?

Sir J. Colonel, you forget to-morrow is Sunday.

Col. Now I always love to begin a journey on Sundays, because I shall have the prayers of the church to preserve all that travel by land or by water.

Sir J. Well, colonel, thou art a mad fellow to make a priest of.

Never. Fie, Sir John! do you take tobacco? How can you make a chimney of your mouth?

Sir J. [*To Neverout.*] What! you don't smoke, I warrant you, but you smock. (Ladies, I beg your pardon.) Colonel, do you never smoke?

Col. No, Sir John; but I take a pipe sometimes.

Sir J. I'faith, one of your finical London blades dined with me last year in Derbyshire: so, after dinner, I took a pipe: so my gentleman turned away his head: so, said I, What, sir, do you never smoke? so he answered, as you do, colonel, No, but I sometimes take a pipe: so he took a pipe in his hand, and fiddled with it till he broke it: so, said I, Pray, sir, can you make a pipe? so he said, No: so, said I, Why then, sir, if you can't make a pipe you should not break a pipe: so we all laughed.

Smart. Well; but, Sir John, they say, that the corruption of pipes is the generation of stoppers.

Sir J. Colonel, I hear you go sometimes to Derbyshire; I wish you would come and foul a plate with me.

Col. I hope you will give me a soldier's bottle.

Sir J. Come and try. Mr. Neverout, you are a Town wit: can you tell me what kind of herb is tobacco?

Never. Why, an Indian herb, Sir John.

Sir J. No; 'tis a pot herb; and so here's t'ye in a pot of my lord's October.

Lady S. I hear, Sir John, since you are married, you have foreswore the town.

Sir J. No, madam; I never foreswore anything but the building of churches.

Lady S. Well; but, Sir John, when may we hope to see you again in London?

Sir J. Why, madam, not till the ducks have eat up the dirt, as the children say.

Never. Come, Sir John: I foresee it will rain terribly.

Smart. Come, Sir John, do nothing rashly; let us drink first.

Spark. I know Sir John will go, though he was sure it would rain cats and dogs: but pray stay, Sir John; you'll be time enough to go to bed by candlelight.

Smart. Why, Sir John, if you must needs go, while you stay, make use of your time; here's my service to you, a health to our friends in Derbyshire: come, sit down; let us put off the evil hour as long as we can.

Sir J. Faith, I could not drink a drop more if the house was full.

Col. Why, Sir John, you used to love a glass of good wine in former times.

Sir J. Why, so I do still, colonel; but a man may love his house very well, without riding on the ridge; besides, I must be with my wife on Tuesday, or there will be the devil and all to pay.

Col. Well, if you go to-day, I wish you may be wet to the skin.

Sir J. Ay; but they say the prayers of the wicked won't prevail.

Sir John takes his leave and goes away.

Smart. Well, miss, how do you like Sir John?

Miss. Why, I think he's a little upon the silly, or so: I

believe he has not all the wit in the world: but I don't pretend to be a judge.

Never. Faith, I believe he was bred at Hog's Norton, where the pigs play upon the organs.

Spark. Why, Tom, I thought you and he were hand and glove.

Never. Faith, he shall have a clean threshold for me; I never darkened his door in my life, neither in town nor country; but he's a queer old duke, by my conscience; and yet, after all, I take him to be more knave than fool.

Lady S. Well, come; a man's a man, if he has but a nose on his face.

Col. I was once with him and some other company over a bottle, and, egad, he fell asleep, and snored so hard that we thought he was driving his hogs to market.

Never. Why, what! you can have no more of a cat than her skin; you can't make a silk purse out of a sow's ear.

Spark. Well, since he's gone, the devil go with him and sixpence; and there's money and company too.

Never. Faith, he's a country put. Pray, miss, let me ask you a question.

Miss. Well; but don't ask questions with a dirty face: I warrant, what you have to say will keep cold.

Col. Come, my lord, against you are disposed: here's to all that love and honour you.

Spark. Ay, that was always Dick Nimble's health. I'm sure you know he's dead.

Col. Dead! well, my lord, you love to be a messenger of ill news: I'm heartily sorry; but, my lord, we must all die.

Never. I knew him very well: but, pray, how came he to die?

Miss. There's a question! you talk like a poticary: why, because he could live no longer.

Never. Well; rest his soul: we must live by the living, and not by the dead.

Spark. You know his house was burnt down to the ground?

Col. Yes; it was in the *News.* Why, fire and water are good servants, but they are very bad masters.

Smart. Here, take away, and set down a bottle of Burgundy. Ladies, you'll stay and drink a glass of wine before you go to your tea.

All taken away, and the wine set down, etc.

Miss gives NEVEROUT *a smart pinch.*

Never. Lord, miss, what d'ye mean? d'ye think I have no feeling?

Miss. I'm forced to pinch, for the times are hard.

Never. [*Giving miss a pinch.*] Take that, miss; what's sauce for a goose, is sauce for a gander.

Miss. [*Screaming.*] Well, Mr. Neverout, that shall neither go to heaven nor hell with you.

Never. [*Takes miss by the hand.*] Come, miss, let us lay all quarrels aside, and be friends.

Miss. Don't be so teasing; you plague a body so! can't you keep your filthy hands to yourself?

Never. Pray, miss, where did you get that picktoothcase?

Miss. I came honestly by it.

Never. I'm sure it was mine, for I lost just such a one; nay, I don't tell you a lie.

Miss. No; if you lie, it is much.

Never. Well; I'm sure 'tis mine.

Miss. What! you think everything is yours, but a little the king has.

Never. Colonel, you have seen my fine picktoothcase; don't you think that is the very same?

Col. Indeed, miss, it is very like it.

Miss. Ay; what he says, you'll swear.

Never. Well; but I'll prove it to be mine.

Miss. Ay; do, if you can.

Never. Why, what's yours is mine, and what's mine is my own.

Miss. Well, run on till you're weary; nobody holds you.

NEVEROUT *gapes.*

Col. What! Mr. Neverout, do you gape for preferment?

Never. Faith, I may gape long enough, before it falls into my mouth.

Lady S. Mr. Neverout, my lord and I intend to beat up your quarters one of these days: I hear you live high.

Never. Yes, faith, madam; I live high and lodge in a garret.

Col. But, miss, I forgot to tell you, that Mr. Neverout got the devilishest fall in the park to-day.

Miss. I hope he did not hurt the ground: but how was it, Mr. Neverout? I wish I had been there to laugh.

Never. Why, madam, it was a place where a cuckold had been buried, and one of his horns sticking out, I happened to stumble against it; that was all.

Lady S. Ladies, let us leave the gentlemen to themselves; I think it is time to go to our tea.

Lady A. and Miss. My lords and gentlemen, your most humble servant.

Smart. Well, ladies, we'll wait on you an hour hence.

The Gentlemen alone.

Smart. Come, John, bring us a fresh bottle.

Col. Ay, my lord; and pray let him carry off the dead men, as we say in the army.   [*Meaning the empty bottles.*

Spark. Mr. Neverout, pray, is not that bottle full?

Never. Yes, my lord, full of emptiness.

Smart. And, d'ye hear, John, bring clean glasses.

Col. I'll keep mine; for I think wine is the best liquor to wash glasses in.

THE THIRD DIALOGUE

The Ladies at their tea.

Lady S. Well, ladies; now let us have a cup of discourse to ourselves.

Lady A. What do you think of your friend Sir John Spendall?

Lady S. Why, madam, 'tis happy for him that his father was born before him.

Miss. They say he makes a very ill husband to my lady.

Lady A. But he must be allowed to be the fondest father in the world.

Lady S. Ay, madam, that's true; for they say, the devil is kind to his own.

Miss. I am told my lady manages him to admiration.

Lady S. That I believe; for she's as cunning as a dead pig, but not half so honest.

Lady A. They say she's quite a stranger to all his gallantries.

Lady S. Not at all; but, you know, there's none so blind as they that won't see.

Miss. O, madam, I am told she watches him as a cat would watch a mouse.

Lady A. Well, if she ben't foully belied, she pays him in his own coin.

Lady S. Madam, I fancy I know your thoughts, as well as if I were within you.

Lady A. Madam, I was t'other day in company with Mrs. Clatter; I find she gives herself airs of being acquainted with your ladyship.

Miss. O the hideous creature! did you observe her nails? they were long enough to scratch her grannum out of her grave.

Lady S. Well, she and Tom Gosling were banging compliments backward and forward: it looked like two asses scrubbing one another.

Miss. Ay, claw me, and I'll claw you: but, pray, madam, who were the company?

Lady S. Why there was all the world and his wife; there was Mrs. Clatter, Lady Singular, the Countess of Talkham (I should have named her first), Tom Gosling, and some others, whom I have forgot.

Lady A. I think the countess is very sickly.

Lady S. Yes, madam; she'll never scratch a grey head, I promise her.

Miss. And pray, what was your conversation?

Lady S. Why Mrs. Clatter had all the talk to herself, and was perpetually complaining of her misfortunes.

Lady A. She brought her husband £10,000: she has a town-house and country-house: would the woman have her a— hung with points?

Lady S. She would fain be at the top of the house before the stairs are built.

Miss. Well, comparisons are odious; but she's as like her husband as if she were spit out of his mouth; as like as one egg is to another: pray, how was she dressed?

Lady S. Why, she was as fine as fi'pence; but, truly, I thought there was more cost than worship.

Lady A. I don't know her husband: pray what is he?

Lady S. Why, he's a counsellor of the law; you must know he came to us as drunk as David's sow.

Miss. What kind of creature is he?

Lady S. You must know, the man and his wife are coupled like rabbits, a fat and a lean; he's as fat as a porpus, and she's one of Pharaoh's lean kine: the ladies and Tom Gosling were proposing a party at quadrille, but he refused to make one: Damn your cards, said he, they are the devil's books.

Lady A. A dull unmannerly brute! well, God send him more wit, and me more money.

Miss. Lord! madam, I would not keep such company for the world.

Lady S. O, miss, 'tis nothing when you are used to it: besides, you know for want of company, welcome trumpery.

Miss. Did your ladyship play?

Lady S. Yes, and won; so I came off with fiddler's fare, meat, drink, and money.

Lady A. Ay; what says Pluck?

Miss. Well, my elbow itches; I shall change bed-fellows.

Lady S. And my right hand itches; I shall receive money.

Lady A. And my right eye itches; I shall cry.

Lady S. Miss, I hear your friend Mrs. Giddy has discarded Dick Shuttle: pray, has she got another lover?

Miss. I hear of none.

Lady S. Why, the fellow's rich, and I think she was a fool to throw out her dirty water before she got clean.

Lady A. Miss, that's a handsome gown of yours, and finely made; very genteel.

Miss. I am glad your ladyship likes it.

Lady A. Your lover will be in raptures; it becomes you admirably.

Miss. Ay; I assure you I won't take it as I have done: if this won't fetch him, the devil fetch him, say I.

Lady S. [*To Lady A.*] Pray, madam, when did you see Sir Peter Muckworm?

Lady A. Not this fortnight; I hear he's laid up with the gout.

Lady S. What does he do for it?

Lady A. I hear he's weary of doctoring it, and now makes use of nothing but patience and flannel.

Miss. Pray, how does he and my lady agree?

Lady A. You know he loves her as the devil loves holy water.

Miss. They say she plays deep with sharpers, that cheat her of her money.

Lady A. Upon my word they must rise early that would cheat her of her money; sharp's the word with her; diamonds cut diamonds.

Miss. Well, but I was assured from a good hand, that she lost at one sitting to the tune of a hundred guineas; make money of that!

Lady S. Well, but do you hear that Mrs. Plump is brought to bed at last?

Miss. And pray what has God sent her?

Lady S. Why, guess if you can.

Miss. A boy, I suppose.

Lady S. No, you are out; guess again.

Miss. A girl, then.

Lady S. You have hit it; I believe you are a witch.

Miss. O, madam, the gentlemen say, all fine ladies are witches; but I pretend to no such thing.

Lady A. Well, she had good luck to draw Tom Plump into wedlock; she ris with her a— upwards.

Miss. Fie, madam; what do you mean?

Lady S. O, miss, 'tis nothing what we say among ourselves.

Miss. Ay, madam; but they say hedges have eyes, and walls have ears.

Lady A. Well, miss, I can't help it; you know, I'm old Telltruth; I love to call a spade a spade.

Lady S. [*Mistakes the teatongs for the spoon.*] What! I think my wits are a wool-gathering to-day.

Miss. Why, madam, there was but a right and a wrong.

Lady S. Miss, I hear that you and Lady Coupler are as great as cup and can.

Lady A. Ay, miss, as great as the devil and the Earl of Kent.[1]

Lady S. Nay, I am told you meet together with as much love as there is between the old cow and the haystack.

Miss. I own I love her very well; but there's difference between staring and stark mad.

Lady S. They say she begins to grow fat.

Miss. Fat! ay, fat as a hen in the forehead.

[1] An old English saying that obtained from the reign of Edward the Confessor, no way complimentary to Goodwin, Earl of Kent.

Lady S. Indeed, Lady Answerall (pray forgive me), I think your ladyship looks thinner than when I saw you last.

Miss. Indeed, madam, I think not; but your ladyship is one of Job's comforters.

Lady A. Well, no matter how I look; I am bought and sold: but really, miss, you are so very obliging, that I wish I were a handsome young lord for your sake.

Miss. O, madam, your love's a million.

Lady S. [*To Lady A.*] Madam, will your ladyship let me wait on you to the play to-morrow?

Lady A. Madam, it becomes me to wait on your ladyship.

Miss. What, then, I'm turned out for a wrangler?

The Gentlemen come in to the Ladies to drink tea.

Miss. Mr. Neverout, we wanted you sadly; you are always out of the way when you should be hang'd.

Never. You wanted me! pray, miss, how do you look when you lie?

Miss. Better than you when you cry. Manners, indeed! I find you mend like sour ale in summer.

Never. I beg your pardon, miss; I only meant, when you lie alone.

Miss. That's well turn'd; one turn more would have turn'd you down stairs.

Never. Come, miss, be kind for once, and order me a dish of coffee.

Miss. Pray, go yourself; let us wear out the oldest; besides I can't go, for I have a bone in my leg.

Col. They say, a woman need but look on her apron-string to find an excuse.

Never. Why, miss, you are grown so peevish, a dog would not live with you.

Miss. Mr. Neverout, I beg your diversion: no offence, I hope; but truly in a little time you intend to make the colonel as bad as yourself; and that's as bad as can be.

Never. My lord, don't you think miss improves wonderfully of late? Why, miss, if I spoil the colonel, I hope you will use him as you do me; for you know, love me, love my dog.

Col. How's that, Tom? Say that again: why, if I am a dog, shake hands, brother.

Here a great, loud, long laugh.

Smart. But pray, gentlemen, why always so severe upon poor miss? On my conscience, colonel and Tom Neverout, one of you two are both knaves.

Col. My Lady Answerall, I intend to do myself the honour of dining with your ladyship to-morrow.

Lady A. Ay, colonel, do if you can.

Miss. I'm sure you'll be glad to be welcome.

Col. Miss, I thank you; and, to reward you, I'll come and drink tea with you in the morning.

Miss. Colonel, there's two words to that bargain.

Col. [*To Lady Smart.*] Your ladyship has a very fine watch; well may you wear it.

Lady S. It is none of mine, colonel.

Col. Pray, whose is it then?

Lady S. Why, 'tis my lord's; for they say a married woman has nothing of her own but her wedding-ring and her hair-lace: but if women had been the law-makers, it would have been better.

Col. This watch seems to be quite new.

Lady S. No, sir, it has been twenty years in my lord's family; but Quare put a new case and dial-plate to it.

Never. Why, that's for all the world like the man, who swore he kept the same knife forty years, only he sometimes changed the haft, and sometimes the blade.

Smart. Well, Tom, to give the devil his due, thou art a right woman's man.

Col. Odd so! I have broke the hinge of my snuff-box; I'm undone, besides the loss.

Miss. Alack-a-day, colonel! I vow I had rather have found forty shillings.

Never. Why, colonel, all that I can say to comfort you is, that you must mend it with a new one.

Miss laughs.

Col. What, miss! you can't laugh, but you must show your teeth.

Miss. I'm sure you show your teeth when you can't bite: well, thus it must be, if we sell ale.

Never. Miss, you smell very sweet; I hope you don't carry perfumes?

Miss. Perfumes! No, sir; I'd have you to know, it is nothing but the grain of my skin.

Col. Tom, you have a good nose to make a poor man's sow.

Spark. So, ladies and gentlemen, methinks you are very witty upon one another: come, box it about; 'twill come to my father at last.

Col. Why, my lord, you see miss has no mercy; I wish she were married; but I doubt the grey mare would prove the better horse.

Miss. Well, God forgive you for that wish.

Spark. Never fear him, miss.

Miss. What, my lord, do you think I was born in a wood, to be afraid of an owl?

Smart. What have you to say to that, colonel?

Never. O, my lord, my friend the colonel scorns to set his wit against a child.

Miss. Scornful dogs will eat dirty puddings.

Col. Well, miss, they say a woman's tongue is the last thing about her that dies; therefore, let's kiss and be friends.

Miss. Hands off! that's meat for your master.

Spark. Faith, colonel, you are for ale and cakes: but after all, miss, you are too severe; you would not meddle with your match.

Miss. All they can say goes in at one ear and out at t'other for me, I can assure you: only I wish they would be quiet, and let me drink my tea.

Never. What! I warrant you think all is lost that goes beside your own mouth.

Miss. Pray, Mr. Neverout, hold your tongue for once, if it be possible: one would think you were a woman in man's clothes, by your prating.

Never. No, miss; it is not handsome to see one hold one's tongue: besides, I should slobber my fingers.

Col. Miss, did you never hear that three women and a goose are enough to make a market?

Miss. I'm sure, if Mr. Neverout or you were among them, it would make a fair.

FOOTMAN *comes in.*

Lady S. Here, take away the tea-table, and bring up candles.

Lady A. O, madam, no candles yet, I beseech you; don't let us burn day-light.

Never. I dare swear, miss, for her part, will never burn day-light, if she can help it.

Miss. Lord! Mr. Neverout, one cannot hear one's own ears for you.

Lady S. Indeed, madam, it is blindman's holiday; we shall soon be all of a colour.

Never. Why, then, miss, we may kiss where we like best.

Miss. Fogh! those men talk of nothing but kissing.

[*She spits.*

Never. What, miss, does it make your mouth water?

Lady S. It is as good to be in the dark as without light; therefore pray bring in candles: they say women and linen show best by candlelight: come, gentlemen, are you for a party at quadrille?

Col. I'll make one with you three ladies.

Lady A. I'll sit down, and be a stander by.

Lady S. [*To Lady A.*] Madam, does your ladyship never play?

Col. Yes; I suppose her ladyship plays sometimes for an egg at Easter.

Never. Ay; and a kiss at Christmas.

Lady A. Come, Mr. Neverout, hold your tongue, and mind your knitting.

Never. With all my heart; kiss my wife, and welcome.

The COLONEL, *Mr.* NEVEROUT, LADY SMART, *and* MISS *go to quadrille, and sit there till three in the morning.*

They rise from cards.

Lady S. Well, miss, you'll have a sad husband, you have such good luck at cards.

Never. Indeed, miss, you dealt me sad cards; if you deal so ill by your friends, what will you do with your enemies?

Lady A. I'm sure 'tis time for honest folks to be a-bed.

Miss. Indeed my eyes draw straws.

She's almost asleep.

Never. Why, miss, if you fall asleep, somebody may get a pair of gloves.

Col. I am going to the land of Nod.

Never. Faith, I'm for Bedfordshire.

Lady S. I'm sure I shall sleep without rocking.

Never. Miss, I hope you'll dream of your sweetheart.

Miss. O, no doubt of it. I believe I shan't be able to sleep for dreaming of him.

Col. [*To miss.*] Madam, shall I have the honour to escort you?

Miss. No, colonel, I thank you; my mamma has sent her chair and footmen. Well, my Lady Smart, I'll give you revenge whenever you please.

FOOTMAN *comes in.*

Footman. Madam, the chairs are waiting.

They all take their chairs and go off.